Physiology
of the Skin II:
Revised Edition

By Peter T. Pugliese, MD

---

*An expanded scientific guide
for the skin care professional.*

Allured Publishing Corporation
Carol Stream, Illinois USA

Physiology of the Skin II
6th Printing

ISBN 978-0-931710-86-5

Global Information Leader

Allured Publishing Corporation
336 Gundersen Drive, Suite A,
Carol Stream, IL 60188 USA
Phone: 630/653-2155 • Fax: 630/653-2192
E-mail: books@allured.com

Contents

About the Author . . .

Peter T. Pugliese MD, earned a Bachelor of Science degree from Franklin and Marshall College in Lancaster, Pennsylvania, and in 1957, a Doctor of Medicine from the School of Medicine at the University of Pennsylvania in Philadelphia. He studied nuclear physics in 1955 at the Oak Ridge Institute of Nuclear Studies in Oak Ridge, Tennessee, and from 1964–1967 did post-graduate research at the Johnson Foundation of Biophysics of the University of Pennsylvania. He has held academic positions at the University of Pennsylvania and Hershey Medical School. For six years he conducted cancer research under a grant from the Cancer Institute of the National Institutes of Health on the bioenergetics of cell division.

Dr. Pugliese conducted a private rural practice in 1958–1978. Since 1972, he has been engaged in the study of skin physiology. From 1970–1978, he conducted a methadone treatment clinic for heroin addicts and during the same period he was consultant physician to the Berks County Prison. For his work with drug addiction, he was awarded the B'nai Brith Americanism Award and the Italian Citizenship Award. A member of the Society of Cosmetic Chemists since 1972, Dr. Pugliese was awarded the Maison De Navarre Gold Medal for outstanding contribution to the field of cosmetic chemistry.

He is a member the American Academy of Dermatology, the Society of Investigative Dermatology, the Society of Bioengineers of the Skin, the American Chemical Society and the Society of Cosmetic Chemists. He has written more than 60 scientific papers, given more than 100 world-wide presentations at scientific meetings, has contributed more than ten chapters to scientific texts, and has published four books including **Advanced Professional Skin Care**.

Dr. Pugliese and Joanne, his wife since 1949, have four children, three grandchildren and reside in Bernville, Pennsylvania.

Introduction

This second edition of Physiology of the Skin has been revised and updated with the addition of 11 new chapters. This book is written for estheticians, to help them understand current scientific developments and prepare for future developments in science. Many new subjects have been added, including basic chemistry and an introduction to biochemistry. The topic of immunology is covered in sufficient detail to allow the serious student to explore the subject further. While the subject of molecular chemistry will grow increasingly important, it is not an appropriate topic for a small book on physiology. The field of enzymology, however, is an area of biochemistry that estheticians will apply often in their practices, both in exfoliating treatments and in specific treatments for acne and other skin conditions. The chapters of the book are organized in two sections—Science and Application. I strongly recommend that you read the Science section first, if even lightly. This will provide you with a basis for understanding the latter chapters in Applications. A brief description of the chapters follows.

Chapter 1—"Behavior of Normal Skin." Even advanced professionals need to review material from time to time, for as waves against the sand, our shoreline of knowledge constantly is being eroded. Several new concepts are presented, as well as many old ones seen from a different point of view. Chapter 2—"The Desquamation Process." An entirely new chapter with up-to-date information on the enzymes of the stratum corneum responsible for exfoliation, this information will prepare you for new exfoliation treatments and help you understand the complexity of the stratum corneum. Chapter 3—"The Appendages." A review with new information on some of the functions of the appendages and some surprises as to how hair really grows! Chapter 4—"The Lymphatic System." A good grounding in the physiology of the lymphatic system is necessary. While knowledgeable estheticians are a leg up on other professions, when it comes to the lymphatic system, there always is more to learn. Chapter 5—"Pigmentation." Always complex and unpredictable, melanin will be a major contender for your time and interest. Understanding the melanocyte and chemistry of melanin is a step up on this pathway. Chapter 6—"Basic Chemistry of Life." This chapter provides the foundation for biochemistry, introducing atomic particles, pH and chemical reactions. Chapter 7—"Biochemistry." Protein, carbohydrates and lipids make up the stuff of life. An appreciation of the structure and reactions of these substances, as well as knowledge of enzymology, is essential to understanding the new science in esthetics. Chapter 8—"Free Radicals and the Skin." A complex chapter, but necessary information if you want to understand antioxidants, ultraviolet radiation and the fundamental processes of life. Chapter 9—"Sun's Effect on the Skin." A tan may look healthy, but it indicates damaged skin! Read all about it here. Chapter 10—"Herpes-type Viral Infections." Fever blisters, shingles and a lot more—how to tell what that little blister means. Chapter 11—"Elastin: The Youth Protein." No protein in the body adds more to our appearance than elastin. Saggy cheeks and droopy eyes mean poor elastin. Elastase is the culprit. Learn how to combat this effect. **Chapter 12—"The Biological Role of Oxygen."** A subject dear to my heart. More nonsense is written about oxygen than is written in political campaigns. These are the known facts backed by science and presented in a manner that can be understood easily.

The section on applications will contain some basic scientific information; such is the case with **Chapter 13—"Immunology and the Skin Care Specialist."** The basics of immunology are tough, but like any meat, it is digestible if taken in small chunks. As you read this chapter make sure you understand each concept before going to the next. Much of the new science of skin care will relate in some fashion to immunology. **Chapter 14—"How Wrinkles Develop."** While a great deal is understood about wrinkle formation, the last word has not been written. Working in esthetics we must contend with wrinkles, but the wrinkle is only a more obvious manifestation of the serious problem of aging. Both problems are dealt with in this chapter. **Chapter 15—"Biology of Acneic Skin."** The pathophysiology of acne slowly is becoming known. Using the information we have on this subject helps to apply effective therapy. **Chapter 16— "Sun-related Disorders."** This chapter builds on information gathered in Chapters 8 and 9. Many skin problems relate to ultraviolet damage, some are quite obvious and others are very subtle. Your knowledge in the area will be expanded to help you recognize and understand several sun-related conditions. **Chapter 17—"Systemic Lupus Erythemato- sus."** Lupus is a very complex, multifaceted disease that is yielding its secrets bit by bit. You will see a significant number of clients with lupus and this chapter will take you into the pathophysiology for a better understanding of how best to handle this problem. **Chapter 18—"Males and Females: Physiological Differences."** As much as some liberals would deny, there are biological differences of great magnitude between men and women. Failing to appreciate the physiological differences could blind you to the needs for varied treatments between the sexes.

Chapter 19—"Estrogens and Phytoestrogens." The biochemistry of estrogens and phytoestrogens is found in this new chapter, and it also includes information on hormone receptors and how phytoestrogens work and their benefits to estheticians. **Chapter 20—"Menopausal Skin."** Menopause induces a major physiological change in women and skin is a very critical target of these changes. This chapter will explain the basic physiological changes and offer some remedies to help your client through this period. **Chapter 21—"New Concepts in Aging."** Aging is one of my favorite subjects and each year it becomes more interesting to me. Is aging a disease, or is it natural to undergo aging changes? Actually, scientists are divided. I see aging as a disease, something we can slow, or reverse. **Chapter 22—"Supplements and Beyond."** A wide range of nutritional supplements are available now, so what to take, and how to take them are questions of importance. A new class of agents called nootropics are designed to increase brain power. This chapter leads you into some exciting new areas. **Chapter 23—"The Power of Chemical Peels."** Chemical peels are here to stay. New peels are available today and some old ones have been "souped-up." The more you understand about peeling chemistry and physiology, the more versatile and effective you will be using peels. **Chapter 24—"Cellulite."** There is new scientific evidence that cellulite is a condition related to estrogen. This chapter outlines the information on what can be done to combat cellulite. **Chapter 25—"Phytotherapy."** This chapter is an introduction to the use of plants in esthetics. While phytotherapy requires years of training to use, just a little knowledge will help introduce you to the proper use of plants and help avoid the pitfalls of improper use. **Chapter 26—"Sterilization."** This last chapter deals with the everyday problems of how to keep equipment clean and sterile. This discipline will help you avoid problems and make your life as an esthetician easier.

I hope you enjoy using this book as much as I enjoyed writing it. Remember to take it slowly, give yourself the opportunity to digest the material and understand it before proceeding to the next fact. Don't be discouraged if you can't understand a subject immediately; go over it again. Remember, it took three or four years before we learned to tie our shoes. We start as a single, tiny cell and by adding cells we grow slowly into an intelligent human. So it is with any intellectual discipline—it must be mastered over time with effort.

Peter T. Pugliese, M.D

Skin care professionals should obtain specialized training before offering any new services.

Chapter 1

Behavior of Normal Skin

The smooth, soft, supple skin of a human female face—free of any blemishes—is highly attractive to the human male, as is a smooth male face to the female. This skin is a result of many biochemical and physical factors. Unfortunately, over time, these factors are subject to changes both internally and externally. Sun, smoking, stress, disease and aging alter the structure of the skin, making it sag, and lose its luster and suppleness. Professional skin care maintains skin in its most attractive and healthy state. This chapter will provide an understanding of normal skin behavior in relation to its structure and function.

Structure of the skin

The two layers of the skin, the **epidermis** and the **dermis** really are one system. One layer cannot be affected without some effect on the other layer. This is a very important concept to keep in mind as the structure and function of these two layers are explored. (See **Figure 1-1**.) [1, 2]

The epidermis serves as a barrier to the outside world, keeping out water, sunlight, insects, germs, heat and cold, dirt and gases. It keeps in fluids such as water and blood, and holds safe minerals, vitamins, hormones, proteins and heat. With the dermis, it provides for heat regulation for the entire body by controlling sweat evaporation and dermal blood flow. An incredible self-renewing system provides replacement of the outer cells lost to the environment. It provides a waterproof outer layer, yet permits water to carry nutrients to the outermost living cells. It provides a tough outer layer to resist friction, abrasion and pressure, yet is sensitive to the lightest touch, or softest breeze. Less glamorous, but equally as important, the skin serves as a vast waste disposal system, ridding the body of many toxic substances. (See **Figure 1-2**.)

Stratum corneum

Malpighian layer

Basement membrane

Dermis

Sebaceous glands (far right)

Nerves

Vasculature

Eccrine sweat glands

Panniculus

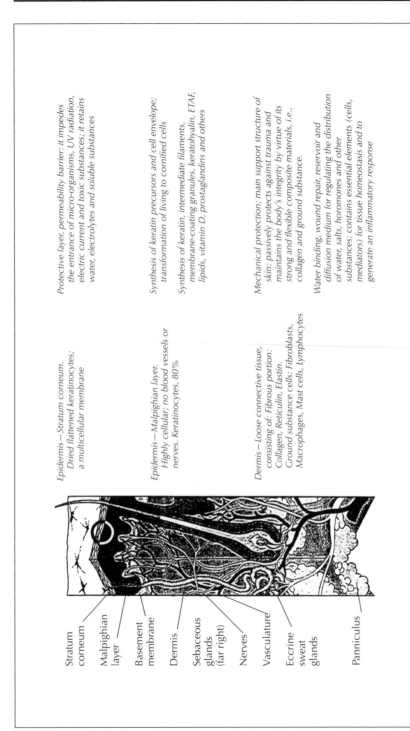

Epidermis—Stratum corneum. Dried flattened keratinocytes; a multicellular membrane

Protective layer, permeability barrier: it impedes the entrance of micro-organisms, UV radiation, electric current and toxic substances; it retains water, electrolytes and soluble substances

Epidermis—Malpighian layer. Highly cellular; no blood vessels or nerves. Keratinocytes, 80%

Synthesis of keratin precursors and cell envelope; transformation of living to cornified cells

Synthesis of keratin, intermediate filaments, membrane-coating granules, keratohyalin, ETAF, lipids, vitamin D, prostaglandins and others

Dermis—Loose connective tissue, consisting of: Fibrous portion: Collagen, Reticulin, Elastin. Ground substance cells: Fibroblasts, Macrophages, Mast cells, Lymphocytes

Mechanical protection; main support structure of skin: passively protects against trauma and maintains the body's integrity by virtue of its strong and flexible composite materials, i.e., collagen and ground substance.

Water binding, wound repair, reservoir and diffusion medium for regulating the distribution of water, salts, horomones and other substances; contains essential elements (cells, mediators) for tissue homeostasis and to generate an inflammatory response

Figure 1-1. Overview of the structure of the skin. The circled area on this figure indicates the cross section of the enlargement in *Figure 1-2.*

Dermatology in General Medicine. Third Edition. Fitzpatrick et al, eds, McGraw-Hill, New York, 1987, p 70

The stratum corneum

The outermost layer of the skin is the **stratum corneum**, or "horn layer." Consider that the whole epidermis is only 0.04-1.5 mm (millimeters) thick; the stratum corneum (SC) is only 15-150 microns thick. To put that into perspective, the paper on which this is written is 70 microns thick. A micron is 1/1,000 of a millimeter; a millimeter is 0.039 inches. The SC is 0.0030 inches thick. That is thinner than a human hair. Most of human life hangs upon this thin structure, for without a SC the epidermis would perish. While the SC is very thin, it also is a very tough little tissue. Here is why. Look at the diagram of the stratum corneum under high magnification in **Figure 1-3**.

Keratin proteins make up the bulk of the SC. Keratin is a helical, or coil-shaped fibrous protein made up of a series of polypeptides. Polypeptides are, in turn, made up of amino acid basic units. These polypeptides vary in different parts of the body so that the skin is not homogeneous, but rather heterogeneous. The protein is resistant to water and many chemicals. It is this complex structure that provides part of the protection from the outside. Manufacturing proteins is one of the major functions of the skin. These proteins are formed with the other important component of the SC—the lipids.

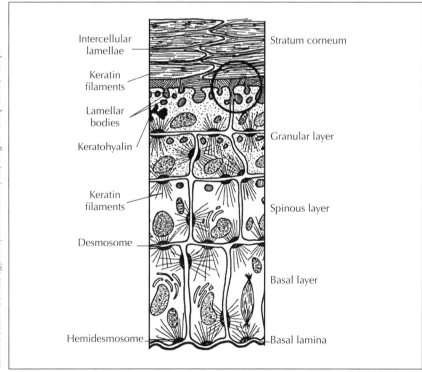

Scientific Basis of Dermatology, Thody and Friedmann, eds, Longman Group UK Ltd, 1986 p 7

Figure 1-2. *Diagram of the four layers of the epidermis. Note the various structures within the cells and the change from oblong, vertical cells in the basal layer to flat, horizontal cells in the stratum corneum. The circled area indicates the cross section of the enlargement in* **Figure 1-5**.

Lipids are water-insoluble, oily substances. They can be classified by their electrical charge and by their structure. The two major groups of lipids are **polar lipids** that have an electrical charge. Examples of this type of lipid are phospholipids, glycolipids and cholesterol. **Non-polar lipids** have no electrical charge. Triglycerides, squalene and waxes are examples of this group.

The six major structural groups of lipids are: **triglycerides**, the most abundant lipids in the body, which function as energy storage compounds and make up between 12–25% of the lipids in the SC; **fatty acids**, which give the oily feel and make up between 12–20% of the lipids in the SC; waxes, which make up 6% of the lipids in the SC; and **cholesterol**, **sphingolipids** and **ceramides**, which make up between 14–25% of lipids in the SC.

The lipid composition of the stratum corneum remains a mystery. While a great deal of work has been done, much of it by Peter Elias, MD, the final word remains to be written. The following is quote from a presentation by Dr. Elias at an international meeting on the stratum corneum held in Cardiff, Wales, in 1998:

"The structure of this barrier is a unique two-component system of lipid-depleted corneocytes embedded in a multi-lamellar, lipid-enriched extracellular matrix. Formation of this matrix is a multi-step sequence, beginning with the synthesis of the three SC lipids, cholesterol, ceramides and fatty acids. This is followed by packaging of these lipids as their precursors, along with lipid catabolic enzymes, within lamellar bodies. The next steps are: (a) secretion of lamellar body contents; and (b) extracellular processing of secreted lipid precursors by co-localized hydrolytic enzymes leading to barrier formation. Each step of this sequence is regulated tightly by alterations in barrier requirements allowing for rapid restoration of barrier homeostasis after most types of acute perturbation. The regulatory signals that link the SC with the nucleated layers,

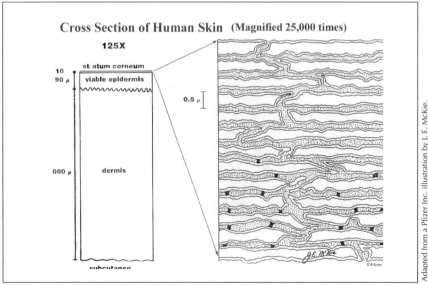

Figure 1-3. A diagram of the stratum corneum under high magnification.

thereby driving the epidermal metabolic apparatus, are beginning to be characterized. For example, alterations in extracellular divalent cations and other ions, resulting from loss during barrier perturbations, regulate lamellar body secretion from the outermost granular cells. Whereas cytokine and growth factor expression and release also are modulated by barrier perturbations, the role of these signaling molecules in re-establishing barrier homeostasis in unknown."

Making of the barrier

Here are the mechanisms, outlined briefly, that make up the final SC cell. The cells are called **keratinocytes** until they are finally cornified at which time they are called **corneocytes**. Follow the process in **Figure 1-4** showing the various layers of the skin.

The basal layer, or bottom layer, is the active, growing, dividing layer of the epidermis. Each cell divides under control of a very sophisticated biochemical system. As these cells divide, a series of biochemical reactions, or pathways, are set into motion. Two of these pathways are protein or keratin synthesis, and lipid synthesis. All of the biochemical action in these two pathways is designed to produce a tough, protective SC.

Step 1: Formation of keratin fibrils and early lipids. Keratin fibrils are formed from keratin filaments in the basal cells. They are part of the inner cell, the cytoplasm, which changes as the cell moves upward to the next layer.

The lipids of the basal cell differ from those in the SC in that there are more polar lipids and less free fatty acids, and almost no sphingolipids. They are mostly phospholipids and neutral lipids.

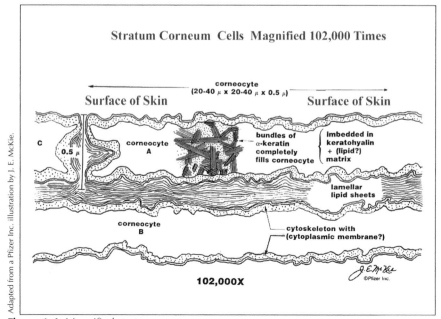

Figure 1-4. Magnified stratum corneum.

Step 2: The spiny layer and early differentiate. The keratin fibrils now become more plentiful and begin to change shape. A process of cross-linking takes place and the keratin is seen more easily in microscopic examination of the skin. The lipids in the spiny layer are not much different than those in the basal layer.

Step 3: The granular layer—the zone of transition. The keratin proteins in the granular layer are visible as dark aggregates and begin to almost completely fill the cell interior. They now are longer than they were in the spiny layer.

The first signs of lipid changes now occur. Free sterols are increased, ceramides and glycolipids now are seen and cholesterol sulfate is detected.[3] The lamellar body makes its appearance at this stage and the drama of the SC begins.

Step 4: Cornification—making the barrier. At this stage the keratinocyte has lost most of its enzyme functions, but not all. It hovers between life and death, but has reached its destiny and must become inanimate to serve its purpose. These cells are mostly protein, flat, very thin and hardy, and are stacked in layers. The outer layer easily sloughs off with mild force and new cells move up to replace it.

Between the cells, in the intercorneocyte space, a dramatic process occurs. Small, complex structures called lamellar bodies are scattered within the spaces between the corneocytes and appear to secrete free sterols, sphingolipids and other compounds such as glycoproteins. This arrangement permits both hydrophilic and hydrophobic materials to pass through the intercorneal space. (See **Figure 1-5.**)[3]

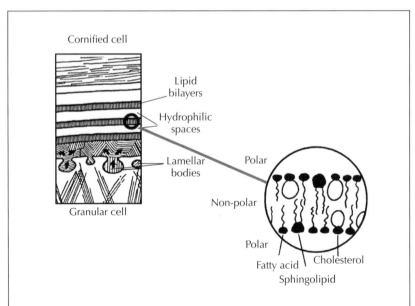

Scientific Basis of Dermatology, Thody and Friedmann, eds, Longman Group UK Ltd, 1986 p 28

Figure 1-5. *Left, diagram of intercellular substances showing lamellar bodies and neutral lipids. Note the circular enlarged area at right, showing the polar and non-polar lipids.*

Remember that the SC must permit the passage of water or hydrophilic material through the skin, as well as allow gases and oils, or hydrophobic material generated in the tissue, to escape. At the same time it must keep out undesirable environmental elements.

Notes on desquamation

The interest today in peeling the stratum corneum and the epidermis is extraordinary, yet the actual process of normal desquammation remains a mystery. We know there are enzymes and initiators, but how it all fits together is largely unknown. Here is a quote by Dr. Elias from the same meeting in Cardiff on the stratum corneum.

"The process of **desquamation** involves a well-regulated transition of a highly resistant tissue consisting of strongly cohesive cells to a loosely attached surface layer of cells among which most of the intercellular cohesion has been eliminated, and eventually shedding these cells to the surroundings. The mechanisms of stratum corneum cell cohesion and dissociation can be predicted to be complex and is far from fully understood. There are, however, a number of basic concepts that are reasonably well supported by experimental evidence collected during recent years.

"One of these concepts is that modified desmosomes in the stratum corneum are of major importance in stratum corneum cell cohesion, and that degradation of proteins responsible for corneocyte cohesion is a crucial prerequisite for a normal desquamation. Another established fact is that changes in the composition of the stratum corneum intercellular lipids can have effects on the rate of desquamation. So far it is not known, however, whether this effect is mediated via direct effects on cell cohesion, or via, for example, physico-chemical effects on involved enzymes such as proteases. The identification and characterization of the proteases involved in desquamation has not yet been fully achieved. There are, however, a number of candidate enzymes. Of these, stratum corneum chymotryptic enzyme, SCCE, has been most extensively studied. SCCE has catalytic properties and a tissue localization compatible with a role in the degradation of desmosomes in the stratum corneum, and it is uniquely expressed by cornifying squamous epithelia at sites where desquamation-like processes take place.

"In addition to SCCE a trypsin-like stratum corneum enzyme with a suggested role in desquamation has been described. This enzyme may also take part in desmosomal degradation. Another possibility is that it acts as an activating enzyme for SCCE, which is produced as an inactive precursor which becomes catalytically active after partial tryptic cleavage. To fully understand desquamation we have to know a lot more about what can be postulated to be very complex interactions between enzymes, enzyme inhibitors, lipids, water, proteins, and probably a number of other substances in the stratum corneum intercellular space with molecular structures of at least the same complexity at the outer surface of the corneocyte."

In this summary of skin physiology, a detailed explanation of this new information on enzymation desquamation would require a great deal of background information.

Control of epidermal growth and differentiation

Much is being learned about the intricacies of growth control and the associated feedback mechanisms involved. The epidermis is a very active tissue, both anatomically and metabolically, being able to replace itself completely in 45–74 days. The SC in the young can be fully replaced in about 14 days, while individuals over 50 can require as long as 37 days to replace the SC.

Changes in the SC send messages to the basal layer to produce cells at different rates. For instance, where there is pressure, such as on the sole of the foot, more cells are produced to make a thicker SC—a callus.

The skin care specialist should be aware of the various disorders of the skin that are associated with a high growth rate of the epidermis. These skin diseases are called **proliferative disorders** and are treated by dermatologists. Psoriasis and certain ichthyoses, or scaling conditions, are two examples of this disorder. The underlying cause of proliferative disorders is either a lack of control mechanism in the epidermis or in the

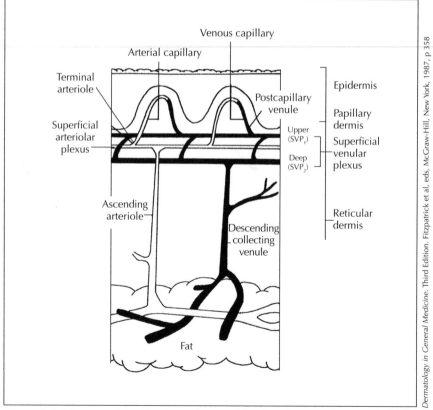

Dermatology in General Medicine. Third Edition. Fitzpatrick et al, eds, McGraw-Hill, New York, 1987, p 358

***Figure 1-6.** Diagram of the blood circulation of the skin showing the arterioles, venules and the capillary loops. The vessels are not drawn to scale, but are excellent graphic representations of the blood vessel system in the skin.*

dermis. This may be either an over-response reaction or lack of some inhibitory chemical. In any case, it demonstrates the interdependent relationship between the dermis and the epidermis.

The dermis

The dermis accounts for more than 90% of the skin mass and for the greatest part of its physical strength. The major divisions of the dermis are the **papillary layer** and the **reticular layer**.

The papillary dermis is the most outer part of the dermis in direct contact with the epidermis. It is thin, contains small and loose elastin and collagen fibers, and the lymphatic and blood vessels. In addition, there are connective tissue cells and interfibrillar gel in the papillary dermis.

The reticular dermis is under the papillary dermis and is found to have fewer cells, relatively few blood vessels, dense collagen bundles and coarse elastin fibers. This is the area that carries most of the physical stress of the skin.

Blood vessels in the dermis

The blood supply to the skin and the sweat glands, along with heat receptors and the central and sympathetic nervous system, are the chief players in the skin's role as a heat control organ. At this point the focus mainly is in the blood vessels of the skin.

The Physiology and Pathophysiology of the Skin, Volume 2, Jarret, ed, Academic Press, New York, 1973, p 620

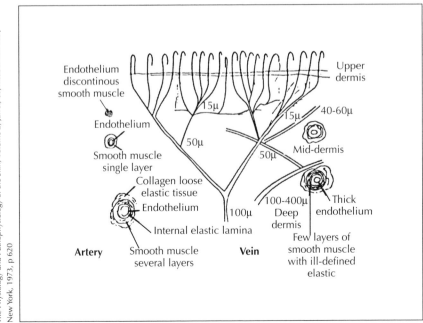

Figure 1-7. *Scematic diagram of the blood supply to the skin showing the various sizes and vessel wall structures.*

The peripheral blood vessel system is a three-dimensional maze of both large and small arterial and venous vessels. Starting with the cutaneous arteries, a number of smaller arterioles are given off to form the subcutaneous vascular bed. At the top of this system the fine capillaries of the papillary dermis serve to nourish the epidermis. (See **Figure 1-6**.) The vertical vessels connecting these two plexuses are the major skin blood vessels employed in heat control. The capillary is the key structure in the skin for our purpose and this small vessel needs to be understood in detail.

Capillaries develop in the embryo about the fourth month of gestation. By the fifth month, new vessels form from existing vessels by budding. In a fetus at this stage the skin is very thin, only a few cells thick, but it now increases rapidly and there is active and rapid blood vessel proliferation. The tiny capillaries now form into arterioles and venules, developing muscular coats and spreading the underlying tissue. These vessels will be the adult subcutaneous blood vessels. The ability of skin to repair itself after injury lies in this primitive ability to grow new vessels from capillaries.

Visualize the capillary network as a series of loops that arise from arteries which become smaller and smaller until they form tiny vessels of a few microns (μ) then loop over and become tiny venules that reverse the direction and grow larger as they return to the dermis. (See **Figure 1-7**.)

In one square mm of skin on the face, there is on an average 150 loops, 38 on the ears, 100+ on the neck, 45 on the arms, 60 on the hands, 20 on the fingers and 40 on the legs and the feet.

The cutaneous nerves

The skin is the largest sensory organ in the body. It must be able to detect many sensations such as pain, pressure or touch, itch, heat, cold and tickle. The sensory nervous system is discussed first and then the motor nerves of the skin. The distribution or cutaneous pattern is shown in **Figure 1-8**.

The sensory nerves

The sensory nerves all arise from the spinal nerve branches, or from the trigeminal nerve in the case of the face. These nerve branches are arranged in a pattern on the surface of the skin so that one branch serves an area that is called a **dermatome**.

Notice that on the trunk the dermatomes are horizontal while on the arms and legs they are more vertical and irregularly distributed. It is of interest that there is a very sharp line of demarcation of the nerves between the right and left sides of the body—the midaxial line, but not between adjacent nerves on each side where there is considerable overlap. Remember also that we are not dealing with a static system; these nerves are changing constantly according to the body's needs. For every cubic millimeter of nerve, there are about 57,000 nerve fibers. These fibers join to sensors in the skin to relay messages to the brain.

The vast majority of sensory system receptors are free nerve terminals that do not have a specialized ending. They are associated with pain and itch sensations. (See **Figure 1-9**.) **Hair follicle endings** are another type of sensory nerve.

Hederiform endings. These are thought to be mechanoreceptors for touch and other internal functions. Hederiform refers to a nerve that occurs in hairless skin. Hederiform endings also are called Merkel's discs by some anatomists since they were first described by Merkel.

Miessner's corpuscles. These are found in frictional areas of the skin, that is, the hands, fingers and soles of the feet and the toes. They transmit both touch and pressure. **Pacinian corpuscles** occur in the deep part of the dermis of the palms and fingers near the bones. They also are found in the external genitalia and the breast. They are believed to transmit vibration and pressure.

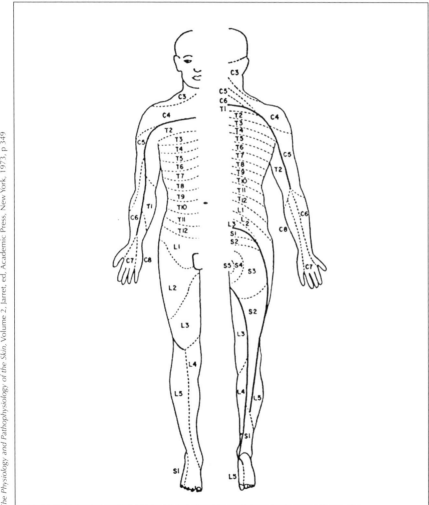

Figure 1-8. *Diagram of the cutaneous nerves. Also called dermatomes. Note that those nerves do not cross the midline of the front or back of the chest or abdomen.*

Mucocutaneous corpuscles. These previously were called Krause end-bulbs and occur in the dermis in transitional zones between the skin and mucous membranes such as the penis, clitoris, lips and tongue, and the eyelids. They do not occur in the hairy, or frictional skin areas. They resemble hair bulb endings and are probably pressure receptors. **Pilo-Ruffini** corpuscles are cylindrical encapsulated nerve endings encircling hair follicles just below the sebaceous duct. These receptors are believed to function as transmitters of slow mechanoreceptors.

Now all these nerve endings and receptors sound confusing, but keep in mind that it's necessary to know what is happening around us all the time. Only special sensors can detect and relay that information. You will see in **Figure 1-9** that these receptors are scattered in the dermal part of the skin, starting under the epidermis with the fine unmylenated nerves. The endings that detect more intense pressure are the Pacinian corpuscles, located deeper in the dermis. Since hands and feet are the major pressure sensitive areas, there are more Pacinian corpuscle on these areas.

Motor nerves

The motor nerves of the skin supply the sweat glands, the pilomotor apparatus and the muscle and the external coat of the microvasculature. It consists of "postganglionic sympathetic fibers" that are part of the sympathetic nervous system or autonomic nervous system over which we have no control.

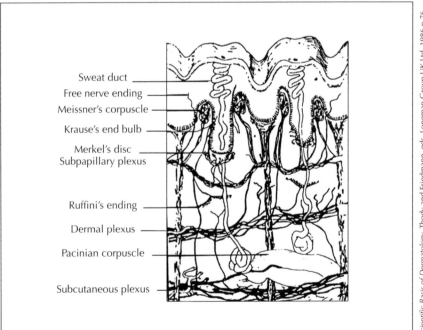

Sweat duct
Free nerve ending
Meissner's corpuscle
Krause's end bulb
Merkel's disc
Subpapillary plexus
Ruffini's ending
Dermal plexus
Pacinian corpuscle
Subcutaneous plexus

Scientific Basis of Dermatology, Thody and Friedmann, eds, Longman Group UK Ltd, 1986 p 76

Figure 1-9. *Diagram of the cutaneous nerves and nerve endings. Note the relationship of the various receptors to the epidermis and the dermis.*

Structural proteins—collagen and elastin

Collagen is derived from the Greek words *kolla* for "glue" and *gennan* for "to produce." It is true that glue has been made from the hides of animals for centuries and a very effective glue it is. As in all tissue the collagen fiber is made up of many fibrils which, in turn, are made up of smaller microfibrils. The microfibrils are made up of molecules of rod-like structure. These molecules consist of three polypeptide chains, wrapped around each other as a triple helix which provides rigidity to the molecule.[5, 6]

Hydroxyproline, an amino acid molecule, comprises 10% of the total amino acid content of collagen. Without hydroxyproline, no triple helix is formed and the alpha chains are degraded. Vitamin C is essential for the formation of hydroxyproline by the enzyme prolyl hydroxylase. Scurvy results from lack of vitamin C and produces many signs of connective tissue abnormalities.

Collagen does not stretch very well and, in fact, this is one of its functions—to resist stretching. The ability of collagen to respond to physical stress changes with age and sun damage. It is believed that sunlight in the range of 310–400 nanometers, UVA, is capable of inhibiting the action of the enzyme prolyl hydroxylase.

There are at least eight major types of collagen and some sub-types as well. For the skin care specialist, Types I and IV are the most important.

In this chapter the story of collagen is discussed briefly, but the interested reader is referred to a general article by Uitto and Eisen for a comprehensive review of collagen. The article reads easily and contains superb references.[7]

Elastin is beginning to command more and more attention from research workers in dermatology, reconstructive surgery and in the basic science disciplines. It is elastin that gives the skin its resiliency and elegant feel. It provides the spring and "snap" to the young face.

Elastin is a fibrous protein that makes up 0.6–2.1% of the dry weight of the skin compared to 72% for collagen. At present only one genetic type of elastin is known. The structure of the elastin molecule has not been defined completely. It is not known if the fibrous protein elastin forms one of the two proteins making up elastic fibers. The elastic fibers are cross-linked by desmosine, a special amino acid that occurs only in elastin. Some investigators feel it is the desmosine cross-link that provides the spring in the elastin molecule. The other component in the elastic fibers is a microfibrillar structure. These microfibrils surround the elastin molecule and the combination produces the elastic fibers.

Within the dermis, the collagen and elastin are in a fluid matrix called the "ground substance." This matrix consists of water and a class of large molecules—macromolecules—known as proteoglycans. These will be discussed briefly.

In order for the dermis to react instantly to changes in external pressures on the skin, it requires a system that is capable of passing through a phase of almost complete liquid to a phase of almost complete solid. This action is mediated by water bonding to macromolecules called proteoglycans. The basic structure of these molecules is a polysaccharide and a protein. The polysaccharides are called glycosaminoglycans. One of these glycosaminoglycans is called hyaluronic acid, another is dermatan sulfate, and together they account for a major portion of the proteoglycans. The total content of these compounds in the skin is only 0.1–0.3% of dry weight of the skin. The proteoglycans serve to maintain water balance in the dermis, to add support for other dermal components and to act as a matrix for cell migration, metabolism and growth. Much more needs to be learned about this material for it is the substance that gives skin its elegant feel.

Notes on the barrier function of the skin

Is there a difference in barrier function among the various races—and between the genders? What effect does aging having on barrier function? The answers are complex, but these are two questions that are important for the esthetician who treats skin daily. Here is some data that will help explain the basis of these differences.

Many scientists use **transepidermal water loss**, or TEWL, as a measure of barrier function. This is the water that escapes through the stratum corneum into the air. Do not confuse this with sweat. The essential difference is that TEWL is not detectable by the eye or touch, while sweat easily is seen and felt. TEWL is measured as either milligrams of water per square centimeter per hour, written as $mg/cm^2/hr$, or as grams per meter squared per hour, written as $gm/m^2/hr$. They are exactly the same quantity, just expressed over different areas. There are 10,000 square centimeters in a square meter.

It is well known that anything that distrubs the skin barrier increases the TEWL. Using tape stripping to remove the stratum corneum and disrupt the barrier, scientists found that skin type, that is the Fitzgerald Classification, correlates with barrier function. They showed that dark skin, types V and VI, showed a more resistant barrier after tape stripping and healed faster than white or light skin, types I to IV. Race and gender had no influence on the results. A light-skinned African had more water loss then a dark-

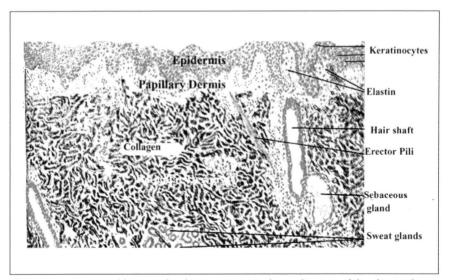

Figure 1-10. A normal human skin biopsy compared to a diagram of the skin and the basic parts of the skin section—epidermis, papillary dermis, reticular dermis and a few major adnexal components.

skinned Caucasian. Clinically, this means that you will have greater absorption of products in light-skinned individuals than in darker-skinned individuals.[8]

A second note on barrier function related to mature skin. It has been found that older skin, that is 89 years or older, has a deficient stratum corneum and cannot make lamellar bodies as well as young skin. As a result the barrier is more permeable, heals more slowly and is more susceptible to environmental insult.[9]

Introduction to skin histology

Many times, during slide presentations, lecturers will use microscopic sections of skin to explain the action of some product, or to define a disease or skin disorder. These microscopic sections of skin represent microscopic anatomy, or histology, the study of the fine structure of skin. *Histo* is a Greek word meaning "web or tissue."

To prepare a histological section of skin, it first must be removed from the patient. This is called a **biopsy**, from the Greek word *opsis* meaning "vision." A piece of skin is removed by cutting, or punching out a small section, then placing the section in formalin, solution of 10% formaldehyde, to fix, or denature it. By fixing it, all living reactions are stopped, such as enzyme reactions, and bacterial and oxidative damage is prevented. The section is then passed through a series of chemical baths to condition it for embedding in paraffin. Once embedded, the section can be cut with a special instrument called a microtome. The cut section is placed on a glass slide, allowed to dry and then stained.

The colors seen on a histological slide actually are dyes, or stains. The most common one is called an H & E stain, for hemotoxylin and eosin, two widely used biological dyes. A normal human skin biopsy compared to a diagram of the skin is shown in **Figure 1-10**, and the basic parts of the skin section, epidermis, papillary dermis, reticular dermis and a few major adnexal components have been outlined.

Conclusion

This is the story of skin. All of the components of the skin contribute to what is seen on the outside. Although researchers have learned a lot about the behavior of skin, there is much more to be learned. No research, however, has explained fully why one person's skin behaves differently from another person's. That is the challenge and the opportunity for estheticians and all skin care specialists: ***to know and use both the science and the art of skin care.***

References

1. Odland GF, Structure of the skin, *Biochemistry and Physiology of the Skin*, Volume 1, L Goldsmith L, ed, Oxford Press: New York, 3 (1983)

2. Baden HP and Kubilus J, The fibrous proteins of the epidermis, *The Stratum Corneum*, Marks R and Plewig G, eds, Springer-Verlag: New York, 2 (1983)

3. Elias P, et al, The intercorneocyte space, *The Stratum Corneum*, Marks R and Plewig G, ed, Springer-Verlag: New York, 61 (1983)

4. Ryan TJ, Structure and shape of blood vessels in the skin, *The Physiology and Pathophysiology of the Skin*, Volume 2, Jarret, A, ed, Academic Press: New York, 589 (1974)

5. Prockop DJ, et al, The biosynthesis of collagen and its disorders, *New Eng J Medicine* 301:77–85 (1979)

6. Bauer EA and Uitto J, Special tissue collagen: skin, *Collagen in Health and Disease*, Churchill Livingstone: Edingburgh, 474–487 (1982)

7. Uitto J and Eisen A, Collagen, *Dermatology in General Medicine*, Third Edition, TB Fitzpatrick TB, et al, eds, McGraw Hill: New York, 259–287 (1987)

8. Reed JI, Ghadially R and Elias PM, Skin type, but neither race or gender influence epidermal permeablility barrier function, *Arch Dermat* 131:1134–1138 (1995)

9. Ghadially R, et al, The Aged Epidermis Permeability Barrier, *J Clinical Invest* 95:2281–2290 (1995)

General References

Champion RH, Gillman T, Rook AJ and Sims RT, eds, *An Introduction to the Biology of the Skin*, Blackwell Scientific: Oxford (1970). An excellent first book for an overview of the skin. Easy reading.

Fitzpatrick TB, Eisen AZ, Wolff, K, Freedberg IM and Austen KF, eds, Dermatology in General Medicine, Two Volumes, McGraw Hill: New York (1987)

Goldsmith LA, ed, *Biochemistry and Physiology of the Skin*, Two Volumes, Oxford University Press (1983). A comprehensive text for the serious advanced student of skin. An excellent reference book for the skin care school.

Jarret A, ed, *The Physiology and Pathophysiology of the Skin*, Six Volumes, Academic Press: New York (1977)

Marks R and Plewig G, eds, *The Stratum Corneum*, Springer-Verlag: New York (1982)

Mier PD and Cotton DWK, *The Molecular Biology of the Skin*, Blackwell Scientific: Oxford (1976). Provides an excellent starting point for in-depth skin biology.

Montagna W, Bentley JP and Dobson RL, eds, The Dermis, Appleton-Century-Crofts: New York (1970). A classic and easy reading.

Regan JD and Parrish JA, eds, *The Science of Photomedicine*, Plenum: New York (1982)

Thody AJ and Friedman PS, eds, *Scientific Basis of Dermatology*, Churchill Livingstone: New York (1986)

Chapter 2

The Desquamation Process

Estheticians usually are concerned with mechanisms to either hydrate or remove the stratum corneum. Desquamation, the shedding of corneocytes, is the biological mechanism of removing the stratum corneum. While it may seem to be a simple process, it actually is extremely complex, with only a few known details.

There is a complex relationship between epidermal cell production, maturation and desquamative loss. Corneocyte hydration, stratum corneum barrier function and enzymatic corneodesmolysis are involved in a dynamic interrelationship. In addition to these mechanisms, many physiological and environmental factors acting in a different time frame influence desquamation. Alteration, or changes in some of these factors, result in several skin conditions, two of which are xerotic, or dry, skin; and ichthyotic, or fish scale, skin.

Purpose of the stratum corneum

The major purpose of the skin is to form a protective barrier, preventing loss of body fluids. Yet, this barrier must be permeable to certain fluids and gases, must constantly regenerate, and must serve to detoxify it and manufacture essential compounds for the rest of the body. Achieving these functions requires an organ system that is responsive to many stimuli—one that can produce a tough, waterproof layer of cells that can be thick or thin, rugged or beautiful, and which can be shed easily. This process—**epidermal keratinization**—is not our topic for it is far too complex a subject for a single chapter. This chapter will concentrate instead on understanding how these specialized keratinocytes, called **corneocytes**, are shed—a process known as **desquamation**.

Overview of keratinization

The names of the basic four layers of the epidermis actually describe the function of each layer. This is shown in **Figure 2-1**, a diagram well-known to estheticians.

Basal layer. This is a fully active, multi-potential layer of cells capable of almost endless replication to supply new cells to the outer surface.

Spiny layer. This is the first step of cellular differentiation, the process of changing from an immature cell to a fully functional end cell, no longer able to divide or to grow.

Granular layer. A second cellular differentiating step in which the nucleus is completely taken apart and degraded and new tough keratin fiber continue to form.

Stratum corneum. The last differentiation step in which the young keratinocyte is formed into a hard, water-resistant cell—corneocyte.

In the process of arriving at the top of the skin, the keratinocyte goes through many, many changes until finally it can function as a barrier cell. The cytoplasm of the cell is completely replaced with keratin protein, a complex process that requires many enzymes. The outer membrane being replaced by lipids and proteins requires even more enzymes. A basic knowledge of enzymes is essential to understand both normal physiology and the pathological conditions that afflict the skin. A brief introduction to enzymes is needed.

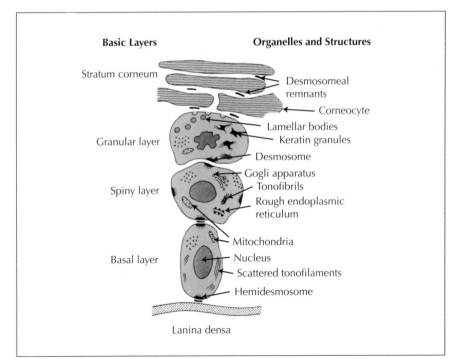

Figure 2-1. Four basic layers of the epidermis.

Enzymology

Without enzymes, there is no life. So what are they and why are they so important? All enzymes are proteins—not ordinary proteins, but special proteins that are able to interact with other substances, called **substrates**, and change that substance into something else, and yet not be altered or used up in the process.

Here is an example. Sugar, or glucose, must be changed from simple glucose to a more complex form known as glucose-6-phosphate before it can be used by the body. What actually happens is a phosphorus group is added to the number 6 carbon of the glucose, hence the name glucose-6-phosphate. The enzyme that adds the phosphate to the glucose is called hexokinase, which means an enzyme that adds a phosphate to a 6-carbon sugar. Note that the last three letters of the enzyme are **–ase**, the identifying ending of enzymes. Writing this out as an equation provides a quick picture of what happens:

Glucose + phosphorus + hexokinase ==> glucose-6-phosphate + hexokinase

In this reaction, one substance—phosphorus—has been added to another—glucose—producing a third chemical—glucose-6-phosphate. Three terms are needed to understand this reaction—**substrate**, **enzyme** and **product**. Glucose is the substrate; hexokinase is the enzyme; and glucose-6-phosphate is the product.

Here is another example, changing lactic acid to pyruvic acid, a reaction that occurs millions of times a day in the body:

Lactic acid + lactic dehyrogenase ==> pyruvic acid + lactic dehyrogenase (LHD)
Substrate   **Enzyme**   **Product**

Now, it is not quite that simple because a few things need to be added to make that equation really work. These two acids are quite different chemically. Here is the full reaction:

Lactic acid + NAD$^+$ + LDH ==> pyruvic acid + NADH$^+$ + H + LDH
<==

Note that this reaction can go both ways. ***It is a reversible reaction, using the same enzyme.*** Lactic acid is an alpha hydroxy acid, meaning it has an **OH** group on the alpha carbon. Pyruvic acid is a keto acid, meaning it has an **=O**, double-bond oxygen, on the alpha carbon. The complete chemical reaction is shown in **Figure 2-2**, and is part of the big picture in the metabolism of glucose.

A third example is more general. Let's chew up a protein so it can be made smaller. Take any protein and add a protease, for example bromelain from pineapples. It's a simple reaction:

Protein, such as keratin + bromelain ==> peptides + bromelain
Substrate   **Enzyme**   **Product**

Note this is not a reversible reaction. The arrow goes in only one direction. Some enzyme reactions are reversible and some are not. You can learn from further study which ones go both ways. This is the basic enzyme reaction—***a substrate is acted on*** *by an enzyme to produce a product of some type.* The enzyme is not used up and is able to do the same thing again and again, thousands of times in minutes.

The stratum corneum

Fibrous proteins and lipids make up the corneocytes of the stratum corneum. Each corneocyte is made as a single cell and then is integrated into the structure called the stratum corneum. Most scientists are impressed with how thin the stratum corneum is on the face and back of the hands. A layer less than 20 microns thick provides the protection needed. **Figure 2-3** shows the dimensions of the stratum corneum compared to the rest of the skin layers.

Forming these corneocytes is a complex process, and although many of the details are known, the complete process is not. Each step requires one or more enzymes. Many of the details have been reduced to present as clear a picture as possible in the formation of a simple corneocyte. Knowing the names of the proteins involved in cell adhesion and desquamation is important as corneocyte formation is followed.

Basal cell

How is the basal cell bonded to the dermis? The basal cell is anchored to fibers in the dermis called the lamina densa by means of a structure called **hemidesmosomes**, from the Greek words *desmos*, which means "a band," *soma*, which means "body," and *hemi*, which means "half."

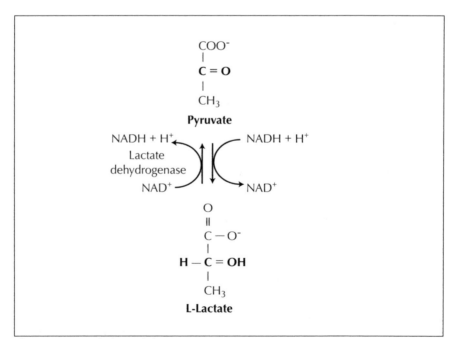

Figure 2-2. Metabolism of glucose.

The structure of the hemidesmosome is complex, consisting of a dense plaque on the plasma membrane that contains integrin molecules that pass into the lamina densa and attach to fibronectin fibers. Within the cell, the integrin molecules are attached to cytoskelatal intermediate filaments.

Integrins are extracellular matrix receptors in the cell membrane. That is, they are special glycoproteins on the cell membrane that bind to extracellular proteins in the dermis. This is shown in **Figure 2-4**. **Fibronectin** is an adhesive glycoprotein found in the dermis to which integrin bind. **Intermediate filaments** are intercellular proteins that bind to the fibrous components of the cell, the cytoskeleton, and then bind to the hemidesmosome plaque. **Laminin** is an adhesive protein that attaches the cell surface to the basal lamina, often through integrins.

Step 1: Forming the daughter cell—the spiny layer. First the basal cell must break the attachment to the dermis, round up, and undergo mitotic division of the nucleus and split into two new cells. The mother cell remains able to divide many times. The daughter cell is programmed to become a corneocyte and die, that is, it cannot receive messages or send messages to lower cells in the epidermis. After being formed, the daughter cell is anchored to the basal cell by a structure similar to the hemidesmosome, known as a **desmosome**, since it connects to two cells. The fine whisker-like projections into the cells are shown in **Figure 2-5**.

Step 2: The daughter cell differentiates into a corneocyte in the spiny layer. The daughter cell splits off from the basal cell and becomes a partially differentiated cell, that is, it no longer can go back to being a basal cell. A major change has occurred

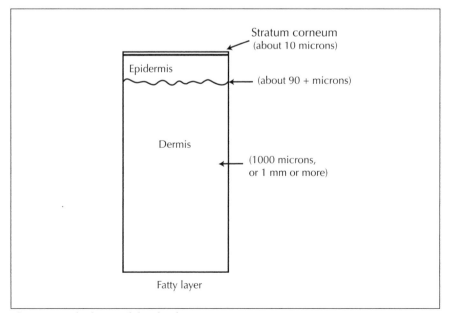

Figure 2-3. Thickness of the skin layers.

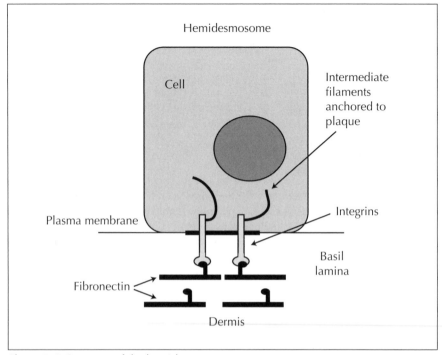

Figure 2-4. *Structure of the hemidesmosome.*

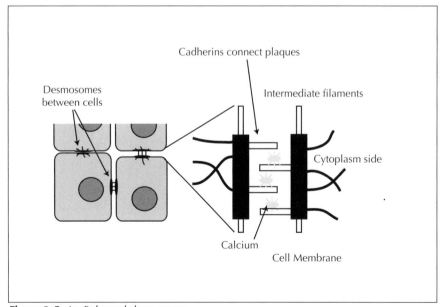

Figure 2-5. *An Enlarged desmosome.*

in the nucleus of the daughter, programming the cell to become a corneocyte. The basal cell pushes the daughter cell up into the epidermis to form a second layer known as the stratum spinosum, or spiny layer. These spines actually are projections of fibrous proteins in the desomosomes, the structures that connect the cells of the epidermis; the cells are hooked together by desmosomes at top, sides and bottom. The spiny cells have several desmosomes that connect them not only to the basal cell, but also to adjacent cells. A desmosome is very much like a hemidesmosome except it joins cells to other cells, not to the lamina densa, or basement membrane. **Figure 2-5** shows an enlarged desmosome.

A complete set of organelles, such as nucleus, Gogli apparatus and mitochondria, remain in the spiny cell, though they are beginning to undergo some changes. Membrane-coating granules and lamellar bodies are starting to form and can be seen in the cytoplasm. A great deal of enzyme activity is creating lipids and proteins, while other enzymes are beginning to take apart the interior of the cell, getting it ready for the next step.

Step 3: *The granular layer.* The granular layer also is known as the stratum granulosum, a layer in which marked changes in the kerantinocyte occur rapidly. The cell is flattened, though still viable, and many lamellar bodies are seen in the cytoplasm at the upper part of the cell. These lamellar bodies contain stacks of flattened lipid vesicles. As the cell slowly is taken apart and new structures form, a dramatic change occurs.

Step 4: *The stratum lucidum.* An abrupt transition of the granular cell to the stratum lucidum ends in the final stages of differentiation that leads to cornification of the cell. The stratum lucidum often is hard to see with the light microscope, as the cells are further flattened, being quite thin. Proteases and nucleases destroy the cellular organelles, leaving only the keratin filaments in the intracellular matrix composed of broken down keratohyalin granules. The membrane-coating granules fuse with the cell membrane and release their contents into the intercellular spaces forming intercellular lipids that are organized into a multi-lamellar domain. These lipids are cholesterol, ceramides and fatty acids, a group of non-polar compounds. The final stage is the addition of a protein envelope called involucrin to the cell membrane, forming the cornified cell, and giving it greater strength.

Step 5: *Corneocyte.* This is the end stage of all the activity, for here the final corneocyte is made. The outer membrane is a hard envelope composed of the protein **involucrin**. Under this envelope is a lipid envelope called the corneocyte lipid envelope, and under this layer are the keratin matrix proteins. These are shown in **Figure 2-6**.

In review, this is the sequence of events:

1. The basal cell divides and forms a daughter cell.

2. The daughter cell slowly begins to differentiate into a corneocyte in the spiny layer.

3. The spiny layer cells move into the granular layer where the organelles are taken apart.

4. Lamellar bodies are formed and extruded into the intercellular spaces.

5. All of the organelles are gone and the center of the cell is filled with keratin fibers.

6. The lipid envelope forms, the involucrin surrounds the cells and the lamellar bodies are pushed between the cells forming the intercellular matrix. These components are shown in a simplified diagram in **Figure 2-7**.

Now that the stratum corneum is formed, it can be taken apart through desquamation.

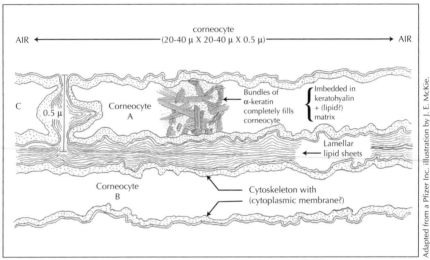

Figure 2-6. *Stratum corneum cells magnified 102,000 times.*

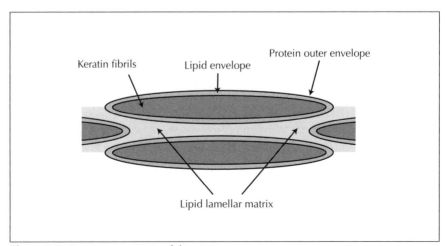

Figure 2-7. *Basic components of the corneocyte.*

An evolving process

In the last five years or so, more has been learned about the complicated process of desquamation—at least enough to understand some of the things that must be known to keep this process normal. Perhaps no other area of skin care is neglected as much as the knowledge of desquamation. Considering all of the peels used by physicians and estheticians, it could be assumed that all is known about this process. This is not the case.

Why desquamate?

The corneocyte shed into the atmosphere each day. Literally millions of cells fly into the air. Consider these numbers.

The average size of a corneocyte is 20–40 microns, although they can be smaller or larger. In a square centimeter of area there are 10 x 10 millimeters or 100 square millimeters. There are 1,000 micron in a millimeter, or 10,000 micron per side. Multiplying 10,000 x 10,000 equals 100,000,000 microns. Divide this by 30 x 30 or 900 square microns for the average size of a corneocyte—100 million micron/900 square micron per cell, and the result is 111,000 corneocyte per square centimeter. Just on the top of the lower arm, which is 8-inches by 2.5 inches, or 20 centimeters x 5.5 centimeters, that equals 110 square centimeters; 111,000 x 110 = 12 million cells, just from the dorsal surface of the lower arm. You shed about one layer of cells a day.

We need to desquamate to get rid of damaged cells and cells that are contaminated with bacteria and other environmental pollutants, such as poison ivy toxins. This is a protective, but also a self-cleansing mechanism. How does it work? Essentially, *it works by enzyme action.*

Desquamation enzymes

The cells are hooked together by desmosomes at the top, sides and bottom. As the cells move to the top of the epidermis, the desmosome are attached, but become weaker. Two known enzymes effectively **break the bonds of the desomosomes** and free the cells to flake off from the stratum corneum. One of these enzymes is chymotrypsin and the other is a special type of trypsin.

Chymotrypsin is an enzyme that breaks up peptide bonds of proteins. This enzyme works best at pH 8, but it also functions at pH 5.5. Since the skin cells below the stratum corneum contain the enzymes and these cells are in a pH 7.4 environment, they are near the optimum pH. It is a very special type of chymotrypsin, known as **stratum corneum chymotryptic enzyme**, or **SCCE**, that occurs only in the skin and hair follicles. It is inactive until acted upon by a trypsin-like enzyme.[1, 2]

The second **trypsin-like enzyme** is less understood than SCCE, but skin scientists believe it interacts with SCCE to activate it, though it has a proteolytic action itself. Chemically, it is known as a **serine protease**.[3, 4] It is a heat-stable enzyme, even above 100-degrees C; is most active at pH 9; and has a higher activity in the upper stratum corneum than in the lower layers.[5]

What regulates desquamation?

The exact mechanism that regulates desquamation is unknown. So far, quite a few factors seem to enter the picture. It's known that proteolytic degradation of the desmosomes is a central event in desquamation, but what starts this action? The precursors of the enzymes must be activated; the inhibitors of the enzymes must be inactivated. Also changes in lipid composition of the stratum corneum intercellular matrix, changes in the water content, pH changes, and the action of other enzymes such as glycosidases, all have been shown to have some effect on the desquamation process.[6, 7, 8, 9, 10]

Consider that the corneocytes are dead and cannot communicate with lower cells. The barrier function must be maintained at all times if the skin is to survive, therefore desquamation within the barrier would be very harmful to the skin.

Any process of desquamation must be programmed in the keratinocytes in the lower levels of the epidermis, that is, the stratum granulosum, or below. It appears that the cells are programmed to stay linked for a certain period of time and then cell cohesion decreases and cells flake off. The process of cell turnover occurs in a period of two to four weeks, depending on a person's age. In most cases, desquamation presents no problems as it is quite imperceptible, but there are a few conditions where it presents serious problems when the enzymes go haywire.

Desquamation disorders

Desquamation disorders are not defined clearly as to etiology since many of them are related to disorders of proteins—keratinization—or lipid disorders, or changes in glycoprotein dysfunction. All of these are very complicated diseases, involving a great deal of biochemistry to understand. Here are some of the major features of a few of the more common disorders associated with desquamation that involve enzyme defects:

Ichthyosis group. This is the name given to a group of skin disorders characterized by persistent, non-inflammatory scaling of the skin surface. The name comes from the Greek word *ichthyos* for "fish," since the scaling appearance suggested the skin of fish to early physicians. One specific enzyme abnormality has been identified as a cause of one form of ichthyosis, but the manifestation of this disease suggests multiple enzyme problems may be involved. In most cases, the disease is inherited as a dominant characteristic.

Clinically, this is a mild disease, often undetected by a casual observer. The desquamation mainly is from the extensor surfaces of the top of the arms and legs. In appearance, it may be a fine scaly type, or plaque-like scales. Some patients have more severe forms that require constant treatment. Generally mild moisturizing and gentle exfoliating are required. The use of 2% salicylic acid in an anhydrous base works well in most cases.

Lamella ichthyosis (LI). A severely disfiguring congenital skin disorder is caused by a genetic defect in the skin enzyme called ***transglutaminase 1 (TGM1)***, which plays a role in the formation of the outermost layer of the skin. Babies with LI often are born encased in a thick, shiny membrane that soon dries and peels off, leaving the baby with bright red underlying skin. Over time, patients develop large, brown plate-like scales all over their bodies, representing a thickening and scaling of the stratum corneum. People with LI may not tolerate heat and may have turned-out eyelids or lips due to tautness of facial skin. Some patients also suffer from scarring hair loss involving the scalp and eyebrows.

Researchers believe that with ichthyosis, the thickening and scaling are due either to runaway production of new stratum corneum cells or a defect in the process by which these cells slough off from the skin's surface. LI is a relatively rare disorder, occurring in about one of every 250,000 births. People with this scaling skin disease often are subjected to societal pressures that lead to isolation, ridicule and misunderstanding.

TGM1 serves to cross-link cellular proteins to form a rigid scaffold within the lifeless cells that form the stratum corneum. This molecular scaffold is an integral part of the cornified cell envelope, a specialized structure that replaces the cell membrane in cells of this outermost layer of the epidermis. The stratum corneum is formed as epidermal cells, keratinocytes, generated in the lowest layer of the epidermis move up toward the skin's surface, pushing older cells ahead of them. As these cells move upwards, they undergo a series of structural and functional changes. In the final stages of this maturation process, known as terminal differentiation, the keratinocytes become more flattened, the cornified cell envelope forms, and the cells eventually die and slough off.

The terminal differentiation process somehow is abnormal in people with LI. How the scaling skin occurs is poorly understood, yet very important, for while it is known that a major cause of scaling is the failure of this one component of the process, the specifics as to exactly what role these cross-links play in producing a normal stratum corneum is still a mystery.[11]

Psoriasis. This is one of the most complicated skin diseases seen by estheticians. Somewhere between 1.5–3% of the population has psoriasis. This is a great number of cases, running into the millions. Asians have less psoriasis than Caucasians, but the reason is not known. Basically, it is a hyperproliferative disease, meaning that the keratincytes grow too fast. This is not the only problem though, for the corneocytes do not desquamate as they should. This results in the formation of large plaques. An inflammatory component also exists, which makes the skin red, due to dilation of capillaries.

There are many causative factors in psoriasis. It is inherited and there are immuno-logical, biochemical and psychological factors involved. One group of enzymes is involved—proteases and protease inhibitors. One of these enzymes is known as **alpha-1-anti-trypsin**, which is found in the bloodstream and functions to inhibit the action of trypsin on proteins. It is known that individuals with high levels of alpha-1-anti-trypsin have more severe psoriasis than those patients with lower levels.

The treatment of psoriasis is forever since there is no cure. There are many types of treatments, but none work very well. Cortisone derivatives are used most often for severe cases, but treatments that suppress proliferation and aid desquamation are helpful. Some day estheticians may be able to treat psoriasis as effectively as physicians do today.

Chapter 2

Summary

The stratum corneum is the end point of all epidermal growth, providing protection from the outside and maintaining the inside of our bodies. A thorough knowledge of the anatomy, biochemistry and physiology of the stratum corneum is essential to the esthetician for rational care of the client. Knowing that the keratinocyte undergoes changes that result in a hard protective cell called a corneocyte is critical to appreciating the physiology of the skin.

When you apply any product to the skin, or even touch the skin, you are perturbing the stratum corneum in some manner. Plucking one hair will induce epidermal growth factor to stimulate keratinocyte proliferation. When you understand the basic chemistry of the stratum corneum, your life as an esthetician will become pure joy, for you will be able to play the skin like a fine-tuned instrument.

References

1. Egelrud T and Lundstrom A, A chymotrypsin-like proteinase that may be involved in desquamation in plantar stratum corneum. *Arch Dermatol Res* 283: 108–112 (1991)

2. Hansson L, Stromquist M, Backman, A, Walibrandt P, Carlstein A and Egelrud T, Cloning, expression and characterization of stratum corneum chymotryptic enzyme, a skin-specific human serine proteinase. *J Biol Chem* 269: 19420–19426 (1994)

3. Suzuki Y, Nomura J, Koyama J, Takahashi M and Horii, I, Detection and characterization of endogenous protease associated with desquamation of stratum corneum. *Arch Dermatol Res* 285: 372–377 (1993)

4. Egelrud T, Purification and preliminary characterization of stratum corneum chymotryptic enzyme: a proteinase that may be involved in desquamation. *J Invest Dermatol* 101: 200–204 (1993)

5. Chang-Yi, c, et al, 30 kDa trypsin-like protease in the plantar stratum corneum, *J Dermatol* 21: 504–509 (1997)

6. Franzke CW, Baici A, Bartels J, Christophers E and Wiedow O, Antileukoprotease inhibits stratum corneum chymotryptic enzyme: evidence for a regulative function in desquamation, *J Biol Chem* 271: 2186–2189 (1996)

7. Williams ML, Lipids in normal and pathological desquamation, *Adv Lipid Res* 24: 211–262 (1991)

8. Warner RR, Water content from analysis of freeze-dried thin section, *J Microsc* 142: 363–369 (1986)

9. von Zglinicky T, Lindberg M, Roomans GM and Forslind B, Water and ion distribution profiles in human skin, *Acta Derm Venereol* (Stockh) 73: 340–343 (1993)

10. Ohman H and Vahiquist A, In vivo studies concerning a pH gradient in human stratum corneum and upper epidermis, *Acta Derm Venereol* (Stockh) 74: 375–379 (1994)

11. Russell LJ, DeGiovanna, JJ, Rogers GR, Steinert PM, Hashem N, Compton J and Bale S, Mutations of the gene for transglutaminase 1 in autosomal recessive lamellar ichthyosis, *Nature Genetics* March (1995)

Chapter 3

The Appendages

The appendages include the hair follicles, the sebaceous glands and the sweat glands.* The one aspect they have in common is that they all reside in the dermis and open either directly or indirectly onto the stratum corneum, the surface of the skin. The esthetician who is not concerned primarily with care of the hair on the head, still needs to know the physiology of the hair because of hair removal treatments used on the face and the extremities, such as waxing and electrolysis.

Hair follicles and the hair

The hair is believed to serve no physiological function in humans. Although of social importance, hair is not a vital organ. There is much speculation over the origin and role of hair that makes delightful reading. In humans, hair remains one of the most considered parts of human anatomy and therefore requires our attention.

Structural characteristics. Hair is a fibrous protein structure that consists of at least three different proteins. The basic structure of the hair arises from a series of six concentric rings in the hair bulb. (See **Figure 3-1**.)

The six concentric rings of cells all arise from a single stem cell group called the matrix of the hair bulb. There must be six populations of keratinocytes in this region, unlike the epidermis where there is only one type. The three inner rings that form the hair are known as the **medulla**, the **cortex** and the **cuticle**, going from the center outward. The outer three layers, again starting inside and moving outward, are the cuticle, the **inner root sheath** and the **outer root sheath**.

Hair growth. Hair grows at varying rates in different regions of the body. Scalp hair grows about 0.37 mm a day. In women, hair on the scalp grows faster than in men, but men have faster growing body hair. Some hair, such as the beard, axillary and pubic,

---

* The fingernails and toenails also are appendages, but are not discussed in this chapter.

require hormones for growth. There remains a question of the exact influence of thyroid hormone and estrogen on hair growth. Androgens, the male hormones, cause hair growth to be coarse in both men and women. In males it is associated with male pattern baldness.[1]

Hair grows in cycles, so growth is intermittent. Unlike many animals, under normal conditions humans do not lose all their hair at one time. Starting with the active period called **anagen**, the hair passes to a transitional phase called **catagen** in which the base of the hair is keratinized to form a "club hair." The base shrinks and finally separates from the follicle pushing the club hair upward. A resting period follows which is called **telogen** in which the club hair is lost and the cycle begins again. (See **Figure 3-2**.)[2]

Hair grows for a period of about three years before falling out. About 100 hairs a day are lost and about as many grow. Without this cyclic, mosaic pattern humans would be totally bald every three years.

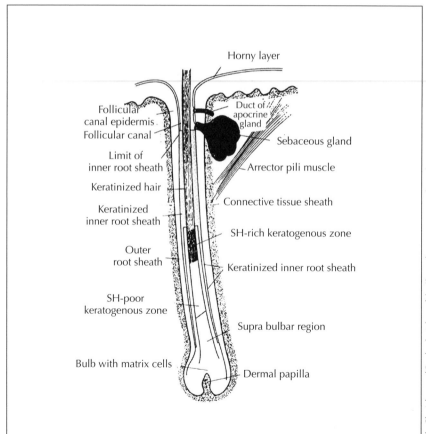

The Physiology and Patahophysiology of the Skin, Volume 4, Jarrett A, ed, Academic Press: New York, 1973, p 1295

Figure 3-1. *Diagram of the hair and hair follicle showing the various zones of growth and development of the hair. Note the attachments of the glands and the arrector pill muscle.*

The stem cell

For many years science has held that hair growth is initiated in the germinal papillae, a small nest of cells at the base of the hair. Recently it was discovered that this is not true. **Stem cells** were found in the area of the hair shaft near the insertion of the erector pili muscle, an area known as the bulb. This startling information was discovered by George Cotsarelis, MD, at the University of Pennsylvania.[3, 4] His findings suggest that there are four types of stem cells in this area—one for the hair shaft, one for the inner root sheath, one for the outer root sheath, and one for the epidermis that surrounds the hair shaft. These stem cells from the epidermis can be the source of new epidermial cells in the wound-healing process. Here are a few notes on stem cells in the event this is a new term.

Stem cells are relatively undifferentiated cells with a tremendous potential to proliferate and are found in all self-renewing tissues. Hair, skin, and the intestines are examples of self-renewing tissues. Cells that are undifferentiated are cells that are capable of becoming differentiated cells or remaining as stem cells when they divide. Fully differentiated normal cells do not divide. Stem cells share certain characteristics:

1. They are ultra-structurally and biochemically primitive.

2. They are very slow to cycle, a process that helps conserve deoxyribonucleic acid (DNA) integrity.

Scientific Basis of Dermatology, Thordy AJ and Friedmann PS, eds, Churchill Livingstone: New York, 1986, p 105

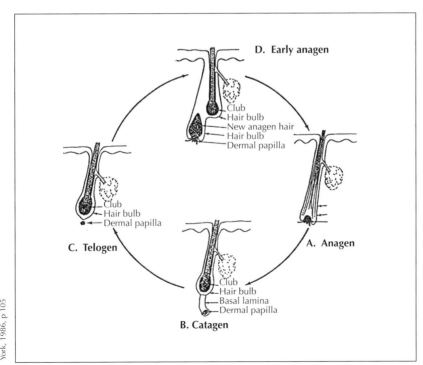

Figure 3-2. *Diagram of the hair cycle. Observe the relationship of the dermal papilla to the hair bulb in the four stages—anagen 1 and 2, catagen and telogen.*

3. They have a large proliferative potential when stimulated by growth factors such as in wound-healing.

4. They often are located near a population of rapidly proliferating cells.

5. They are located in areas that are well protected such as at the bottom of the rete in skin and in intestinal crypts. These area are highly vascular to provide the needed nourishment for growth, and they are richly supplied with nerves to receive signals.

Types of hair. There are three main types of human hair. First, **lanugo** hair—from the Latin word *lana*, meaning "wool"—is soft, unpigmented hair without a medulla. This type of hair generally disappears after the seventh month of gestation, but sometimes is seen in infants and occasionally in adults.

The second type, **vellus** hair—from the Latin word vellus, meaning "fleece"—is soft, unpigmented, unmedullated and is usually less than one-inch long. It normally replaces the lanugo hair. Finally, **terminal** hair is stiff, medullated and pigmented. It replaces vellus hair at puberty and continues through adult life. Not all vellus hairs are replaced at puberty and not all vellus hairs respond to hormones.[5]

Notes on hair removal

Somehow, even among skin care specialists, there remains a belief that shaving the hair causes it to grow thicker and darker. This is just not true. Shaving is an effective way to remove unwanted hair for a short time. The other four methods are mechanical extraction, chemical destruction, electrolytic destruction and laser ablation.

Mechanical extraction. This method employs wax, tweezers and recently, vibrating springs. These methods rarely give permanent results since they merely fracture the hair shaft and fail to remove the germinal hair cell.

Chemical destruction. This method employs certain chemicals that are capable of either dissolving or weakening the hair such as thioglycolates, or stronger depilatories such as thallium, a highly toxic metal, that is a cellular toxin. Chemical methods usually are not permanent unless they destroy the hair germinal cells.

Electrolytic destruction or epilation. This probably is the best method developed to date. It is very important that the user of this technique fully understands the use of the instrument and the technique of application. There are two methods of epilation by electrical current. Direct current of low voltage and low amperage produces a localized chemical cautery. Heat is produced from the formation of alkaline caustic sodium hydroxide at the tip of the negative electrode. Only the negative electrode is used as tissues are softened and the hair root is destroyed. The use of the positive electrode will cause the tissue to harden, the needle to stick in the follicle and the skin to be tattooed from the metal of the needle.

Alternating current epilation uses high-frequency electrical oscillations that cause heat build-up in the tissue because they resist the passage of the oscillations. No matter what system is used, a certain amount of minimal skin damage will result with epilation by electrolysis.

Laser ablation. This newest method uses heat to destroy the hair shaft and bulb.

Sebaceous glands

Sebaceous glands secrete an oily substance known as **sebum**. They are found all over the body except the palms of the hands, and on the soles and top of the feet. They usually are not visible to the naked eye but some very large openings can be seen. Sebaceous glands are associated with hair follicles except in the mucus membranes such as the lips. They are most numerous and largest on the face—400–900 per square centimeter—but they still are plentiful on the middle of the back and chest. On the extremities they are less numerous and smaller, about 100 per square centimeter. They are seen in the nipple area, the labia minora, the prepuce and the eyelids.

Structure of the sebaceous glands. Structurally the sebaceous gland is either unilobular or multilobular, and varies greatly in size from site to site. The glands have a sac-like, or acinar form, at the bottom of the follicular canal. The canal opens onto the surface with a widely dilated follicular orifice. This opening is called a **pore**. Within the canal there are a variety of materials including sebum, keratin cells and bacteria. All of these materials contribute in some way to the genesis of **acne**, a disorder of the oil glands characterized by the formation of clogged pores, called blackheads, and pustules, or pimples. Sebaceous follicles always are associated with a vellus hair, though at times the vellus hair cannot be seen. **Figure 3-3** shows the relationship of the glands in the follicle.

The word pore comes from the Greek *poros,* which means "a small opening." A pore is this and nothing more, an opening. A pore is not a stand-alone structure; it must always be associated with some structure, such as a sweat gland or a sebaceous gland. Like the doughnut hole, it has no meaning by itself. It can be helpful to remember that pores do not pass completely through the skin, but rather always are terminated in a gland at the level of the dermis.

Pores do not breathe. They act only as openings onto the skin from which pour out sweat and various oils. Pores sometimes do act as channels and carry certain substances that are placed on the skin down into the deeper dermal layers of the skin. That is why skin covered with hair can absorb more applied material than hairless skin. Keep this thought in mind when you apply products. The ingredients will penetrate faster in hairy areas where there are many pores, that is the infundibuli of the hair follicles.

Function of the sebaceous glands. The sebaceous gland produces lipids in the cells of the acinus and these cells then rupture and are secreted into the canal. This type of secretion is called **holocrine**. The process of holocrine secretion requires that the entire cell of the gland be disrupted and discharged into the sebaceous duct. This process takes about 14 days from the time the cell is formed until it finally discharges. The sebaceous gland is under hormone control being dormant before puberty and springing to life after puberty. The tragedy of acne is a result of some malady of the sebaceous apparatus.

Sebum is the end product of the sebaceous gland. It is a fatty material that is secreted into the hair shaft below the opening of the hair follicle. The word sebum is taken directly from the Latin word for *suet*, which is a type of greasy animal fat. The function of sebum is not known. It appears to have no positive function. There are problems; however, related to sebum production with which estheticians must deal. It is possible that the sebaceous gland is a vestige of the water proofing of hair seen in aquatic mammals.

At one time great importance was given to sebum as a barrier substance of the skin as a component of "skin mantel" or "acid mantle." This has been put to rest by new research into skin lipid function, and sebum plays no known role as a barrier or as a natural moisturizer.

Variations in sebum production. The production of sebum varies with an individual's sex and age. The pre-puberty levels in males and females are very low. During the teen years 16–19, the female level is higher than that seen in males. Overall, the rates of sebum production are higher in the male than in the female for the androgen content of males is much higher. Estrogen in the female acts to suppress sebum production; however, high levels of androgens will reverse this inhibition of estrogen. This is seen in the hormonal changes associated with the menstrual cycle, and with women on

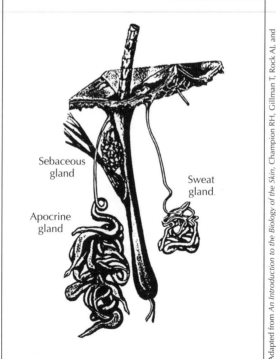

Sebaceous gland

Sweat gland.

Apocrine gland

Adapted from *An Introduction to the Biology of the Skin,* Champion RH, Gillman T, Rock AJ, and Sims, RT, Blackwell Scientific: Edinburgh, 1970, p 89.

Figure 3-3. *Diagram of the relationship of the apocrine gland, the sweat gland and the sebaceous gland to the hair follicle.*

hormone therapy. Steroids, such as cortisone, are notorious for producing acne associated with increased sebum production.

The area about the nose and the forehead is the most active facial area for sebum secretion. This area, known as the "T-Zone," is the source of much worry by skin care center clients. Speculation on the effectiveness of products to suppress sebum goes on each year. Current physiological findings suggest that sebum is produced at a constant rate under hormonal control rather than neurogenic control. Efforts to suppress sebum have met with varying success. Sebum is secreted in higher levels in the acne-prone individual. In mild acne the level can be only 25–30% higher than the normal level, whereas in severe acne, it can be twice the normal value.

There is much to learn about the relationship of sebum, the sebaceous duct keratin and acne. It is apparent that free fatty acids in the sebaceous duct tend to induce inflammatory reactions. Bacteria play a role here as well.

Apocrine sweat glands

The **apocrine gland** is one of two types of sweat glands in the skin; the other sweat gland is the **eccrine gland**. The apocrine gland is a mystery gland, a vestigial organ that also appears to be a remnant of primitive sexual attraction. Apocrine comes from the Greek word *apokrinesthai*, which means "to be secreted."

Structure of the apocrine gland. In humans, apocrine glands are found in the axilla or arm pit, and in the genital area, or perineum. They are associated with hair follicles and are located deeper than the sebaceous glands. They also are larger than the sebaceous glands and open on the hair follicle orifice at a site above the duct of the sebaceous follicle.

Function of the apocrine gland. The apocrine gland does not develop fully until puberty. Once developed; however, it appears to be independent of hormonal influences. The gland secretes a sticky, milky, odorless fluid. Bacterial action causes the gland to break down and produce the characteristic odors of unwashed humanity. Excitement, particularly sexual excitement, seems to be the major inducer of apocrine secretion. Many scientists believe that the apocrine secretion of dehydroepiandrosterone (DHEA), an androgen hormone, forms the basis of a pheromone for humans. Unlike lower animal life, pheromones in humans appear to be auto-stimulatory, that is they work via the olfactory system to develop a person's awareness of his, or her, attractiveness and desirability. In some manner the pheromones are able to cause the person to project these qualities to others.

Eccrine sweat glands

Humans are the sweatiest animal. There are more than three million eccrine sweat glands in the human body that can produce several liters of sweat a day, if necessary. In cases of strenuous exercise, as much as ten liters of sweat a day can be lost. The sweat glands are located all over the body, but are more numerous in the palm and the soles of the feet, about 400 glands per square centimeter, while the face has 270 per square centimeter. (See **Figure 3-3**.)

Structure of the sweat gland. The sweat glands lie deep in the dermis and consist of a coiled tube rising to the surface on the stratum corneum. The long-coiled configuration allows salts and other essential ingredients of the sweat to be resorbed as the sweat passes upward to the surface. The gland is divided into the secretory portion and the duct for matters of anatomical clarity. Cells lining the secretory portion are of two types, dark cells and clear cells. The clear cells secrete sweat. Each gland is supplied with abundant blood vessels and nerve fibers (See **Figure 3-4.**)

Function of the sweat gland. The sweat gland is under control of the sympathetic nervous system. If the nerve supply is lost, there is no function of the sweat gland. The major function of sweating is to lower the body heat. This is called **thermoregulation.** Sweating also occurs under emotional stress, but mainly in the hands, feet, forehead, axilla and pubic area. Gustatory sweating, associated with eating, occurs only on the forehead.

The absence of sweating is called **anhydrosis** and can be a sign of a serious disorder under certain circumstances. Prickly heat is a condition produced by sweat trapped in the epidermis at the level of the granular layer. This condition is seen in hot, humid areas.

The entire mechanism of sweat regulation is exceedingly complex. It is not necessary for the skin care specialist to know all the fine details. One must recognize that sweating is a normal function of the skin that is regulated by both external and internal heat, and that sweat glands are an opening to the dermis and a potential systemic route of delivery for topically applied products.

Remember that the skin is a living, dynamic, unpredictable and unforgiving organ. It has a long memory for insults and injuries. The skin will react in unexpected ways and

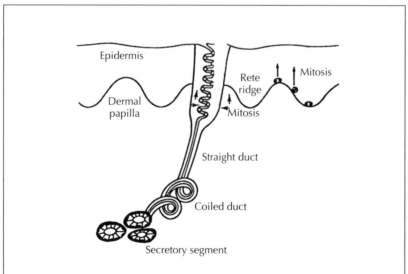

The Physiology and Patahophysiology of the Skin, Volume 4, Jarrett A, ed, Academic Press: New York, 1973, p 1544

Figure 3-4. Diagram of the sweat duct and the relationship to the epidermis. Note the coiled nature of the secretory segment and the wide top duct, the acrosyringium. This is where the action of antiperspirants is believed to occur.

at the same time, will respond favorably to treatments that are scientifically worthless. The characteristics of the appendages impact strongly with the other skin structures. This is why it is so important for an esthetician to understand the roles played by all facets of the skin.

References

1. Spearmen RIC, Hair follicle development, cyclic changes and hair form, *The Physiology and Pathophysiology of the Skin*, Volume 4, Jarrett A, ed, New York: Academic Press, 1253–1292 (1977)

2. Ebling FJ, Biology of Hair Follicles, *Dermatology in General Medicine*, Third Edition. Fitzpatrick TB, et al., eds, New York: McGraw Hill, 213–219 (1987)

3. Corsarelis G, Hair follicle development, cycling and stem cells. *Prog Dermatol* 32:2 (1998)

4. Paus R and Corsarelis G, The biology of hair follicles, *N. Eng J of Med* 341:481–497 (1999)

5. Spearman RIC, The structure and function of the fully developed follicle, *The Physiology and Pathophysiology of the Skin*, Volume 4, Jarrett A, ed, New York: Academic Press, 1293–1349 (1977)

General References

Champion RH, Gillman T, Rook AJ and Sims RT, eds, *An Introduction to the Biology of the Skin*, Oxford: Blackwell Scientific (1970). An excellent first book for an overview of the skin. Easy reading.

Goldsmith LA, ed, *Biochemistry and Physiology of the Skin*, Two volumes, Oxford University Press (1983). A comprehensive text for the serious, advanced skin care student. An excellent reference book for the skin care school.

Chapter 4

The Lymphatic System

The lymphatic system is one of the least studied systems in the body, yet this system is extremely important since it serves to control microcirculation, which is the movement of interstitial fluid in the body tissues. I believe the major reason for this apparent lack of interest is the great difficulty encountered in studying this system.

In this chapter, I will present the anatomy and physiology of the lymphatic system with some clinical information on how this knowledge can be used in the practice of skin care. Since our understanding of the lymphatic system is improving, more ways are being found to assist the function of this system both in medicine and in skin care.

Anatomy of the lymphatic system

The **lymphatic vessels** essentially are a system of channels that develop in pools of fluid within the tissues. These channels serve as a self-cleaning system. At first this may appear to be a difficult concept to visualize, but it is the primary key to understanding the lymphatic system.

Consider that tissues are composed of cells bathed in the interstitial fluid that serves as a means of transporting materials between cells, collecting food elements from the bloodstream and picking up waste products from the same cells. These tissue spaces are organized into the lymphatic system by **endothelial cells** that line the channels. They allow easy passage of fluid from the tissues into the lymph vessels. Depending on various body stresses the endothelial cells are able to form valves and smooth muscles in order to direct the flow of the lymph fluid in one direction.[1]

The lymph vessels are both deep and superficial. All of the body lymph fluid flows into the venous system through two major lymph vessels. The **thoracic duct** collects superficial lymph from the legs, abdomen, left arm, left chest and the left face. The deeper lymphatic system and the lymphatic vessels arising from the gastrointestinal tract flow into the thoracic duct. This large duct, which actually is no bigger than a small soda straw, travels up the abdomen and empties into the internal jugular vein. (See **Figure 3-1**.)

The **right lymphatic duct** collects lymph fluid from the right arm, the right chest and the right side of the face, and from the top of the liver. It empties into the right subclavian vein. (See **Figure 4-1**.)

Micro-anatomy of lymph vessels

In order to see these lymph channels in the tissue, special techniques of histology are needed. This is the science that studies tissue, often employing special stains that color the tissues. The word histology comes from *histos*, the Greek word for "web," since many tissues resemble webs when viewed with a microscope. The lymphatic vessels within the sub-papillary dermis are very thin.

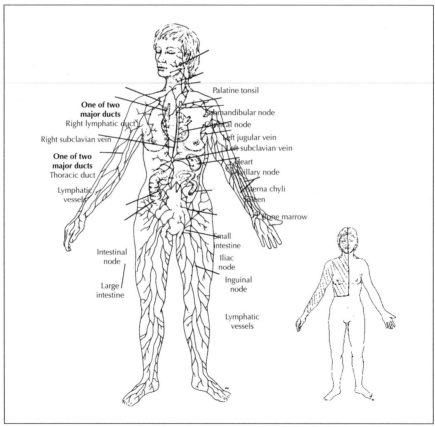

Figure 4-1. The anatomy of the lymphatic system. This diagram shows mostly deeper lymph vessels. The superficial vessels, if depicted, would be so numerous as to obscure the deeper vessels. Note the inset showing the area drained by the right lymphatic duct. All the other lymphatic vessels flow into the thoracic duct.

There is a rich network of lymph vessels in the upper dermis and a wide mesh in the deep dermis and the subcutaneous tissues. In **Figure 4-2** there is a diagram of a lymphatic vessel in the skin. Notice that there are openings between some of the cells. In the fatty tissue, also called adipose tissue, the lymphatic vessels are positioned only on the periphery of the fat lobules. This arrangement makes drainage of fatty tissue a slow process. Within the tissues the superficial vessels penetrate the fascia over the muscles to enter the deep collecting lymphatic vessels.[2, 3]

Unlike the capillaries associated with the circulation of the blood, the lymphatic vessels end in a blind loop. They branch off from a slightly larger vessel to collect fluid from a specific area. There appears to be no lymphatic vessels in the upper dermis, yet fluid from the epidermis does collect in this area and must be removed. Since the epidermis is nourished by diffusion of nutrients from the capillaries through the dermis to the epidermis, the flow is favored as an upward movement of fluid. It has been reported, however, that a vast network of micro-tubular pre-lymphatics exists in and around the basal layer of the epidermis. When normal skin is examined, however, lymphatic vessels clearly can be seen only in the mid-dermis.

The position of the lymphatic vessels and their connection to the stroma, or fibrous tissue, of the dermis provides for a system of movement of the vessel walls. This movement opens and closes, dilates and compresses the lymphatic vessels thus forcing the fluid to move. This again is a key concept to understand the disorders of the skin that arise when the lymphatic system does not function well.

Understanding the function of the endothelial cell is the second key to understanding the lymphatic system. Endothelial cells line the lymphatic spaces. They are flat cells that line the interior of many body structures. For example, blood vessels are lined with endothelial cells under the muscle layer. (See **Figure 4-3**.)

The endothelial cells in the smaller lymphatic vessels are joined at isolated points on the cell surface. This arrangement provides gaps and permits the cell to separate for passage of proteins and fluids. A very important feature of these cells is that they are connected to the surrounding tissue by collagen and elastic fibers. As the tissues move,

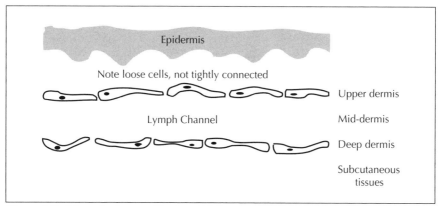

Figure 4-2. *A lymphatic vessel in the mid-dermis. Note that the vessel lies well below the epidermis, and that it is composed of loosely connected cells.*

they pull on the endothelial cells and open up the spaces between them permitting tissue fluid and even blood cells to pass into the lymphatics. The "bunching up" of cells creates the valves in the vessels system, giving the appearance of tiny knots along the vessels.[4, 5] (See **Figure 4-4**.)

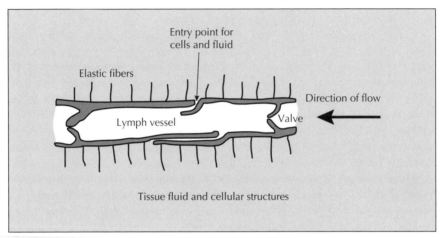

Figure 4-3. *Diagram of the endothelial cells of a lymphatic vessel showing associated elastic fibers connected to surrounding tissue. The valves are highly schematic, for in fact, they are cells that constrict the vessels by conformational changes.*

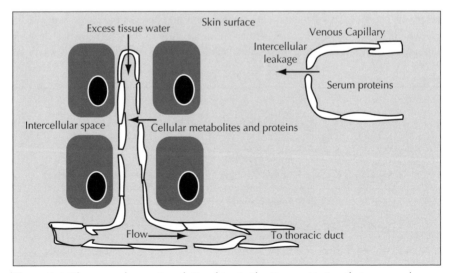

Figure 4-4. *The normal osmotic relationships in the tissues. Notice that a normal amount of protein leakage from the venous capillaries easily can be handled by the lymphatic vessels. Normal tissue pressure and normal flow must be present.*

The physiology of the lymphatic system

As previously mentioned, the first key to understanding the lymphatic system is to view the system as a body-cleansing system. All of the excess body fluid, waste products of cellular metabolism and degradation products are swept into the lymphatic system. The **macrophage**, a large free-living cell with many functions, is an integral part of the lymphatic system since it acts as a scavenger to remove both proteins and cellular debris. The macrophage enters the lymphatic system and is carried to the lymphatic nodes by the lymphatic vessels. Some of these cells and the protein they ingest are destroyed within the lymph nodes, while other cells and proteins are returned to the bloodstream. Many essential enzymes are returned to the bloodstream by this route. No one really knows what is actually happening inside the lymph node with any great degree of certainty. It is known that some immune processing takes place, but beyond that, skin care specialists are operating in the dark.[6]

Osmosis is the force that moves fluids. A very basic concept in understanding the movement of tissue fluid into the lymphatic system is the concept of **osmotic pressure**. When two fluids of different concentrations are separated by a semi-permeable membrane, they have a tendency to become equal in concentration on both sides of the membrane. For example, if you place a concentrated solution of sugar, such as molasses, in a cellophane bag and place it in water, it will "pull" water into the bag until it reaches a certain concentration of water. Since the sugar molecules cannot get out of the bag, they serve as the high concentration inside the bag, but the water is in high concentration on the outside of the bag, so it will move into the bag where it is in low concentration. The principle is: substances will move from an area of high concentration to an area of low concentration. Since the proteins in the bloodstream are higher in concentration than they are in the tissues, they will move first into the tissues and then into the lymph vessels.[7]

Associated skin problems

As long as the pressure within the tissue is normal, the protein content of the blood is normal and there is no obstruction to lymph flow, the lymphatic system works very well. However, if only one of these three conditions is changed, the system will fail. Let us look at each of these conditions to see what actually happens when changes occur.

Continuous external pressure. Increased pressure in the tissue from forces outside of the body will result in a compression of the cells and intercellular spaces with a resultant decrease in lymph flow. The lymphatic vessels are constricted, actually pressed flat, and the lymph fluid cannot clear the tissues. This results in increased back pressure in the tissues so that nutrients cannot reach the cells by diffusion from the bloodstream. Eventually even the capillaries will constrict and collapse. The end result of this condition, if not corrected, is tissue death or *necrosis*. A common problem seen with this condition is bedsores. (See **Figure 4-5**.)

Internal pressure. Another common condition associated with increased tissue pressure is dependent **edema**. Fluid increases in the intercellular spaces because there is insufficient tissue movement. This condition is seen commonly in sales clerks and hair designers, television watchers (couch potatoes) and long-distance airline travelers. In this case one needs only to walk about to get the tissue moving again, which in turn will pump the fluid up into the lymphatic system. Lymphatic edema from standing for long periods without moving about can be prevented or reduced by wearing elastic stockings or, even better, elastic pantyhose. (See **Figure 4-5**.)

Poor nutrition. Poor protein intake, destruction of body protein or rapid elimination of body protein as seen in certain kidney disorders will reduce the amount of protein in the bloodstream and thus upset the osmotic pressure difference which is needed to move the fluids back into the lymphatic system. While true nutritional protein deficit is rare in the United States, infants, the homeless and elderly individuals occasionally have low protein intake that will exhibit edema of the lower extremities. This type of edema requires medical attention. (See **Figure 4-5**.)

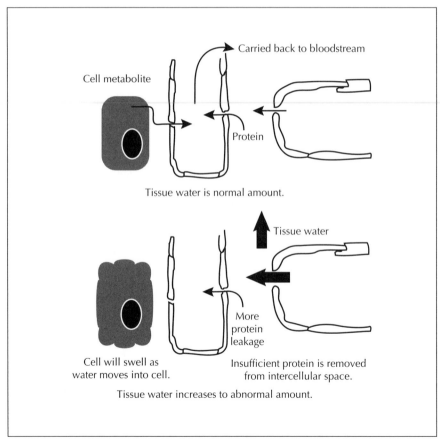

Figure 4-5. *Comparison of normal and abnormal tissue conditions. Under abnormal conditions—a. increased protein leakage causes increase in tissue osmotic pressure; b. fluid is retained to dilute the protein; c. lymph vessels are constricted and flow is decreased; and d. edema, the swelling of tissues, occurs.*

Inflammatory edema. Most skin infections are associated with redness and some swelling. Dilated capillaries produce the redness and at the same time leak proteins into the intercellular spaces. The increased protein content within the tissue spaces cause fluid to be retained and swelling results. This type of edema requires medical attention. (See **Figure 4-5**.) In the presence of inflamed tissue, lymphatic drainage is neither indicated nor advised.

Post-operative edema. One of the most common types of post-operative edema seen a few years ago was edema of the arm following radical mastectomy. Since fewer of these procedures are done today, the condition is not as common, but still is seen. The esthetician trained in lymphatic drainage would be of great assistance to a patient with this disorder. Unfortunately, most physicians are unaware that this service is offered by estheticians. It also is unfortunate that not all estheticians are trained in this technique.[8]

Lymphatic drainage and massage therapy

Lymphatic drainage massage is a specialized massage technique that requires specific training. Do not offer this service unless you are certified in this technique.

It is well established that moving the tissue that surrounds the vessels can move lymphatic fluid within the lymphatic vessels. The most effective method that is applicable to most areas of the body is massage. Vibration of the skin also has been shown to be effective in mobilizing lymph fluid. Heavy massage is not needed, but it makes sense if one is attempting to move fluid into the lymphatic system and then into the venous system that the direction of massage follows the natural flow of lymph.[9]

Using gravity to assist this movement also is practical. Holding an arm above the chest will aid in moving the fluid toward the chest with less effort. For my purpose, I do not think the fingers can be replaced by any instrument or machine for lymphatic massage. The skilled skin care specialist will have learned the feedback signals coming from the client's skin and can thereby make an infinite number of adjustments in technique.

I believe the experienced esthetician will have more uses for lymphatic drainage than I, so I shall limit my comments to the applications with which I am most familiar. If you understand the functioning of the lymphatic system, you can use this knowledge in a wide number of skin care applications.

Edema of the lower eyelid (baggy eyes). This is a very distressing condition for many clients. At all ages, it occurs most often in the morning, but usually clears up in about 30 minutes with simple blinking of the eyes. The condition is due to lymphatic stasis at night, not to the innumerable causes one sees in many "beauty books." Very few true medical conditions are associated with edema of the lower lid alone; most involve both lids. Hypothyroid disease and advanced kidney disease are two conditions that come to mind that often are associated with swollen lids. Allergies and crying also produce this type of swelling. If both lids are swollen, refer the client to a physician. Occasionally some cases will benefit from light lymphatic drainage, but do the whole face, not just the eyelids. ***Do not massage the upper lid as pressure on the upper lid may trigger a reflex that can slow down the heart rate.***

Puffy faces. Puffy faces are the result of impaired venous return and thus impaired lymphatic flow. This condition is seen in long-standing lung disorders from chronic smoking, often appearing in women as early as 38–42. If these are recalcitrant smokers, there is no hope for them and I would advise no attempt at therapy. For clients who have stopped smoking, the lung condition will improve and they will benefit from facial lymphatic drainage.

There is no hard and fast technique for facial massage, except to avoid any inflamed areas. I do not recommend massage at any time on inflamed skin, particularly on the face.

Breasts, back and arms. Periodic massage with lymphatic drainage of these areas will benefit the client in terms of removing sluggish lymph and the associated accumulated toxins. These are dependent areas with a tendency to retain fluid and are frequently neglected.

Sprains, strains and post-fractures. Sprains and strains of the ligaments are associated with increased tissue fluids. Initial application of cold compresses, followed by gentle lymphatic drainage, will help a great deal to reduce the swelling in the affected area. After the cast is removed from a fractured arm or leg, there usually is a fair amount of swelling. The skin often shows some hyperkeratosis as well. This condition will respond very well to lymphatic drainage, as well as to general measures in good skin care to restore the epidermis to normal.

Post-surgical lymphedema (associated with mastectomy). Most surgical procedures are associated with tissue fibrosis as a consequence of the healing process. Fibrosis tends to reduce the intercellular spaces by replacing the loose interstitial tissues with compact fibrotic tissues. Lymphatic flow is difficult in these areas. In those patients with lymphedema of the arm following mastectomy, the use of lymphatic drainage is very helpful. The schedule of treatment is dictated by the severity of the edema and here experience helps. I would not recommend that you undertake this type of treatment unless you have had training in lymphatic drainage for this condition.

Varicose veins. Today varicose veins and spider veins on the legs of women are seen more than previously has been recorded. I think this is due to tight bikini underwear and the "jean plague." Traditionally, severe varicose veins were seen in women who had children, though they also were seen in men. One sees spider veins and mild varicose veins even in teenage females today. The major problem with varicose veins is that they impede normal return of blood from the legs, and this impedes the transfer of tissue fluid to the lymphatic system.[10]

Walking, removing the restrictive clothing and wearing a support type of hose will help to correct mild varicose veins. In the absence of corrective measures, many individuals will go on to full blown varicose veins that generally require corrective surgery. Leg treatments for clients with large varicose veins must be done with certain cautions. Again, any inflammation is an indication for referral, and the presence of a hard or tender vein also should be an indication for referral to a physician.

While lymphatic drainage will help to relieve the swelling of the legs, instruct the client in the preventive measures as well. Keep in mind that as long as the client continues to follow the pattern of life that initially produced the condition, an uphill battle exists.

Topical products to help varicose veins

The major ingredients that have been tested in the treatment of venous system disorders are the **flavonoids**. Most herbal treatments for varicose veins include them since these compounds aid the circulatory system and strengthen capillaries. Flavonoids are pigments found in herbs and plants; they are the chemical source of the intense colors seen in autumn leaves, brightly colored flowers, and dark colored fruits.

Flavonoids, such as anthocyanidins and proanthocyanidins such as grape seed-skin extract, reduce capillary fragility, increase the integrity of the venous walls, inhibit the breakdown of collagen and increase the muscle tone of the vein. In studies, they have shown to benefit varicose veins and hemorrhoids. This is a safe product to take orally in doses of 50–200 mgs a day. Gotu kola strengthens collagen and reduces hardening of connective tissue. It has had impressive results in varicose veins and venous insufficiency. Gingko biloba increases peripheral circulation and alleviates vascular insufficiency.

Flavonoid-rich foods include cherries, rose hips, blackberries, apricots, buckwheat, bell peppers, onions, asparagus, brussels sprouts, apples, pears and the thin inner layer of citrus rinds. Herbal sources of flavonoids include hawthorn (*Crataegus spp.*), ginkgo (*Ginkgo biloba*), German chamomile (*Matricaria recutita*), calendula (*Calendula officinalis*) and bilberry (*Vaccinium myrtillus*).

Horse chestnut as a vein strengthener

Horse chestnut (*Aesculus hippocastanum*) products, including both oral and topical dosage forms, are the single most widely prescribed remedy in Germany for edema with chronic venous insufficiency, a condition sometimes associated with varicose veins. There are seven placebo-controlled, double-blind studies published between 1973–1996 indicating that oral standardized horse chestnut relieves chronic venous insufficiency. Horse chestnut extracts help veins withstand damage, reduce capillary wall permeability and prevent absorption of damaging UV radiation. A component compound called aescin, or escin, helps seal tiny openings in capillary walls, reducing the outflow of fluid into surrounding tissue.

Studies show the extracts reduced leg edema, improved vascular tone, and lessened subjective symptoms such as a feeling of heaviness in the legs, nighttime calf muscle spasms, itching and swelling. Topical products are not absorbed systemically; they do, however, absorb into the tissues to which they're directly applied. I have used this agent topically with good results, but have not advocated oral use. I would suggest if you are interested in oral use, consult a qualified herbalist, as few physicians have knowledge of this treatment.

Massage oils

Finally, a few words about massage oils and lymphatic drainage. I know of no published reports that any particular oil, when applied to the skin with massage, will improve the flow of the lymph fluid. Only the mechanical action of the massage is known to move the lymph fluid. While many vendors say this or that oil can stimulate lymph flow, there is no scientific data to support such a claim. On the other hand, the use of vegetable oils with a few drops of essential oils will add to the pleasant experience of the client and can produce a further benefit by inducing a state of physical and mental relaxation.

References

1. Ryan TJ and Champion RH, Disorders of lymphatic vessels, Ch 14 in *Textbook of Dermatology*. Champion RH, Burtos JL and Ebling FJG, eds. London: Blackwell Scientific Publications p 2015–2017 (1992)

2. Branerman IM and Yen A, Microcirculation in psoriatic skin. *J Invest Dermatol* 62: 493–501 (1974)

3. Takada M, The ultrastructure of lymphatic values in rabbits and mice. *Am J Anat* 132: 207–217 (1971)

4. Klika E, et al, Inceptions and manner of development of lymph vessels in the chick embryo heart. *Lymphology* 5: 137–148 (1972)

5. Leak LU and Burke JF, Fine structure of the lymphatic capillary and adjoining connective tissue area. *Am J Anat* 118: 785–809 (1966)

6. Ryan TJ, The lymphatics of the skin, in *The Physiology and Pathology of the Skin*, Vol 5, Jarrett A, ed, London: Academic Press p1753 (1978)

7. Guyton AG, Granger HJ and Taylor AE, Interstitial fluid pressure. *Physiol Rev* 51: 523–563 (1971)

8. Wolfe JHN, The progress and possible causes of severe primary lymphedema. *Ann Roy Coll Surg Eng* 66: 251–257 (1984)

9. Ryan TJ and Salter DC, The effects of vibration on skin blood flow. *Biblio Anat* 16: 180 (1977)

10. BorschbergvE, ed, *The Prevalence of Varicose Veins of the Lower Extremities*. S Karger, Basale (1967)

General References

Pugliese PT, *Advanced Professional Skin Care*. Bernville, Pennsylvania: APSC Publishing (1991)

Ryan TJ and Curri SB, Blood vessels and lymphatics. In: Cutaneous Adipose Tissue. *Clinic in Dermatology* 7: 25 (1989)

Daroczy J, *The Dermal Lymphatic Capillaries*. Berlin: Springer Verlag (1988)

Chapter 5

Pigmentation

How could we even conceive of a world without color? Most colors in biological materials are due to complex molecules, the most complex of which is melanin—the predominant pigment in mammals. Melanin, also known as pigment, is found in brain tissue, in the eye, in the ear and in mucous membranes.

Skin color will be discussed in this chapter, but the major emphasis will be on the role of melanin in the skin and hair. Melanin is one of the most fascinating substances in biology, but like many beautiful and intriguing things in nature, melanin does not give up its secrets easily. First, let us look at skin color in general, and then the role of melanin as a component of skin color will be explored.

Skin color

Human skin has red, yellow, brown or blue tones. The red color is due to a blood pigment called oxygenated hemoglobin, and the yellow to the pigments called carotenoids. Carrots contain beta-carotene. The blue color is due to the hemoglobin in the veins, which is called reduced hemoglobin, and the major brown color to the presence of the pigment melanin, which is produced in cells called melanocytes.

Skin tones are a combination of melanin, hemoglobin, carotenoids and the condition of the stratum corneum. Flakey skin of any color looks whiter or lighter because it can't absorb light. What is perceived in skin color is the reflected light off the skin.*

This is an important concept to remember when examining a client. Skin seen under fluorescent lights is quite different from skin seen under incandescent light bulbs. The best way to check skin color is in natural sunlight. Skin color will be discussed, but first let's look at the pigment producing cell—the **melanocyte**.

---

* The reader is referred to a discussion of reflected light included in Chapter 9, "Physiology of the Skin: Sun's Effect on the Skin." While in color analysis, blue is considered a cool color and red a warm color, the discussion shows that in fact in the color spectrum the blue light is the hotter light and the red light the cooler light! This chapter also discusses melanin in more depth with regard to the affects of sun on the skin.

The melanocyte–the maker of pigment

Skin pigment originates in a cell called a melanocyte. *Melas* is a Greek word meaning "black." These cells are in the basal layer of the epidermis at a ratio of about 1:4–1:10 melanocytes to basal keratinocytes. One melanocyte will provide melanin pigment to about 36 keratinocytes. The association of the melanocyte with these keratinocytes has been called the epidermal melanin unit.

Melanin produced in the melanocyte is transferred to the keratinocytes in packets called **melanosomes**. The melanosomes are transferred to the keratinocytes by the dendritic projections of the melanocyte. Dendrites are spidery-like projections that extend in all directions from the body of the melanocyte. Langerhans cells also are called dendritic cells. The action of the dendrites transferring the melanosomes into the keratinocyte is very similar to the process of injection with a hypodermic needle.

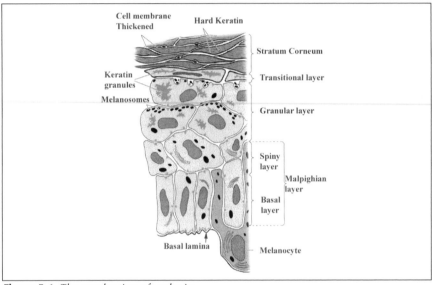

Figure 5-1. The production of melanin.

Definitions

Caucasian Members of the white race as composed of persons of European, North African or Southwest Asian ancestry.

Mongoloid Members of a major racial group native to Asia including people of Northern and Eastern Asia, Malaysians, Eskimos and often American Indians.

Negroid Members of the black race as composed of the majority of the people of Africa, Melanesia and New Guinea.

The production of melanin

Let us look at melanin itself, how it is formed and what kind of pigment it is. Understanding the basic process of pigment production will help you to understand the differences that occur in blond, red, and brown to black hair.

Melanin is a biopolymer, that is, a large complex molecule formed of many smaller units. The basic unit is tyrosine, an amino acid. Tyrosine is acted upon by an enzyme called tyrosinase that converts the tyrosine to L-dopa (DihydrOxy-PhenylAlanine). Next L-dopa is converted to dopa quinone and melanin starts to form as the molecule undergoes polymerization. There are two different types of melanin: eumelanin and pheomelanin.

Tyrosinase is synthesized by the ribosomes of the rough endoplasmic reticulum (rER) and transported through the smooth endoplasmic reticulum (sER) to the Golgi apparatus. It is then released within membrane-bound vesicles. Meanwhile, structural melanosomal proteins also are synthesized on the rER and are then incorporated into vesicles at the sER. Fusion of the two types of vesicles—tyrosinase and structural melanosomal proteins—results in the formation of a melanosome. As the melanosome matures and more melanin is deposited on its lamellar matrix, it passes into the dendrite of the melanocyte. This process is outlined in **Figure 5-1**.

Eumelanin is the brown-black melanin seen in brown skin and black hair. It is an oblong, or spherical granule about 0.9 microns long and 0.3 microns wide. **Pheomelanin** is the red-yellow seen in red hair. It is a spherical granule about 0.7 microns in diameter.

Recent research has found that the melanocyte first will produce a premelanosome organelle that has an internal matrix of melanofilaments. It is interesting that the filaments are well organized in eumelanosomes, but highly disorganized in pheomelanosomes. Pheomelanin is synthesized from tyrosine and cysteine. This combination makes it less stable to ultraviolet light so that it undergoes photo-oxidation, explaining why red hair is relatively rare.

As the melanosome-laden keratinocytes rise to the stratum corneum, the melanin undergoes a degenerative process and eventually is sloughed from the skin. The most heavily pigmented cells, therefore, are in the lower layers of the epidermis. This is the basic process governing skin pigmentation.

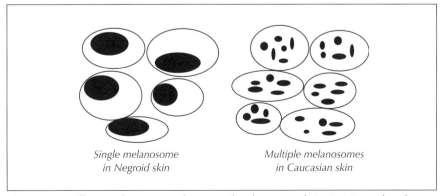

Single melanosome
in Negroid skin

Multiple melanosomes
in Caucasian skin

Figure 5-2. Difference between melansome distribution and size in Negroid and Caucasian skin.

Genetic aspects of skin pigmentation

Melanocytes have both a morphological difference as well as a racial difference in arrangement within the cell. In Caucasians and Mongoloids the melanosomes occur in groups, whereas in Negroids and Australian aborigines, they occur singularly. (See **Figure 5-2**.) There is no explanation for this phenomenon to date.

A further note about skin color and light—the structure of melanin absorbs both ultraviolet light and visible light. The more melanin in the skin, the more light is absorbed and the darker the skin looks. In the case of Negroid, or black, skin with more melanin, the broad absorption of light by melanin allows less light to reflect, so what is seen mainly is the reflected brown hues. It is this broad absorption band of melanin that gives black skin its protective quality against ultraviolet light.

Caucasian skin, so-called white skin, actually is a red-brown hue. But because Caucasian skin does not contain as much melanin as black skin, white light is reflected from surfaces that do not absorb specific colors so the total spectrum, which is white light, is perceived.

While a complete understanding of the genetics of skin pigmentation awaits further investigation, there appear to be three or four pairs of genes that contribute to skin color. One of the genes involved in skin color is on the X chromosome, but just how this fits into the total skin color scheme is not known.

Factors that affect pigmentation

Permanent versus temporary pigmentation. Pigment production in the skin is under control of a number of internal and external factors. It is obvious that both stimulatory and inhibitory forces must be in play constantly. There are two pigmentation components in the skin that contribute to skin color. Constitutive skin color is the basic melanin inherited according to genetic programs and is without any direct effect by solar irradiation. Facultative skin color is inducible, is the result of sun exposure and includes immediate tanning and delayed tanning. As a result, it is reversible and will decrease to the level of constitutive skin color.

Hormone effects. Pregnancy and birth control pills will produce a temporary change in skin pigmentation. This is limited to the breast and the midline of the abdomen in the case of pregnancy, and on the face in the case of birth control pills. Addison's disease, adrenal gland insufficiency, has a similar effect on the skin pigment, but there is a more generalized increase in skin pigmentation. This is a complex relationship between hormones, sun and genetic factors on the melanocyte that is not fully understood.

There are receptors on the surface of melanocytes for melanocyte-stimulating hormone (MSH). MSH, ACTH—similar to MSH in the arrangement of first 13 amino acids, estrogen and progesterone, all stimulate pigmentation through increasing cAMP and tyrosinase activity, resulting in increased melanin formation and transfer. It still is unknown why the sexes differentiate in skin pigmentation during adolescence. The process apparently is genetic in origin. In a carefully controlled study at a residential school, it was found that the boys and girls steadily diverged in skin color after puberty despite their following the same regimen of indoor/outdoor activities and wearing uniforms that prevented tanning. In a study on monozygotic twins,[1] Omoto found that intra-pair variance for skin color did not change as girls lightened in complexion during adolescence, again suggesting a minimal role for non-genetic factors.[2]

The occurrence of this sexual differentiation after puberty suggests that the sex hormones are responsible. Both androgens and estrogens increase skin pigmentation by promoting melanin synthesis and cutaneous blood flow; the effect of androgens, however, is stronger. This stronger effect in itself might explain why the sexes differentiate in skin color during adolescence, except that this differentiation occurs because girls lighten in color and not because boys darken.[3]

Sunlight and skin pigmentation. Melanocytes respond to sunlight with an increase in melanosomes, an increase in melanocytes and a rearrangement of the melanosomes. This is essentially a protective mechanism and one of the prime purposes of melanin production. Within the keratinocyte of the epidermis, the melanosomes form a cap-like structure over the nucleus of the living cells. This obviously is a protective arrangement to prevent ultraviolet damage to the nucleus. It is reported by some investigators that constitutive pigmentation is far superior in protection from ultraviolet radiation (5–30 times) than is the protective quality of facultative pigmentation (2–3 times).[4, 5]

Immediate tanning with light exposure is most marked with exposure between 380–500 nm (nanometers). The tanning appears immediately, but can fade within minutes to 24 hours depending on the exposure. With this type of exposure, the nuclear cap formation of melanin is most noticeable in the basal layer of the epidermis. There does not appear to be an increase in melanosomes or melanocytes with immediate tanning.

Delayed tanning is a facultative type of pigmentation that occurs with repeated exposure to the sun. Delayed tanning can occur with both UVA (320–400 nm) exposure, or with UVB (290–320 nm) exposure. The appearance and duration of the tan is related to the total exposure to sun. Delayed tanning usually appears in 26–48 hours after exposure and can last for weeks or even up to a year.

An increase in the number of melanocytes has been reported for both UVA- and UVB-induced tanning, but only with repeated exposures.[6] A single dose of ultraviolet exposure will increase only the functional activity of the melanocytes while multiple exposures will increase both the number of epidermal melanin units and the number of melanosomes.

One must not be lulled into a sense of complacency about this, however, for the ultraviolet light also induces an inflammation of the skin. Nucleic acids and proteins are damaged and free radicals abound, cell membranes are injured and a generalized inflammatory reaction is set up. Keep in mind that tanning is a protective mechanism, not a therapeutic mechanism, and that it is designed to help protect us against our foolish selves.

Hair color

There are three major types of hair in the human population. Straight hair, as in Mongoloids; curly or kinky hair, as seen in Negroids; and mixed straight and curly, as seen in Caucasians. Mongoloid hair on cross-section is round and larger than Caucasian hair. Negroid hair is flattened and elliptical in cross-section and often is tightly coiled.

Caucasian hair is intermediate in cross-section and often is wavy. One thing is certain, there is no genetic relationship between hair color and hair type.

All pigment in the hair arises from the hair bulb from a line of melanocytes that produces the melanosomes for the keratinocytes of the hair shaft. The mechanism is exactly the same as in the epidermis. Pigment is added to the hair only during the growing or anagen stage. There is no pigment production during the resting or telogen stage. The perceived color of hair is the result of structural proteins, the luminance and color dilution.

Black and brown hair is due to eumelanin melanosome. Variations in the number of melanosomes and the characteristics of the melanosome granules provide the shades of black or brown color. Blond hair also is composed of eumelanin, but the degree of melaninization is arrested in an early stage so that very little melanin is present in blond hair.

Red hair is composed of pheomelanin. It is characterized by a soluble red pigment that is spherical in shape and rather disorganized. The same type of melanin, but far less in quantity, exists in albino hair. In addition, the activity of tyrosinase in albino hair is extremely low.

It is not known for certain, but current studies suggest that melanocytes are capable of producing both eumelanin and pheomelanin. It is not unusual to see males with black hair and red beards. The genetics are not worked out for this type of phenomenon.

Gray hair is devoid of melanin. When the hair bulb ceases to make melanin, the hair will continue to grow, but will be colorless. This usually occurs about age 40-50. No one can become totally gray overnight, as often is reported, since graying is a long process. Actually, it is easier to become totally bald overnight than totally gray. Gray hair is perceived early in dark-haired individuals, but appearance of complete graying occurs earlier in light-haired individuals. To date no one knows the role played by melanin in the aging process, though there appears to be some connection. Occasionally gray hair will get darker. This observation is related to an inflammatory reaction in the scalp.[7]

Nutritional and metabolic disorders can change hair color. This is a complex topic, but one of the more unusual manifested disorders is the "flag sign" in alcoholism. Alternate layers or stripes of light and dark hair are associated with malnutrition.[8]

Green hair is associated with copper exposure, usually in swimming pools. Mercury also has been associated with green hair. These metal deposits on the surface of the hair decrease in concentration as the inner portion of the hair is approached. Treatments for this condition have included hydrogen peroxide at 3% for one to two hours. The most effective treatment has been a three-minute application of a 1.5% solution of 1-hydroxyethyldiphosphonic.[9]

Melanin and skin inflammation

It has been known for a long time that infections and injuries often are associated with hyperpigmentation of the skin. With an infection in Caucasians, a red papule is formed, then a pustule, and finally a return to either a papule again or a tawny brown flat macula. The redness is due to capillary dilations and an actual increase in the number of capillaries around the pimple. The brown color occurs because an increase in melanocyte activity results in the production of more melanin. In Negroids this phenomenon is more pronounced and a deeply pigmented black spot results.

Increased melanocyte activity arises in response to stimulation from inflammatory mediators, whose object is to heal the area and return it to normal, and results in the production of more melanin. When the inflammation subsides, the inflammatory mediators revert to normal levels and so does production of pigmentation. In due course, the cells causing the hyperpigmentation will rise to the stratum corneum and slough off; hyperpigmentation will disappear.

There is only circumstantial evidence that pigmented cells play a role in the initiation of the inflammatory response in the skin. Some investigators feel that hyperpigmentation with inflammation is a sign that the melanocyte is functioning well. In fact, the melanocyte is believed to be an integral part of the homeostatic mechanism.

The homeostatic mechanism keeps the system, that is, the human body, the same. For example, there are parts of the mechanism whose function is to maintain a normal pH or a normal temperature. One of the melanocyte's functions is to maintain even skin tones. From a cosmetic point of view, however, this is not a favorable condition while the hyperpigmentation lasts. Bleaching agents have been developed to help this problem.

Bleaching agents and how they work

Hydroquinone. For many years the only agent available to treat hyperpigmentation was hydroquinone (HQ), which acts by blocking the action of tyrosinase in the formation of melanin. It is considered one of the most effective inhibitors of melanogenesis in vitro and in vivo; however, HQ causes reversible inhibition of cellular metabolism by affecting both DNA and RNA synthesis. The cytotoxic effects of HQ are not limited to melanocytes, although the dose required to inhibit cellular metabolism is much higher for cells other than melanocytes. HQ is considered a potent melanocyte cytotoxic agent with relatively high melanocyte-specific cytotoxicity.

Contact dermatitis occurs in a small number of patients and responds promptly to topical steroids. An uncommon, yet important, side effect of HQ is exogenous ochronosis. This disorder is characterized by progressive darkening of the area to which the cream containing HQ is applied. Histologically, degeneration of collagen and elastic fibers occurs followed by the appearance of characteristic ochronotic deposits consisting of crescent-shaped, ochre-colored fibers in the dermis. Exogenous ochronosis generally has been observed in black patients and after use of high concentrations of HQ for many years. However, cases occurring after use of 2% HQ also have been reported. A South African epidemic of exogenous ochronosis due to HQ has been reported. For this reason, it generally is agreed that the use of HQ should be discontinued if no improvement occurs within 4–6 months. Because of its potential mutagenic properties, HQ currently is banned in Europe for use as a depigmenting agent. Hydroquinone-induced ochronosis often responds to topical steroids and chemical peeling.

By itself hydroquinone is not very effective, so some physicians have combined it with hydrocortisone for a more effective product. Other combinations have been tried, including hydroquinone, hydrocortisone and Retin-A.** A combination of one-third of each ingredient is used. There are no commercial preparations available containing all three ingredients. Over-the-counter preparations usually contain 2% active hydroquinone.

** Retin-A is a registered trade mark of Ortho-McNeil Pharmaceutical, Raritan, NJ

Azelaic acid. Naturally occurring azelaic acid is dicarboxylic acid isolated from Pityrosporum ovale, a fungus. It functions as a weak competitive inhibitor of tyrosinase in vitro. Azelaic acid has both antiproliferative and cytotoxic effect on melanocytes. The cytotoxicity of melanocytes is due to a potent inhibition of thioredoxin reductase, an enzyme involved in mitochondrial oxidoreductase activation and deoxyribonucleic acid (DNA) synthesis. Thioredoxin reductase is a very important enzyme in free radical protection.

Azelaic acid is prescribed topically as a 20% cream and has been combined with 15% and 20% glycolic acid, and its efficacy has been compared with HQ 4% in the treatment of facial hyperpigmentation in dark-skinned patients. It has been reported that the combination formula was as effective as HQ 4% cream, although with a slightly higher rate of local irritation.

Kojic acid. A fungal metabolic product, kojic acid (5-hydroxy-4-pyran-4-one-2-methyl), inhibits the catecholase activity of tyrosinase, which is the rate-limiting, essential enzyme in the biosynthesis of the skin pigment melanin. Melanocytes treated with kojic acid become non-dendritic with a decreased melanin content. Additionally, it scavenges reactive oxygen species that are excessively released from cells or generated in tissue or blood. Kojic acid is used in concentrations ranging from 1–4%. Although effective as a skin-lightening gel, it has been reported to have high-sensitizing potential and cause irritant contact dermatitis. In a study comparing glycolic acid/kojic acid combination with glycolic acid/hydroquinone, no statistical difference in efficacy existed between kojic acid and HQ. However, the kojic acid preparation was reported to be more irritating.

Arbutin. A glycosylated hydroquinone, arbutin (hydroquinone-beta-D-glucopyranoside), is found at high concentrations in certain plants and capable of surviving extreme and sustained dehydration. Arbutin has been shown to inhibit melanin synthesis by inhibition of tyrosinase activity. This appears to be due to inhibition of melanosomal tyrosinase activity, rather than suppression of the synthesis and expression of this enzyme. Arbutin does not hydrolyze to liberate hydroquinone, the latter agent is not responsible for the inhibitory effect of arbutin on melanogenesis. Inhibition of melanin synthesis is about 40% in tissue culture. The effective topical concentration in treating disorders of hyperpigmentation has not been evaluated formally and published, several manufacturers are marketing arbutin as a depigmenting agent. When contacted, these manufacturers report arbutin as an effective depigmenting agent at a concentration of 1%. Some products may contain 3–5%.

Melatonin. Secreted by the pineal gland, melantonin is considered to be responsible for lightening the color of amphibians. Melatonin, while able to effect a dose-related inhibition of melanogenesis, the inhibition of melanogenesis seems to occur at the post-tyrosinase step in the melanin biosynthetic pathway, not by inhibiting tyrosinase. Melatonin has been shown to inhibit adenosine 3′, 5′-cyclic phosphate (cAMP) driven processes in pigment cells. The topical use of melatonin for hyperpigmentation disorders is being investigated, but no published results for dosage has come forth. Topical melatonin also has been reported to have anti-inflammatory properties when applied at

0.6 mg/cm2. Melatonin seems to be an effective antioxidant when topically applied at a concentration of 1%.

Magnesium ascorbyl phosphate. Magnesium-L-ascorbyl-2-phosphate (MAP) is a stable derivative of ascorbic acid. When used as a 10% cream, MAP was shown to suppress melanin formation. Significant lightening effect was seen clinically in 19 of 34 patients with melasma and solar lentigos. Furthermore, MAP has been shown to have a protective effect against skin damage induced by UVB irradiation.

Pigmentation disorder skin diseases

There are many disorders of pigmentation from something as benign as freckles to malignant melanoma. Freckles, or ephilides, are pigmented spots under 0.5 cm (approximately 3/16 inch in diameter) that occur in childhood. More freckles are seen in persons with red or red-brown hair as there appears to be a genetic link between these two traits.

Some freckles are visible to the naked eye and some are not. With sun exposure of 300–400 nm (the UVA range), they become darker. Since this band of sunlight is not filtered out by window glass, freckles will become darker even with indoor exposure. This range of light energy also is emitted by fluorescent light, so if you have freckles you need to wear a UVA sunscreen if you work under fluorescent lighting.

Lentiges are brown spots 0.5–1 cm in size. Although sometimes mistaken for freckles, they are larger than and histologically different from freckles. I recommend you become familiar with pigmented lesions and refer any lesion that looks suspicious to a physician.

Vitiligo is a skin disorder characterized by spotty areas of hypopigmentation. It is a common disorder, perhaps afflicting 1–2% of the population of all races and both genders. The peak age of occurrence is between 10–30, but vitiligo can occur at any age.[10]

The cause is unknown, though there are several theories. A very strong theory is the immune theory based on the finding that about 15% of subjects with vitiligo also are afflicted with autoimmune disorders. Since only 1% of the population has autoimmune disorders, this is good evidence. The depigmented areas of skin in vitiligo do not have melanocytes and have a reduced number of Langerhans cells.

The clinical picture is variable, but the disease often starts at the knees and the elbows. The perioral area, nose, eyes, nipples, anus and genitalia frequently are involved since these are heavily pigmented areas.

Treatment is less than satisfactory. Camouflage makeup helps even out the skin tones. Medical treatment that entails the use of oral psoralen and ultraviolet light is effective in 50–70% of patients. This is a long treatment course with 25 or more treatments needed for initial improvement, with perhaps 100–200 additional treatments needed.[11] Some surgeons are trying micro-grafting techniques and have been successful in some selected cases.

A newer agent has made the scene in recent years called kojic acid. Chemically this compound is 5-hydroxy-2 (hydroxymethyl)-4-pyrone, somewhat related to the quinone family. It is used as a flavor enhancer in foods, so it is safe. I believe it works much like the quinones which it seems to potentiate. It often is sold in preparations with alpha hydroxy acids. It seems to work fairly well.

One of the best agents is vitamin C, or ascorbic acid. It must be made fresh, kept free of light, iron and air. There will be new preparations available within a year. If you want to try it, use 10% vitamin C powder in distilled, absolutely iron-free water. Put it in a dark glass or dark plastic container with a tight, narrow cap, such as a squeeze bottle. Instruct your client to keep it in the refrigerator between use. If there is no iron present in the water, it will keep this way for 30 days or longer. If it turns deep yellow, it has lost its activity, so throw it out and make up fresh material. It works well if applied three times a day and is excellent for the brown spots on the back of the hands.

Summary

Pigmentation is a broad term to explain the red, blue, yellow and brown tones seen in the skin. What actually is seen depends on how much or little light is reflected or absorbed by the skin. This is an important concept to keep in mind when you are examining a client. Understanding pigmentation will help you to anticipate the reactions of a client's skin to salon services as varied as facials with extraction and makeup applications.

References

1.	Kalla AK and Tiwari SC, Sex differences in skin colour in man. *Acta Geneticae Medicae et Gemellologiae* 19:472–476 (1970)

2.	Omoto K, Measurements of skin reflectance in a Japanese twin sample. *Journal of the Anthropological Society of Nippon* (Jinruigaku Zassi). 73:115–122 (1965)

3.	Frost P, Human skin color: a possible relationship between its sexual dimorphism and its social perception. *Perspectives in Biology and Medicine* 32: 38–58 (1988)

4.	Olson RL, et al, Skin Color, Melanin, and Erythema, *Arch Dermatol* 108: 541–544 (1973)

5.	Kaidbey KH and Kligman AM, Sunburn Protection by Longwave Ultraviolet Radiation-Induced Pigmentation, *Arch Dermatol* 114: 46–48 (1978)

6.	Pathak MA, et al, Effects of UVA, UVB, and Psoralen on In Vivo Human Melanin Pigmentation; Cellular and Subcellular Characterization on Delayed Tanning Reaction Induced By Single or Multiple Exposure of to UVA, UVB or UVA Plus 8-Methoxypsoralen; In: Pigment Cell, Vol. 3, V. Riley, ed., pp. 291–298, S. Karger, Basel (1976)

7.	Pinkus H, Post-Inflammatory Hair Darkening, *Arch Dermatol* 82: 253–264 (1960)

8.	MacNamara H, et al, The Flag Sign in the Hair of an Alcoholic, *Aust J Dermatol* 22: 68–80 (1981)

9.	Melnik BC, et al, Green Hair: Guidelines for Diagnosis and Therapy, *J Amer Acad Dermatol* 5: 1065–1068 (1986)

10.	Nordlund, JJ and Lerner AB, Vitiligo: It is Important, *Arch Dermatol* 118: 5 (1982)

11.	Nordlund JJ, et al, The Proliferative and Toxic Effects of Ultraviolet Light and Inflammation on Epidermal Pigment Cells, *J Invest Dermatol* 77: 361 (1981)

Chapter 6

Basic Chemistry of Life

Why should an esthetician study chemistry? What good is the knowledge of chemistry in esthetics? Who really needs it? Chemistry is a tough subject ... too difficult for the average person ... so why bother? Estheticians ask these questions time and time again. There's no easy answer, but estheticians serious about advancing their treatment skills, as well as providing the very best client care, will profit from a basic understanding of chemistry. As in every aspect of life, some effort is required to gain a foothold in new territory.

What is chemistry?

Every material substance in the universe is chemical. Hydrogen and helium make up the bulk of the universe, and the remaining chemicals make up only a tiny part of it in comparison. The human body is composed of chemicals—mostly hydrogen, oxygen, carbon and nitrogen. Every action made ... every thought ... every emotion experienced ... is based on biochemical reactions.

Chemistry is the study of matter, and there are three aspects to the study of chemistry:

1. The study of structure and composition of matter.
2. The study of changes matter undergoes.
3. The phenomenon that occurs with these changes.

As an example, what is fire? Fire is a phenomenon that happens when material such as carbon combines rapidly with oxygen to produce carbon dioxide, water and heat. What is carbon and what is water, and what is meant by "combines with?" These questions can be answered only with chemistry. This chapter will cover the structure and composition of matter, atoms and elements, compound molecules, chemical reactions, and biochemistry—the chemistry of life.

Chemistry Shorthand

IA																	VIIIB
H 1 HYDROGEN 1.0794																	**He 2** HELIUM 4.003
0.0899	**IIA**											**IIIA**	**IVA**	**VA**	**VIA**	**VIIA**	0.1785
Li 3 LITHIUM 6.941	**Be 4** BERYLLIUM 9.01218											**B 5** BORON 10.811	**C 6** CARBON 12.01	**N 7** NITROGEN 14.006	**O 8** OXYGEN 15.999	**F 9** FLUORINE 18.998	**Ne 10** NEON 20.179
0.534	1.848											2.34	2.25	1.25	1.429	1.699	0.900
Na 11 SODIUM 22.98768	**Mg 12** MAGNESIUM 24.305											**Al 13** ALUMINUM 26.981	**Si 14** SILICON 28.085	**P 15** PHOSPHORUS 30.97	**S 16** SULFUR 32.066	**Cl 17** CHLORINE 35.456	**Ar 18** ARGON 39.948
0.971	1.738	**IIIB**	**IVB**	**VB**	**VIB**	**VIIB**		**VIII**			**IB**	**IIB**	2.33	1.82	2.07	3.214	1.783
K 19 POTASSIUM 39.0983	**Ca 20** CALCIUM 40.078	**Sc 21** SCANDIUM 44.956	**Ti 22** TITANIUM 47.88	**V 23** VANADIUM 50.941	**Cr 24** CHROMIUM 51.996	**Mn 25** MANGANESE 54.938	**Fe 26** IRON 55.847	**Co 27** COBALT 58.933	**Ni 28** NICKEL 58.69	**Cu 29** COPPER 63.546	**Zn 30** ZINC 65.39	**Ga 31** GALLIUM 69.723	**Ge 32** GERMANIUM 72.61	**As 33** ARSENIC 72.921	**Se 34** SELENIUM 78.96	**Br 35** BROMINE 79.904	**Kr 36** KRYPTON 83.90
0.862	1.55	2.989	4.54	6.11	7.19	7.44	7.874	8.90	8.902	8.90	7.133	5.904	5.323	5.727	4.79	3.12	3.733
Rb 37 RUBIDIUM 85.467	**Sr 38** STRONTIUM 87.62	**Y 39** YTTRIUM 88.905	**Zr 40** ZIRCONIUM 91.224	**Nb 41** NIOBIUM 92.906	**Mo 42** MOLYBDENUM 95.94	**Tc 43** TECHNETIUM (98)	**Ru 44** RUTHENIUM 101.07	**Rh 45** RHODIUM 102.905	**Pd 46** PALLADIUM 106.42	**Ag 47** SILVER 107.868	**Cd 48** CADMIUM 112.411	**In 49** INDIUM 114.82	**Sn 50** TIN 118.71	**Sb 51** ANTIMONY 121.75	**Te 52** TELLURIUM 127.60	**I 53** IODINE 126.904	**Xe 54** XENON 131.29
1.532	2.54	4.469	6.506	8.57	10.22	11.50	12.46	12.41	12.02	10.50	8.65	7.31	7.31	6.691	6.24	4.93	5.89
Cs 55 CESIUM 132.905	**Ba 56** BARIUM 137.327	**La* 57** LANTHANUM 138.905	**Hf 72** HAFNIUM 178.49	**Ta 73** TANTALUM 180.947	**W 74** TUNGSTEN 183.85	**Re 75** RHENIUM 186.207	**Os 76** OSMIUM 190.2	**Ir 77** IRIDIUM 192.22	**Pt 78** PLATINUM 195.08	**Au 79** GOLD 196.966	**Hg 80** MERCURY 200.59	**Tl 81** THALLIUM 204.383	**Pb 82** LEAD 207.2	**Bi 83** BISMUTH 208.98	**Po 84** POLONIUM (209)	**At 85** ASTATINE (210)	**Rn 86** RADON (222)
1.873	3.5	6.145	13.31	16.654	19.3	21.02	22.57	22.42	21.45	19.31	13.46	11.85	11.35	9.747	9.32		9.73
Fr 87 FRANCIUM (223)	**Ra 88** RADIUM 226.025	**Ac** 89** ACTINIUM 227.027	**Rf 104** (261)	**Ha 105** (262)	**Sg 106** (263)	**Ns 107** (262)	**Hs 108** (265)	**Mt 109** (266)									
	5	10.07															

*LANTHANIDE SERIES	**Ce 58** CERIUM 140.115	**Pr 59** PRAESEODYMIUM 140.907	**Nd 60** NEODYMIUM 144.24	**Pm 61** PROMETHIUM (145)	**Sm 62** SAMARIUM 150.36	**Eu 63** EUROPIUM 151.965	**Gd 64** GADOLINIUM 157.25	**Tb 65** TERBIUM 158.925	**Dy 66** DYSPROSIUM 162.50	**Ho 67** HOLMIUM 164.930	**Er 68** ERBIUM 167.26	**Tm 69** THULIUM 168.934	**Yb 70** YTTERBIUM 173.04	**Lu 71** LUTETIUM 174.967
	6.77	6.773	7.008	7.22	7.52	5.24	7.901	8.230	8.551	8.795	9.066	9.321	6.966	9.841
**ACTINIDE SERIES	**Th 90** THORIUM 232.038	**Pa 91** PROTOACTINIUM 231.005	**U 92** URANIUM 238.029	**Np 93** NEPTUNIUM 237.04	**Pu 94** PLUTONIUM (244)	**Am 95** AMERICIUM (243)	**Cm 96** CURIUM (247)	**Bk 97** BERKELIUM (247)	**Cf 98** CALIFORNIUM (251)	**Es 99** EINSTEINIUM (252)	**Fm 100** FERMIUM (257)	**Md 101** MENDELEVIUM (258)	**No 102** NOBELIUM (259)	**Lr 103** LAWRENCIUM (260)
	11.72	15.37	18.95	20.25	19.84	13.67	13.51	14.00						

Chemistry shorthand

Symbols are used for all chemical names. Knowing a few rules helps make understanding chemistry shorthand easier. Every chemical element is listed in the periodic table where chemical elements are arranged according to their atomic numbers to exhibit the periodic law. This table can be found in any chemistry book. (See **Chemistry Shorthand**.)

One-letter elements are written in capital letters. Elements of two letters are written as a capital and a lowercase letter. For example, **H** is hydrogen; **Fe** is iron, **Ca** is calcium, **C** is carbon and **O** is oxygen. For compounds, capitalize the first letter of each element. **CO** is carbon monoxide and **NaCl** is sodium chloride.

The beginning

For our purpose, ***an atom is the most basic unit of matter***. The word atom comes from the Greek word *atomos* and means "indivisible." This concept of matter was taught thousands of years ago by the ancient Greek Democritus. Today, however, it's known that the atom is divisible.

The atom is the smallest quantity of an element that exists and still has the properties of that element. An element consists of two or more atoms, or molecules, and is a simple substance that cannot be decomposed by chemical means. These are important definitions that form the basis of understanding chemical reactions.

For example, hydrogen is an element that exists as a gas and is written as H_2, which means two atoms of hydrogen are present in the molecule.

$$H_2 \text{ (a molecule of hydrogen)} ===> 2\,H \text{ (two atoms of hydrogen)}$$

The relationship between atoms and molecules will be understood better as this chapter continues. Just remember that elements such as gold or sodium can exist as either molecules or atoms. Elements are more stable in molecular form.

Inside the atom

The ancient philosophers never dreamed that an atom actually consisted of smaller parts. There are only three basic, but very important, principles to learn to understand the fundamentals of atomic chemical structure of matter:

1. The proton is a positively charged particle with mass or weight.
   Proton—mass, positive charge

2. The neutron is a particle with mass, but has no charge.
   Neutron—mass, no charge

3. The electron is a particle that has a negative charge but virtually no mass.
   Electron—no mass, negative charge

The nucleus

The center of the atom is called the **nucleus**. Nucleus is Latin for "little nut," the diminutive of the word *nux*, for a regular-sized nut. This hard, little nut of the atom consists of protons and neutrons locked tightly together by nuclear forces. In nature, positive forces must be balanced with negative forces and so it is with the atom. The negative charge on the electron balances the positive charge on the proton in the nucleus. For every proton in the nucleus, there is an electron whirling about somewhere in the atom. Otherwise the atom would be unbalanced and self-destruct.

Hydrogen is the most basic atom—one proton, one electron. It has a molecular weight of 1 and an atomic number of 1. The atomic number represents its relative position in the periodic table. (See **Figure 6-1**.) Notice that the electron is some distance from the proton, which is in the nucleus. This distance actually is enormous in terms of an atom, for most of an atom is just space. While the pathway of the electron looks circular, it actually is quite irregular, varying in form and place. This pathway is called an **orbit**.

Helium is an example of another atom and is a fun gas since it is used to fill balloons and help sea divers orient under water. Helium was discovered as a component in the sun before it was discovered on earth. The name helium comes from the Greek word *helios* meaning "sun." There are two protons and two neutrons in the nucleus, and two electrons. (See **Figure 6-2**.) It is an interesting fact of science that the formation of helium by the fusion of hydrogen in stars is the source of all life's energy on earth. Helium has a molecular weight of 4, and an atomic number of 2.

For our purpose, the three atom particles—the proton, the neutron and the electron—form the basis of all matter. If you master these three particles, you will have a good beginning to understanding chemistry. As more protons, neutrons and electrons are added to atoms, heavier materials are made that have different physical and chemical properties depending on how many of each particle is present in the atom.

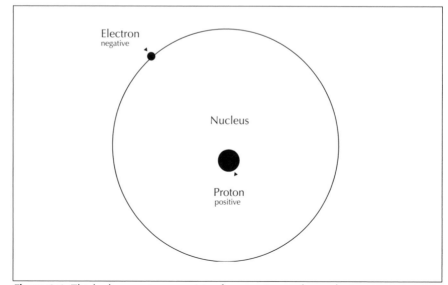

Figure 6-1. The hydrogen atom consists of one proton and one electron.

One more atom, a bit more complex than hydrogen or helium, will illustrate this and introduce the concept of orbits.

The model molecule is sodium, an element essential to life but also a very explosive metal. (See **Figure 6-3**.) It appears to have a bigger nucleus and more electrons than hydrogen or helium. There are 11 protons in the nucleus and 12 neutrons, and 11 electrons whizzing about the nucleus to balance the atom. There are three orbits,

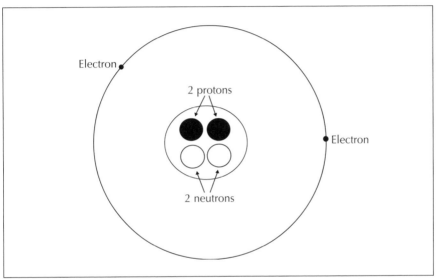

Figure 6-2. *The helium atom consists of two protons, two neutrons and two electrons. The atomic number is 2, but the atomic weight is 4.*

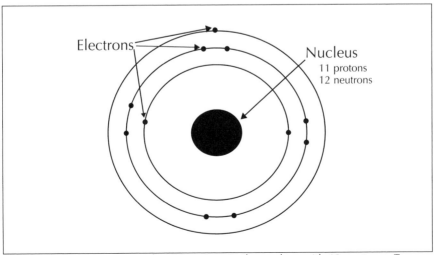

Figure 6-3. *The sodium atom has 11 protons in the nucleus with 12 neutrons. To match the protons, there must be 11 electrons.*

or shells. The one nearest to the nucleus has two electrons, the next one has eight electrons and the third has only one electron. The outer orbit, with one electron, leads to chemical reactions.

Chemical bonds

More confusion can exist in the understanding of chemical bonding than in any other part of first-year chemistry. Knowledge of chemical bonds forms the basis for understanding how chemicals react because chemical reactions involve breaking bonds and reforming them. Three types of chemical bonds will be discussed—the ionic bond, the covalent bond and the hydrogen bond.

Ionic bond. Ionic means "like an ion" and the word *ion* is from the Greek word that means "going." Chemically speaking, an ion is any charged particle, an unneutralized part of an atom or molecule. There are positively charged and negatively charged particles. What does this mean? It means that if an atom or molecule loses an electron, it is positively charged, while a molecule or atom that gains an electron is negatively charged. Electrons and protons must balance in an atom to make it stable and electrically neutral. Ions are unstable and not electrically neutral. They cannot exist alone.

Here is an example: two molecules—sodium and chlorine—are put into water. Sodium is a metal and chlorine is a gas. They react violently and produce table salt—sodium chloride. (See **Figure 6-4**.) Notice that sodium has 11 protons and 11 electrons, while chlorine has 17 protons and 17 electrons. Sodium gives up one electron to

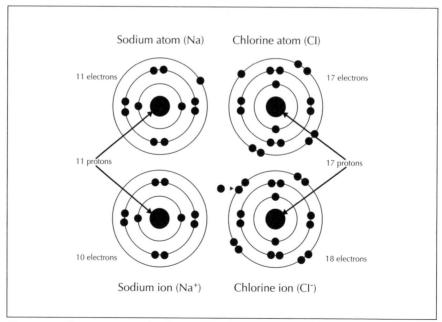

Figure 6-4. *This is an example of an ionic bond. The sodium gives up one electron to chlorine, forming sodium chloride, the common table salt.*

chlorine and the two atoms combine to make one molecule of sodium chloride. The one electron from the sodium goes into the outer orbit of chlorine completing that orbit and making a stable compound—table salt. The importance of eight electrons in the outer orbit is a study in atomic physics and is beyond the purpose of this chapter; however, references are supplied in case you have interest in pursuing the subject. See **Figure 6-5** for the ionic bonded molecule.

   Covalent bond. This bond is the strongest chemical bond and is formed by sharing a pair of electrons. A simple example is the hydrogen atom. It has only one electron. When two hydrogen atoms get close enough, they will share their electron orbits around two nuclei. This pair of electrons now is a covalent bond, which means the two atoms are bonded into a single molecule of hydrogen, now designated as H_2. The valence indicates the number of bonds that a particular atom or molecule can form. A valence of 1 means one bond, while a valence of 4 means four bonds can form. Carbon has a valence of four, so it can form four strong covalent bonds with other atoms.

   Hydrogen bond. This bond is important in science because it involves the type of bonding seen in water, as well as many other molecules. While it is not a strong bond, it is responsible for many biological reactions. The hydrogen bond forms when hydrogen is shared between two molecules. The best example is water. The symbol for water is H_2O, but actually it is H-O-H, as seen in **Figure 6-6**. The small delta signs indicate levels of positive or negative charges. It is the presence of these charges that form the basis of hydrogen bonding. Hydrogen bonding is found in nucleic acids and proteins that undergo constant changes, but which must remain stable most of the time. The hydrogen bonds reinforce each other and provide stability.

   In review, the ionic bond requires a transfer of electrons between atomic orbits; covalent bonds require sharing a pair of electrons; and hydrogen bonds occur when hydrogen is shared between two molecules. The strongest bond is the covalent bond and the weakest bond is the hydrogen bond.

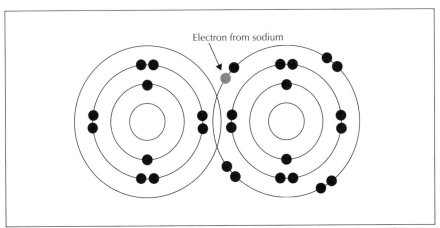

Electron from sodium

Figure 6-5. *Molecule of sodium chloride showing the shared electrons. Note the chlorine atom now has eight electrons in the outer shell.*

Chemical reactions

This is the meat of chemistry and the really neat part! Here you learn what practical chemistry is all about, and how we use all the other bits of chemical information. It will be easier for you to remember chemical reactions if you divide them into six basic kinds of reactions:

1. **Synthesis reactions.** This reaction involves putting two or more chemicals together. Any chemical compound can be made if you know how to put various elements together. Chemical synthesis is both an art and a science. While it is a very tough discipline, at the same time it is one of the most rewarding fields of chemistry. Almost all great advances in medicine and industry in the last 50 years are related in some way to chemical synthesis. A simple example of synthesis is the formation of ethyl alcohol from ethane and water.

$$C_2H_4 + H_2O ==> C_2H_5OH$$

2. **Displacement reactions.** This reaction involves changing one element for another. In displacement, one element, or compound, is changed for another element or compound. Hemoglobin in the blood cells uses displacement to exchange carbon dioxide for oxygen. Pure copper—Cu—can be displaced from copper chloride, $CuCl_2$ by adding metallic zinc.

$$Zn + CuCl_2 ==> ZnCl_2 + Cu \text{ (copper metal)}$$

3. **Decomposition reactions.** This reaction involves breaking down a compound. Everything that decomposes requires some chemical reaction. Burning wood

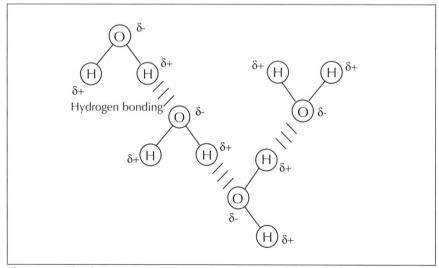

Figure 6-6. *The three components—one oxygen atom and two hydrogen atoms—all have a charge. Note the hydrogen bonding between the water molecules.*

produces heat, water and carbon dioxide. Explosions are decomposition reactions, as is digestion. Water is decomposed with electrical energy. Liquid water can be turned into two gases.

$$2\ H_2O ==> H_2 + O_2 \text{ (hydrogen and oxygen)}$$

4. **Neutralization.** This reaction involves hydrogen transfer from an acid to a base. It is used when acids and bases are combined. It will be discussed in detail in the pH section of this chapter. A base such as baking soda, which is sodium bicarbonate, can neutralize stomach acid safely.

5. **Precipitation reactions.** This reaction involves forming a solid out of water-soluble reactants. These are used to identify, separate and measure substances, and in biological reactions, get rid of toxins and microbes. Antibodies are proteins that are made by white blood cells against bacteria, or viruses called antigens. When an antibody comes into contact with an antigen, it forms a clump, becomes insoluble and falls out of a solution as a solid. Many laboratory procedures depend on antibody-antigen reactions. When proteins come in contact with acid solutions, they are denatured and form an insoluble mass—the precipitate. This is the reaction that occurs when vinegar is added to milk to form curds and whey.

6. **Redox, or oxidation-reduction reactions.** This reaction involves electron transfer between reactants—oxidation-reduction. The nature of life cannot be comprehended without the knowledge of redox reactions. Life essentially is a transfer of electrons, and electron transfer is a redox reaction that occurs in two's. One molecule is reduced; one is oxidized. What does this mean? What is reduced? How can you gain something and be reduced? Just a little molecular chemistry makes it all clear.

Iron, the fourth most abundant material on earth, will be used as the model molecule. The symbol for pure iron is **Fe**. Its atomic number is 26 and its atomic mass is 55.8. Iron normally appears as metallic iron—good old iron gates and rusty hinges. But iron does not stay pure very long because it reacts easily with oxygen to form iron oxide. Pure iron is hard to melt, but iron oxide is easy to melt. Because of this, early iron makers did not need very high temperatures to melt it. Iron oxide must be converted to pure iron by a process called reduction:

$$2\ (Fe_2O_3) + 3C + heat ==> 4\ FE + 3\ CO_2$$

In other words, 2 lumps of iron oxide and 3 lumps of carbon (charcoal) plus heat produces 4 lumps of iron and 3 lumps of carbon dioxide. The lumps could be handfuls, or grams or pounds, or whatever. What has happened?

The carbon reduced the iron's valence, that is, added electrons until the iron could no longer combine with anything else, so it became pure iron. The capacity of iron to react with other chemicals was reduced. The carbon, on the other hand, lost these electrons so it combined with oxygen to gain stability again. In effect, it was oxidized.

If the electrons that moved between the various reactants were counted, it would come out even. Consider Fe_2 combined with O_3. Oxygen has two electrons in its outer orbit.

2 (electrons) x 3 (atoms) ==> 6 (electrons)

Iron must need these electrons. With 2 **Fe**, the six electrons are divided from the oxygen by 2 and we get 3. That's it. Iron has a valence of three, but it is 3+. It is lacking three electrons stolen by the oxygen forming the iron oxide. Carbon has a valence of four since it combines with four hydrogen atoms. There are 12 possible electrons from carbon—4 (electrons) x 3 (carbon atoms).

Now do the arithmetic. Iron got all 12 electrons, the carbon lost 12, but oxygen supplied 12 electrons to the carbon as carbon dioxide. O_2 molecular oxygen, has four electrons, two for each atom. 3 x 4 = 12. Iron dioxide has been reduced to pure iron and carbon has been oxidized to carbon dioxide. Iron has been reduced from the redox sate of 3+ to redox state of 0.

The chemistry of early iron makers has been used to explain oxidation-reduction reactions. You'll need to know this to understand pH and many other chemical reactions.

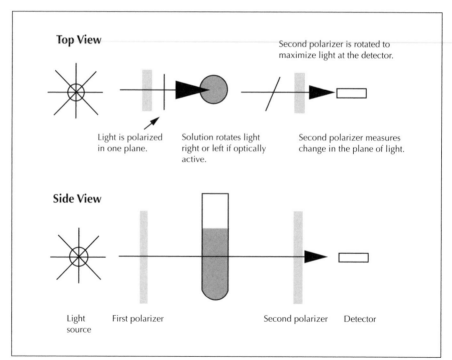

Figure 6-7. *Light passing through the first polarizer selects only vertical vibration of light. This is polarized light. After passing through the sugar solution, the light is rotated clockwise. The second polarizer is rotated to achieve the greatest light intensity at the detector. The direction and degree of rotation describe the optical activity of the solution.*

The full chemical definitions of oxidation and reduction can help you understand the meaning of these terms more clearly. Think of oxidation as electron loss, reduction as electron gain.

Oxidation is the removal of hydrogen, or electrons, from an element, or the addition of oxygen to an element. Oxidation results in a more positive ion.

Reduction is the addition of hydrogen, or an electron, to an element, or the removal of oxygen from an element that results in a more negative ion.

Notes on chirality

It is important for estheticians to know about acids and how they react on proteins such as the keratin of skin.

A term that is being used lately is **chirality**. The word chiral is from *cheir*, the Greek word for "hand." A chiral molecule is one that cannot be superimposed on its mirror image, just as you cannot superimpose your two hands in a mirror image. *Any compound that has four different atoms, or groups, attached to a single carbon is chiral.* You need to think about this for a minute or two before you realize that what you are thinking about is an **asymmetrical figure**, since all chiral compounds lack symmetry by definition.

More and more often, it's being asked if a product's chirality is correct. What should be asked is if the product is **biologically active.** Most chemical compounds in nature are chiral compounds that are biologically active, so they are indeed, correct chirally. Asking if it is "chirally correct" is the same as asking "Is the water in this product really H_2O?" There is no such thing as chirally correct, any more than you can be facially correct. What should be asked is, "Does this product have the correct optical isomerism?" By being correct it is biologically active.

Any compound that has a chiral component, or a degree of asymmetry, will rotate polarized light in solution. That means simply, if you take a solution of glucose—a simple sugar—put it into a beam of plane polarized light and look at it with a second polarizer it will rotate the light to the right, that is, clockwise. (See **Figures 6-7** and **6-7A**.) This is sugar d-glucose because it rotates light to the right, or **dextrorotatory**. In Latin, *dextra* means "right." Ascorbic acid on the other hand will rotate plane polarized light to the left, counterclockwise. This is called l-ascorbic acid for **levorotatory** from the Latin word for *laevus* for "left." If you have a mixture of d- and l-compounds you have a **racemic mixture** that is optically inactive.

There are a few other words that should be understood to appreciate the full significance of the chiral trap. When compounds have *the same formula, but are slightly different in configuration*, they are called **isomers.** If the difference occurs on the same carbon number, they are called **epimers**, and all epimers also are isomers. Glucose, fructose and mannose all have the same formula—$C_6H_{12}O_6$. They cannot be differentiated just by looking at the formula. The difference is in the position of the OH group (See **Figure 6-8**.)

Many sugars have carbon groups arranged in mirror images, and are given the special name of **enantiomers**, from the Greek word *enantios*, which means "opposite." Enantiomers therefore are compounds that are isomers, which are mirror images of each

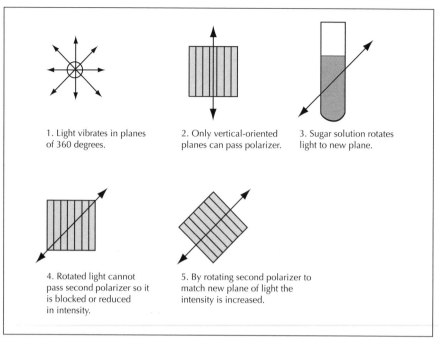

Figure 6-7A. An end view of the polarizer. Vertical light leaves the polarizer. The vertical light leaving the polarizer is rotated by the sugar solution. By turning the polarizer to see the maximum light intensity, the direction of rotation by the solutions is determined. The direction and degree of rotation measures the optical activity of the sugar solution. In this case, it is clockwise, indicating a d-type sugar. The amount of rotation measures the quantity of sugar present in the solution.

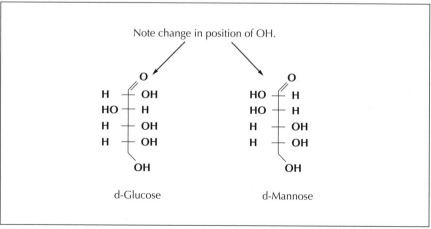

Figure 6-8. The chemical formula is identical, but the OH on the right-hand carbon is on the other side of the molecule. This is called an eipmer. All epimers are isomers.

other. **Figure 6-9** shows the enantiomers of glucose, essentially they are d- and l-forms of the same compound. Note the chemical groups on both end carbons of each molecule point in the same direction.

The importance of d and l is that biologically, the body can use only one of the forms. There are a few exceptions. While most sugars are d-forms, a few l-forms are used. L-fructose, for example, is used by the body to make glycoproteins. Most amino acids are l-forms, again with a few exceptions, but some d-forms are found in antibodies and in bacteria. It is unlikely that any skin care product would not be made with biologically active ingredients. In some cases, a dl-form of a vitamin can be found on an ingredient label. In that case, one of the forms is inactive. At times it is less expensive to use twice as much of a racemic form of a material then to use the pure d- or l-form.

What is pH?

The subject of pH is a vital topic to estheticians who use acid exfoliators in their practices. Symbols used in chemistry have a certain mystique, but they also have a practical use. It is much easier to say "pH" than "the logarithmic of the reciprocal of the hydrogen ion concentration."

Logarithm is Greek in origin. *Logos* means "word" and *arithmos* means "number." So, logarithm means "a word number," or numbers expressed by a word. It became cumbersome for scientists to deal with huge numbers and extremely small numbers so the logarithmic system was developed to make it easier. A number can be multiplied by ten or a million very easily using logarithms (logs). Since pH is based on logs to the base ten, only base 10 logs will be discussed.

You know that 10 x 10 x 10 = 1,000. This can be written by using four zeros or as 10^3—ten to the third power. The ^{3} is an exponent and represents the number of zeros

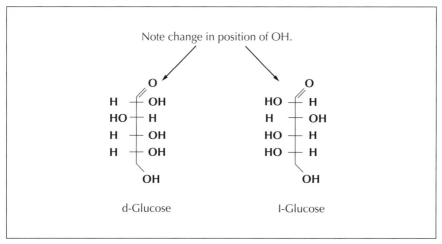

Figure 6-9. *Enantiomers of glucose are the d-form and the l-form. Only the d-form is biologically active. Note that all groups except those on the first carbon and the sixth carbon are on opposite sides of the molecules.*

after the 1. For example, 10^5 is 100,000, and 10^7 is 10,000,000. The exponent 10^2 is converted to a logarithm as "log 2 to the base 10" or log^2. This makes it easy to say 100 million by saying log^{10}. The ten means "to the base 10," but that doesn't need to be said, just "log," since in most cases the base ten is assumed. Knowing that a log really is the exponent to the base 10 makes the rest easy since pH is a logarithmic expression of the hydrogen concentration.

Unraveling the mystery

Water and pH go together. It has been determined that water is not just H_2O, but also $H+$ and $OH-$ ions. For distilled water, the number of $H+$'s and $OH-$'s is equal. In determining the actual concentrations of these two ions, the $H+$ was found to be 10^{-7} mol/l, which means 10 to the minus seven moles per liter. A mole is short for one molecular weight in grams, dissolved in one liter of fluid, such as water. In using 10^{-7} mol/l as the concentration of the hydrogen ion H+, it can be said that hydrogen ions in distilled water are present at a concentration of one 10 millionth of a molecular weight of hydrogen, which is 2 grams. The actual amount of hydrogen ion is 2 grams divided by 10 million. You don't need to bother with grams; however, a concentration of hydrogen ion refers to moles per liter, or mol/l, simply the molecular weight of a substance in grams in one liter of solution. A pH therefore is a shorthand way of writing the hydrogen ion concentration, but since the concentration is so small, it produces a negative logarithm. Divide this tiny concentration into 1, making it a larger number. This is called the **reciprocal**.

The reciprocal of 0.5 is 1/.5 or 2 and the reciprocal of 40 is 1/40 or .025. A small number such as 0.0004 would be 1/0.0004 or 2,500. So, some bright scientist said, "Let's just use the reciprocal of the hydrogen ion concentration and make it easier." The pH equation evolved using logs and reciprocals just to make the life of student estheticians easier. The equation is:

$$pH = log\ 1/[H+]$$

Being a reciprocal, the higher the hydrogen ion concentration, the lower the pH. Each change of whole pH numbers means a tenfold change in hydrogen concentration. A pH of 5 is ten times more acid than a pH of 6, and 10,000 times less acid than pH 1.

The other half of the pH subject is the hydroxyl ion, or OH-. If the pH is 7, there are an equal number of **OH-** and **H+**, that is, 10^{-7} mol/l of H+. In terms of pH, the values range from pH 0 for 1M hydrochloric acid to pH 14 for 1M sodium hydroxide base.

Acids and bases

An **acid** is anything that will donate a hydrogen ion, or a proton, when dissolved in water. A base is anything that will react with an acid to form a salt and water. The classic example is hydrochloric acid and sodium hydroxide:

$$HCl + NaOH ==> NaCl + H_2O\ (a\ salt\ and\ water)$$

By definition, *a salt is any product of an acid and a base reaction*. The base usually is a metal compound.

The more hydrogen an acid can liberate when dissolved in water, the stronger it is. This is a key concept for estheticians to remember. The process of acids dissolving in water is called **dissociation** or **ionization**. Acids that are fully ionized, such as hydrochorlic acid, are very strong. That is why they are not used as skin peeling agents. Sulfuric acid, H_2SO_4, is fully ionized, terribly strong, and is used in car batteries. It is not the concentration of the acid that determines how strong it is, but the degree of ionization that occurs. The hydrogen ions determine the final acidity of the solution.

Acetic, glycolic, lactic and citric acids are examples of weak acids. The term **pKa** is used to represent the dissociation constant of an acid. The lower the pKa, the stronger the acid. This is a more complex concept than pH, and you need to know only that when the pKa is equal to the pH in a solution, the solution is half acid and half salt. Why is this important? Often you will hear that a peeling acid is stronger because it is 10% acid or 20% acid. If you check the pH of that solution and it is equal to the pKa, you have 5% acid and 5% salt in the 10% solution. See **Common Acids**, some of which are used in peeling.

Glycolic acid has the following pH values at various concentrations: at 0.5% (grams/100ml water) the pH is 2.5, while at 10% the pH is 1.7. The increasing concentration by 20 fold from 0.5% to 10% has lowered the pH less than 0.8 of a pH unit. Citric acid also is a weak acid, a 10% solution has a pH of 1.03 and at 60% it is only pH 1.27, actually less acid. Trichloroacetic acid, a strong acid, has a pH 1.2 at a concentration of 1.6%; at higher concentrations it can go below 0. Trichloroacetic acid is used at 30% or more since it is unstable in lower concentration. Crystals of trichloroacetic acid can explode violently. It can be neutralized with sodium bicarbonate solution, but should not be used by estheticians except under supervision of a trained physician.

Common Acids

Acid	Formula	pH of	pKa
Acetic	H(C2H3O2)	6% sol 2.4	4.76
Ascorbid (l)	H2(C6H6O6)	5% sol 2.0	4.10
Boric (l)	H3BO3	0.61% sol 5.1	9.27
Butanoic (l)	H(C4H7O2)		4.83
Carbonic (l)	H2CO3		6.35
Citric (l)	H3(C6H5O7)	1.9% sol 2.2	3.14
Formic	H(CHO2)		3.75
Lactic	H(C3H5O3)		3.08
Phosphoric	H3PO4		2.16

Some values of pKa for weak acids from the Merck Index.

Proteins and acids

Since chemical peeling has become important as a treatment modality for estheticians, acids and proteins are important aspects of life chemistry. Consider that the skin is composed of protein and water, and the rest of the chemicals are minor components. Proteins are very complex chains of amino acids and their structures are very sensitive to the pH of the surrounding solution. When a protein is placed in water, it will hydrate and be surrounded with a type of ion known as the hydronium ion, designated by **H_3O+**. The **hydronium ion** is a water molecule bonded to a free hydrogen ion. You will see it in the references and in other material you may read on pH. It is the hydronium ion that is measured when pH is measured, but for all practical purposes, only the hydrogen ion is discussed in pH studies.

When protein reacts with acid above a certain hydrogen ion concentration, that is, at a low pH, the protein can denature fully to form an irreversible precipitation reaction. This process is called **coagulation**, and occurs with trichloroacetic acid peels. The protein cannot be made normal again; it is destroyed by proteolytic enzymes that take it apart and recycle the amino acids. The whole concept behind the use of chemical peels is to destroy the existing tissues and replace them with new structures. Recognize that the stronger the acid, the more hydrogen ion there is to react with proteins. Here is one proposed reaction that occurs in the stomach, known as acid hydrolysis:

$HCl + H_2O$ + Protein as polypeptide (chicken fried steak) ==> dipeptides and amino acids

The hydrochloric acid in the stomach has a pH between 1 and 2, which is fairly strong. The same process happens on the skin. Note that water is needed in this reaction.

Summary

Knowing basic chemical concepts will help the esthetician appreciate and understand new products as they come on the market. More important, this knowledge will provide the basis for proper use of the products, thereby providing better treatment. It is pure joy to understand the reasons behind any scientific concept. Chemistry is the basis of all physical life. You essentially are a highly sophisticated organization of protons, electrons and neutrons, which make up atom and molecules. Knowing how these tiny components work by obeying certain chemical and physical laws forms the basis of chemistry knowledge.

General References

Author's note: I have used recent chemistry texts as references, as well as a number of Internet sites. A good book in general chemistry is an excellent addition to your library, as is a text on biochemistry.

General Chemistry Books

Hess F and Thomas A, *Chemistry Made Simple*, Made Simple Books (1984). A really easy paperback book to read.

King E, *Chemistry 1979*, Salsaulito, CA: Painter Hopkins. A college-level classic. Good reference book, but not a first chemistry book unless you really are serious about chemistry.

Mascette JA, *Chemistry the Easy Way*, Barron Educational Series (1996). A paperback; one of the best first chemistry books.

Waites G and Harrison, P, *The Cassell Dictionary of Chemistry*, London: Cassell (1998). A quick-and-easy reference for chemical words you don't recognize or can't define.

Biochemistry

Champe PC and Harvey RA, *Biochemistry*, Lippiiincott-Raven (1987). A good first biochemistry book; paperback, easy to read and well illustrated.

Lehninger AL, *Principles of Biochemistry*, Worth Publishers, Inc. (1982). One of the best books ever written on the subject of biochemistry; a true classic.

The Merck Index, An Encyclopedia of Chemicals, Drugs and Biologicals, 11th edition, Rahway, NJ: Merck & Co. (1989). Available either on disc or as a book. Lists basic structures and properties of thousands of chemical compounds. Well worth the investment.

Scientific American Science Desk Reference, Wiley Company (1999). Nice to have on hand for the occasional scientific term you have forgotten, or perhaps not learned. Concise, easy-to-read explanations.

3-D Molecular Modeling, Toronto, ON, Canada: Advanced Chemical Development, Inc. Plenty of programs available; some are great, but expensive. The one I like most is ChemSketch 4.0. Comes with great movies on how to use the program, as well as assorted chemical topics.

Internet sites

antoine.frostburg.edu/chem/senese/101/acidbase/faq/
    Comprehensive, easy to follow, good drawings.

www.borg.com/~lubehawk/biochem.htm
    Easy to read, friendly.

www.chemtutor.com
    One of the best. Great stuff here; needs some effort to follow the first time around.

www.chem.purdue.edu/gchelp/cchem
    A good site for optical qualities of compounds.

Chapter 7

Biochemistry

In the previous chapter, the basics of chemistry, atoms, molecules, acids and bases, and chemical reactions were covered. Now learn the basics of a special type of chemistry that deals specifically with the life processes.

Every minute of every day, thousands of chemical reactions occur in every cell of the body. Biochemistry is the chemical discipline that studies these reactions. Five areas of this discipline are valuable to the esthetician—the three basic foods, **proteins**, **carbohydrates** and **fats**; **energetics**, or how the body stores and uses energy; and **deoxyribonucleic acid (DNA)** and the genetic code.

Proteins

All matter begins with electrons and protons, the building components of the elements. Proteins start with amino acids, which are not difficult to understand. There are 20 essential ones, and a few others, that make up life's proteins. When two amino acids are combined, a new chemical called a **peptide** is formed. The word peptide comes from the Greek word *pepsis* that means "digestion," and that is what happens when a protein is digested—peptides are formed. A **dipeptide** is formed from two amino acids, and a **polypeptide** contains more than two amino acids.

Essential amino acids

With the exception of one, all amino acids consist of a negatively charged carboxyl group ^-COO – and an amino group NH_2+ that is positively charged. In all amino acids these two groups are joined to form a peptide linkage, as seen in this equation:

$$^-COOH + {}^+H_2N \longrightarrow \boxed{\begin{array}{c} O \quad\quad H \\ \| \quad\quad\; | \\ -C-N-C- \\ \;\;\;\;| \quad\; | \\ \;\;\;H \quad H \end{array}} {}^+H_2O$$

The actual linkage is shown rather than the full amino acids that are shown in **Figure 7-1**. The peptide bond always has this configuration: a nitrogen atom between two carbon atoms and a double-bond oxygen on one of the carbons. This is a fundamental concept in protein chemistry. Amino acids have certain properties based on the nature of the side chains, since the end amino group and carboxyl groups usually are bonded together in the protein. **Figure 7-2** represents a few amino acid structures showing the glycine backbone with the side chains.

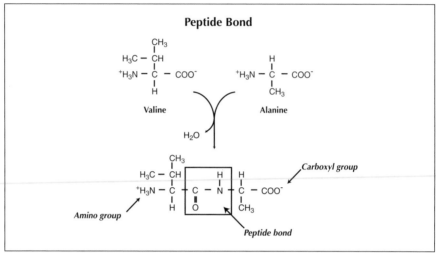

Figure 7-1. *The peptide bond is the critical link between amino acids. There always is a double bond carbon-oxygen atom linked to the nitrogen atom in a peptide linkage.*

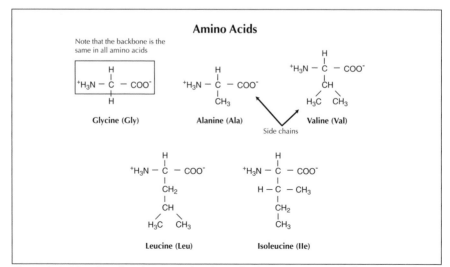

Figure 7-2. *Visualize the glycine molecule as the basic structure of all amino acids. Everything else is attached to this basic structure.*

Amino acids classification

Non-polar amino acids with side chains. Hydrophobic amino acids do not give off protons and do not form ionic or hydrogen bonds. They are not water-soluble. They usually are found in the center of protein molecules and include glycine, alanine, valine, leucine, isoleucine, phenylalanine, tryptophane, methionine and proline.

Uncharged polar amino acids. These amino acids enter into hydrogen bonding even though they have a zero charge. Cysteine contains a sulfhydryl group, -SH, that is an important component of many enzymes. They include serine, threoine, tyrosine, asparginine, cysteine and glutamine.

Acidic side chains. These amino acids are proton donors and are negatively charged at physiological pH (7.4). Two of these are aspartic acid and glutamic acid.

Basic side chains. These amino acids accept protons and at physiological pH they are fully ionized and positively charged. Three of them are histidine, lysine and arginine.

Protein structure

Proteins usually are very large molecules containing hundreds to thousands of amino acids. For example, albumin, the major soluble protein in the blood, is quite small at 40,000 molecular weight while gamma globulin is more than a million molecular weight. Amino acids linked in chains form peptides and the peptides form the proteins. The polypeptide chain forms the backbone of the protein and is called the **primary structure**, but proteins can have **secondary**, **tertiary** and **quaternary** structures as well. These structures relate to the functional properties of the protein.

Two types of protein models are **globular** and **fibrous**. Hemoglobin is a globular protein and collagen is a fibrous protein. There are many types of globular and fibrous proteins in the body, but *all the proteins in the body are formed of exact amino acid sequences that are directed by the genetic code within the cell nucleus*.

Hemoglobin

A first look at the hemoglobin structure could urge you to throw up your hands and run out screaming. It is a very complex molecule, but can be broken down to components. Hemoglobin contains the protein **globin** and four **heme** groups. See **Figure 7-3**.

Hemoglobin is found in the red blood cells where it carries oxygen from the lungs to the tissues and cells of the body. The many chemicals around the iron atom make up a structure known as **porphyrins**, which can be seen in the upper right corner of **Figure 7-3**. The globin proteins surround the heme group, folded in a highly specific manner. While the iron in the heme part carries the oxygen, the protein part of hemoglobin allows the iron to be transported in the red blood cell. All mammals have this basic structure of hemoglobin, though there are some different types, even within human beings. Humans have four hemoglobins known as types A, A2, F and S.

The important concept is that *heme proteins are required to carry oxygen to cells*. These proteins are subject to all the physical and chemical properties of proteins, therefore a normal status of physiology is required for optimum function of oxygen transport. Changing the pH of the blood, a lack of iron, lung disease and poor diet combine to reduce tissue oxygenation.

Collagen

Collagen is the most abundant of all body proteins, making up 25% of all proteins. Collagen is found mainly in skin, teeth, bones and tendons, though small amounts can be in most organs as a structural component. Collagen is an insoluble protein and this chemical characteristic gives it strength, but made it almost impossible for biochemists to study the nature of collagen protein. Collagen consists of many fibers that are cross-linked by special amino acids. In young animals, some collagen is not yet crossed-linked and it was found that this type of collagen could be extracted in soluble form. This is **tropocollagen**, the basic unit of collagen.

Tropocollagen consists of three same-sized polypeptide chains. Two of these chains, called **a1 chains** are identical; the third one, known as **a2**, is similar to the a1 chains. Each chain contains about 1,000 amino acids, while the molecular weight of tropocollagen is 285,000, producing a very large basic unit. Glycine is the most common amino acid in collagen and comprises 25% of collagen's weight. Proline, hydroxyproline and hydoxylysine are other critical amino acids in collagen.

The full details of collagen's structure are far too complex to cover in this chapter, but there are important features to know. The fundamental structural design of the

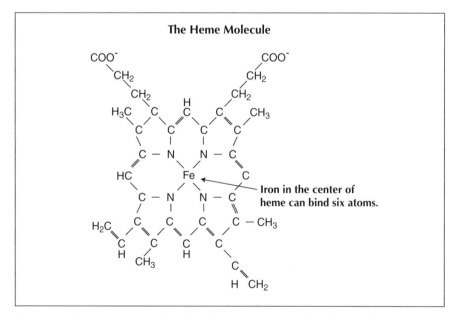

The Heme Molecule

Iron in the center of heme can bind six atoms.

Figure 7-3. The heme molecule is bonded with protein to form hemoglobin, the oxygen-carrying protein in the bloodstream. Fe, the iron atom, is central to the oxygen-carrying capacity of this large molecule.

collagen fiber is a quarter-staggered array of tropocollagen molecules. **Figure 7-4** outlines the sequence of collagen formation. Note that pro-collagen, secreted by the fibroblast, is the precursor of tropocollagen. In the intercellular space, the tropocollagen fibers are bonded by cross-linking with hydroxylysine, while the hydroxyproline amino acids stabilize the tropocollagen fiber internally. The esthetician should be aware of the general complex nature of collagen and its importance in skin as a structural component.

Another fibrous protein

Keratin is the major protein in the epidermis. It also is formed by fibers joined in a complex structure, but unlike collagen, keratin is crossed-linked through amino acids called **cysteine** that join to form **cystine**, a double amino acid. Keratin also is insoluble, tough and resistant to tearing, even though is can be stretched quite a bit. Wet keratin is more flexible and can be stretched twice as far as dry keratin. Keratin and collagen, as with all proteins, can be degraded, or broken down by another class of proteins called **enzymes**.

Enzymes

Life is impossible without enzymes, which make things happen quickly and efficiently. Almost all chemical reactions in the body require one or more enzymes. Sugar alone requires more than 20 enzymes to be converted to carbon dioxide, water and energy. Enzymes can have complex or simple names, such as **trypsin** and **pepsin**, but most of them end in the suffix -ase. **Lipase** breaks down fat and **urease** breaks down urea, but a group of enzymes known as **syntheses** build up compounds. The name

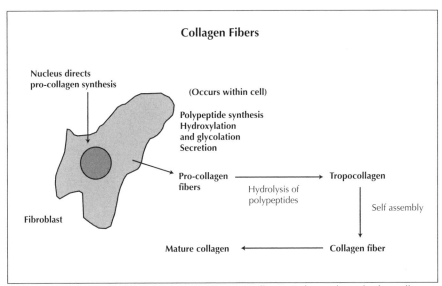

Figure 7-4. This is a multi-step process. The pro-collagen is formed inside the cell, but the cross-linking occurs in the intercellular space.

of the enzyme often describes its action, for example **lactic dehydrogenase** removes hydrogen from lactic acid to make pyruvic acid. There are six major classes of enzymes based on their functions.

How enzymes work

Enzymes are **catalysts**, chemicals that enter into reactions, but are not used up in the process. There are three parts of an enzyme reaction—the **substrate, enzyme** and **product**.

$$[S] + [E] ==> [ES] ==> [P] + [E]$$

Substrate + enzyme becomes enzyme substrate and results in product + enzyme complex

This equation describes an enzyme reaction. The enzymes combine with the substrate forming the enzyme-substrate complex; this action alters the substrate to make the product and then free the enzyme. The reaction is diagrammed in **Figure 7-5**.

Here is a real-life example. A mother wishes to take the clothes off her baby for a bath. The clothed baby is the substrate, the mother is the enzyme and the naked baby is the product. The discarded clothing is a second product. Here it is in equation form:

Clothed baby + mother ==> mother removing clothes ==> naked baby + mother
Substrate + enzyme ==> enzyme substrate complex ==> product + enzyme

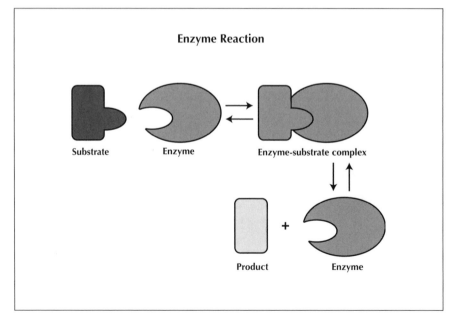

Enzyme Reaction

Substrate   Enzyme   Enzyme-substrate complex

Product   Enzyme

Figure 7-5. An enzyme requires a substrate and an enzyme, times one or more co-factors. The binding of the enzyme to the substrate is the critical step since no reaction can occur unless binding takes place. The enzyme is not used up in the reaction.

This is a very simple concept if you remember the three parts: substrate, enzyme and product, although there can be other components in the reaction such as co-factors and additional products. The actual chemical reactions are described by enzyme kinetics, a branch of biochemistry that provides a great deal of information about enzymes in mathematical terms.

While there are many kinds of enzymes, the six major types can be defined as follows:

1. **Oxidoreductases.** These enzymes catalyze oxidation-reduction reactions. Reduction is the gain of hydrogen or an electron; oxidation is the loss of hydrogen or an electron.

Lactate + lactate dehyrogenase + NAD ==> pyruvate + NADH (hydrogen acceptor)

2. **Transferases.** These enzymes catalyze the transfer of carbon- (C), nitrogen- (N), or phosphorous- (P) containing groups.

Methyl ethyl ketone + glucose + methyl transferase ==> methyl glucose + ethyl ketone
A methyl group is transferred to the glucose molecule from methyl ethyl ketone.

3. **Hydrolases.** These enzymes catalyze cleavage of bonds by addition of water.

Urea + water ==> urease + carbon dioxide + amonia

4. **Lyases.** These enzymes catalyze cleavage of C-C, C-S and certain C-N bonds. Lyases cut, or break bonds. Think of lysis, a breaking up of a molecule. In the reaction illustrated, pyruvate is converted to two smaller molecules.

Pyruvate + pyruvate decarboxylase ==> acetaldehyde + carbon dioxide

5. **Isomerases.** These enzymes catalyze the racemization of optical, or geometric isomers. This means that the chemical groups on a particular molecule are rearranged so that the optical, or chemical, properties are altered.

Methylmalonyl CoA + methylmalonyl CoA mutase ==> succinyl CoA
A branched chain compound ==> a straight-chain compound

6. **Ligases.** These enzymes catalyze formation of bonds between carbon and oxygen, sulfur and nitrogen coupled to hydrolysis of high-energy phosphates. This reaction binds compounds, but requires a high-energy source such as adenosine triphosphate (ATP). Think of ligature as something that binds.

Pyruvate + carbon dioxide + ATP + pyruvate carboxylase ==> oxaloacetic acid
Three carbons + one carbon ==> four carbons

The enzyme **pyruvate carboxylase** joins carbon dioxide (one carbon) to pyruvate (three carbons) to form a new four-carbon compound. Note that pyruvate decarboxylase is present in the lyases enzyme already mentioned.

This very brief introduction can't cover all aspects of enzymes, but at least familiarizes you with some of the nomenclature of enzymes and some of the reactions that require them. Enzymes are proteins and are very sensitive to temperature and pH conditions. Perhaps no chemical compound uses more enzymes than carbohydrates, a major food source.

Carbohydrates

Carbohydrates are the most abundant organic molecules in nature. They not only supply energy for animals but they make up much of the structural components of plants and trees. Structurally, there is one molecule of water for each molecule of carbon, hence the formula $(CH_2O)_n$. The lower case "n" is a multiplication factor. For example, sugar would be written as $(C_6H_{12}O_6)$ or $(CH_2O)_6$ where the "n" stands for 6. Classification probably is the most complex thing about carbohydrates.

Classifying carbohydrates

Monosaccharides and **simple sugars** are the same thing. One can be substituted for the other. The five most common sugars, based on the number of carbon atoms in the molecule, are **trioses** with three carbons; **tetroses**, four carbons; **pentoses**, five carbons; **hexoses**, six carbons; and **heptoses**, seven carbons. Common glucose is a hexose. Carbohydrates can have either an aldehyde or a ketone as their carbonyl group. When simple carbohydrates are linked, they become complex carbohydrates.

Complex carbohydrates

Two simple sugars form a **disaccharide** such as **sucrose**, which is glucose plus fructose, common table sugar. Some other disaccharides are **maltose** from glucose + glucose and lactose from galactose + glucose. If more and more sugars are added, a polymeric carbohydrate such as starch or **cellulose** is produced. The linking of carbohydrates is via the glycosidic bond that is diagrammed in **Figure 7-6**. When three to twelve **saccharides** are linked, the compound is called an **oligosaccharide**. More than 12 monosaccharides linked together form **polysaccharides**, which actually are polymers. **Glycogen**, for example, is a polysaccharide used to store energy and it contains hundreds of glucose molecules.

The glycosidic bond

Many complex structures can be formed with carbohydrates using the glycosidic linkage. For example, **glycoproteins** form when sugars unite with protein as **glycosaminoglycans** in the dermis. Sugars that combine with lipids are called **glycolipids**. One major sugar group called deoxyglucose unites with purines and pyrimidines to form the basic units of deoxyribonucleic acid (DNA). **Figure 7-6** also shows two types of bonding in glycosides, the **O bonding** and the **N bonding**. The O linkage is a C–O–C link, while the N linkage is C–N–C. When a carbohydrate binds to a non-carbohydrate, the non-carbohydrate part is called an **aglycone**. In the pathological process of aging this becomes very important since **glycosylation** of proteins is a glycosidic bonding. These abnormal proteins do not function normally since they interfere with physiological processes. They are one of the major causes of cataracts and abnormal proteins in

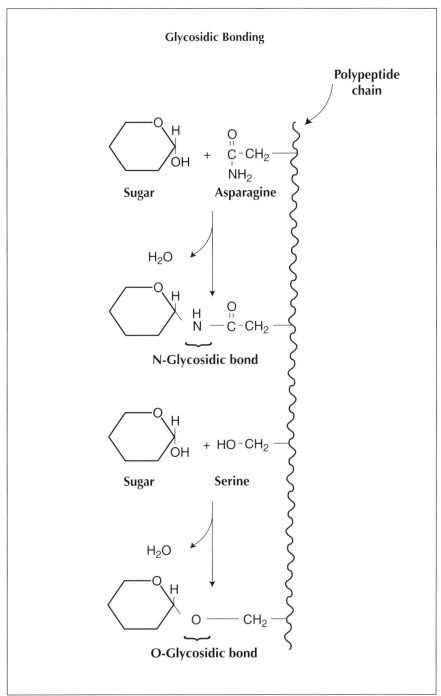

Figure 7-6. *The glycosidic bond of the C–O–C type can join two sugars through a carbon-oxygen-carbon linkage. Amino acids bind to sugars in this manner.*

diabetics, and a major source of reduced functional capacity in aging. Reversal of glycosylation now is possible using special biological agents known as **thiazolidines**.

One more bit of carbohydrate structure is needed to help understand the nomenclature in biochemistry. The terms **alpha** and **beta** are used frequently to designate certain complex carbohydrates. The Greek letters α and β are used to denote what side of the carbohydrate molecule the OH group occurs in a **hemiacetal** structure. In **Figure 7-7**, one of the OH groups forms a ring structure with the carbonyl group at the top of the molecule. This is important because certain carbohydrates cannot be utilized by humans as food unless they have a structure that can be metabolized. These structures change constantly and are called **mutorotations**.

Carbohydrates as food and energy

Carbohydrates are the only food eaten that starts to digest in the mouth. The action of **amylose** in the mouth begins to break down starch. Humans cannot digest carbohydrates with β(1-4) bonds. Cellulose is an example of this type of carbohydrate. There is no digestion of carbohydrates in the stomach because the high acid content inhibits the enzyme reactions. In the small intestine the acid is neutralized and pancreatic amylase continues the digestion. Mucosal cell membrane-bound enzymes continue the digestive process converting the carbohydrates to glucose, fructose and galactose. At this point these simple sugars enter the portal circulation and are transported to the liver. Both fructose and glucose can enter the cells after having phosphorus added to the molecule. These two molecules, known as fructose-1-phosphate and glucose-6-phosphate, then enter the metabolic pathway to be converted to energy, or converted to fat and stored.

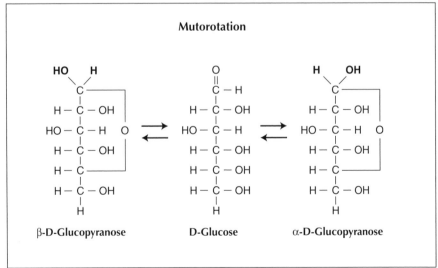

Figure 7-7. Mutorotation frequently occurs in sugars. Note that the OH group has changed sides in the molecule.

Many individuals cannot digest some sugars normally, so they develop an intolerance for these compounds. Lactose intolerance often comes late in life, but it occurs in some infants as a defect in one of more of the enzymes that metabolize lactose. Abdominal gas and diarrhea are common symptoms. Excessive consumption of fructose-bearing foods produce an intolerance leading to liver disease. In some cases, a lack of one or more enzymes can cause hepatic failure. This is condition is treatable by simply removing fructose and sucrose from the diet.

Glucose storage

A constant source of glucose is needed for life. Maintaining an adequate blood glucose level is achieved by three sources: **diet**, **glycogen conversion** and **gluconeogenesis**.

Gluconeogenesis means "generation of new glucose." Briefly, this is the production of glucose from amino acids, glycerol and lactate. It begins four to six hours after a meal and becomes fully active if the liver glycogen is depleted.

Glycogen

Glycogen is a big-branched chained polymeric molecule. A single molecule can have a molecular weight of a hundred million. Only glucose molecules make up glycogen, linked in an α 1, 4 linkage with β 1, 6 linkage every eight to ten glucosyol residues. About 400 grams of glycogen are stored in the muscles, and about 100 grams are stored in the liver.

Synthesis of glycogen introduces a new compound called **uridine**, a component of ribonucleic acid (RNA) that occurs in another form of ATP called **uridine triphosphate (UTP)**. Glycogen is synthesized in the cytoplasm of the cell and requires energy to be produced. While the synthesis is quite complex, it can be reduced to two simple steps.

Step 1. Uridine triphosphate reacts with glucose to produce **uridine diphosphate**, or UDP-glucose, by the action of an enzyme called **UDP-glucose pyrophosphate**.

Step 2. The UPD-glucose is added to a primer molecule consisting of four glucose molecules and starts the chain reaction of polymerization. The enzyme responsible for this action is glycogen synthetase. The branched-chains are added by a second enzyme called the **branching enzyme**. Branching is very important both to glycogen synthesis and the degradation of glycogen.

When glucose is needed, glycogen breaks down. Both the length of the glycogen polymer and the side chains are used in the production of glucose. A new enzyme, glycogen phosphorylase, breaks the α 1, 4 bonds to shorten the chain, and two other enzymes remove the side chains in two steps. These enzymes actually are on a single peptide known as the **debranching enzyme**.

The regulation of the synthesis and storage of glycogen is itself a complex story but quite fascinating. It is enough to know that glucose can be stored in the liver and muscle as glycogen and that this stored glucose is available when the blood glucose drops. One of the peptides that moves glycogen to glucose from the liver very fast is **glucagon**. It often is used to counteract excess insulin.

Glycosaminoglycans

Glycosaminoglycans (GAGs) are large complex polysaccharides that are negatively charged and associated with a small amount of protein. These compounds bind large quantities of water to form a gel-like matrix. Mucous secretions from the nose and other areas of the body are due to the presence of GAGs. Originally these secretions were called mucopolysaccharides.

Structure. GAGs are long linear structures that in most cases are not branched. The basic unit is a repeating disaccharide structure consisting of an acid sugar and an amino sugar. An acid sugar has the carbonyl group (HC=O) replaced by a carboxyl group (-COOH), and the amino sugar has one of the OH groups replaced by an NH group. You can see these the basic components in **Figure 7-8.**

Function. Being linear structures and negatively charged, the GAGs repel each other and are able to slip over each other. Since a shell of water surrounds them, they are able to contract and expand simply by squeezing out or adding water. The six major types of GAGs in the body include:

1. *Chondroitin 4- and 6-sulfates.* This is the most abundant GAG in the body, found in the cartilage tendons, ligaments and aorta.

2. *Keratin sulfate.* This is the only GAG that contains galactose rather than uronic acid. It is very heterogeneous and is found in the cornea and cartilage.

3. *Hyaluronic acid.* Unlike other GAGs, hyaluronic acid is not attached to a protein and has no sulfur component. Besides occurring in animals, it is the only GAG that occurs in bacteria. Hyaluronic acid acts as a lubricant and shock absorber. It is found in the lubricating fluid of joints, in the vitreous humor of the eye, in

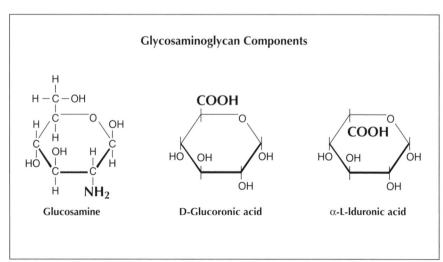

Figure 7-8. *Glycosaminoglycan components are linked in glycosidic linkage to form a glycosaminoglycan.*

the umbilical cord and in loose connective tissue. Commercial hyaluronic acid is obtained from rooster combs, umbilical cords or bacteria. Note that GAGs do not occur in plants and plant-derived hyaluronic acid does not exist.

4. *Dermatan sulfate.* As the name implies, this GAG occurs in the dermal portion of the skin. It also is found in the blood vessels and in the heart valves.

5. *Heparin.* This is an intracellular GAG that is unique because most GAGs are extra-cellular. Heparin is a component of mast cells that line arteries, especially in the liver, lungs and skin. The major function of heparin is as an anticoagulant.

6. *Heparan sulfate.* Found in basement membranes, this GAG is a component of cell surfaces.

Proteoglycans

All GAGs but heparin are bound to a core protein. The relationship between the core protein and the attached GAG molecules in the basic structure can be seen in **Figure 7-9**. These structures can link to a larger protein and form a proteoglycan aggregate. While they have diverse physiological functions, they all essentially have the same role as the basic GAG. The heparin proteoglycan structure has the appearance of a bottle brush as seen in **Figure 7-10**.

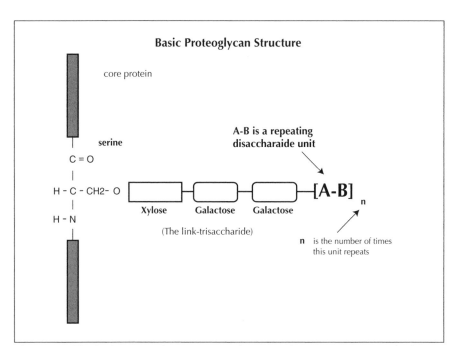

Figure 7-9. The basic proteoglycan structure begins with a protein core to which sugars are linked in series. Notice that a link or key sugar group is needed before the repeating series is attached. These are special triose sugar links.

GAG abnormalities

As in all compounds in the body, sometimes things go wrong with GAGs that can produce serious diseases. These disorders are called **mucopolysaccharidoses**. They are progressive and characterized by accumulation of GAGs in various tissues causing skeletal and extra-cellular matrix deformities. The cause of these disorders is the lack of one or more enzymes that break down the GAGs. They usually are fatal conditions that occur early in childhood. Information sources for these disorders have been listed in the references at the end of the chapter.

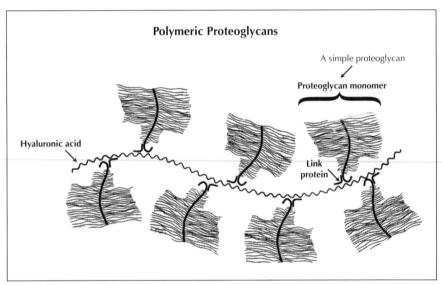

Figure 7-10. Polymeric proteoglycans have a polysaccharide core such as hyaluronic acid, with many proteoglycans attached.

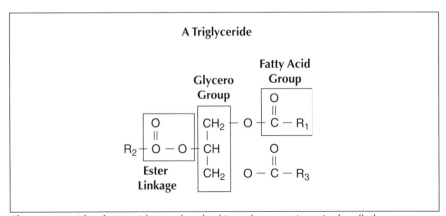

Figure 7-11. After fatty acids are absorbed into the gastrointestinal wall, they are reformed into triglycerides before they can pass into the lymphatic system.

Glycoproteins

Glycoprotein is not the same as a proteoglycan, although they share some similarity. Glycoproteins are very diverse compounds with multiple functions. Structurally they are more branched and not as large as proteoglycans. Membrane-bound glycoproteins function in a broad range of cellular phenomenon such as cell surface recognition; and cell surface antigenicity, such as blood group antigens. They also can act as a protective lubricant in the gastrointestinal and urogenital tracts, but their largest number are in the globular proteins present in human plasma, except albumin.

The structure of the glycoproteins basically is an oligosaccharide, three or more simple sugars, linked to a protein through the glycosidic linkage either as an O or N linkage.

As with the GAGs, glycoproteins are associated with diseases when they are not degraded effectively. Missing or defective enzymes are again the culprits, leading to a deformity and death as the glycoproteins accumulate.

Lipids

Lipids are the least interesting topic to many beginning students of biochemistry but in time they recognize the tremendous importance of lipid chemistry in everyday life. Even lowly **adipocytes** that store **triglycerides**, the fat you eat and store, have assumed an importance as a regulatory organ. Lipids are a dietary component and specific biochemical agents involved in physiology.

Lipids can be defined as biochemicals that do not dissolve in water. While not entirely correct, all lipids are water-insoluble, but not all water insoluble substances are lipids. In biochemistry, there are seven classes of lipids: triglycerides, fatty acids, phospholipids, glycolipids, sphingolipids, steroids, and vitamins A, D, E and K.

Triglycerides

A triglyceride is a lipid compound consisting of glycerol plus three fatty acids. **Figure 7-11** shows the basic structure of a triglyceride. The three Rs represent a fatty acid from 1-20 carbons, although triglycerides usually contain fatty acids with at least 16 carbons. The three glycerol carbons are seen in a straight chain. The fatty acids are linked to the glycerol by an ester linkage that is quite easy to break by enzymes.

Dietary lipids

The intake and fate of fats via the gastrointestinal tract is shown in **Figure 7-12**. After the fatty acids are absorbed into the gastrointestinal wall, they are reformed into triglycerides before they can pass into the lymphatic system. The **chylomicrons** are combinations of lipids and proteins that make the fats water-soluble in the blood stream. The chylomicrons are broken down to fatty acids and glycerol by a special enzyme called lipoprotein lipase. The glycerol goes to the liver for utilization, but the fatty acids can be used directly by many cells including muscle cells, the heart and the adipose tissue. Abnormalities of these lipolytic enzymes produce serious problems.

Chylomicrons require a protein to solubilize them in the plasma. This protein, known as **apolipoprotein B-48**, is synthesized in the intestinal mucosal cells and is used to coat the chylomicron. If this protein is absent, the chylomicrons accumulate in the intestinal wall. This is a genetic condition and is known as **congenital abetalipoproteinemia**. If the enzyme **lipoprotein lipase** is absent, a condition called **type I hyperlipoproteinemia** results. It is a rare condition that results in massive accumulation of chylomicronemia. After the triglycerides are removed from the chylomicrons, they contain only cholesterol esters, phospholipids, protein and some triacylglycerol. These remnants are sent to the liver where they are broken down into their component parts and sent back to the body pool to be recycled. Sometimes this system is defective and produces a condition called **dysbetalipoproteinemia,** or **type III hyperlipoproteinemia**, a serious cardiovascular disorder. These conditions are mentioned only to let you know they exist and make you aware of the importance of enzymes in biology.

Fatty acids

A fatty acid is a long chain hydrocarbon carbon with a terminal carboxyl group (COOH). At physiological pH 7.4, the terminal carboxyl group ionizes and becomes

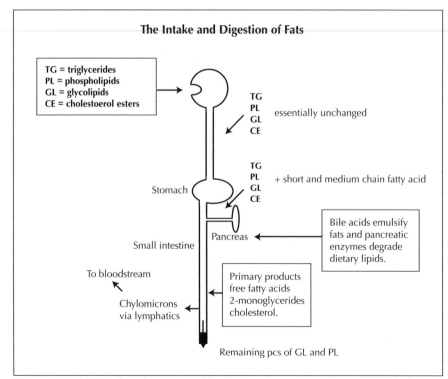

The Intake and Digestion of Fats

TG = triglycerides
PL = phospholipids
GL = glycolipids
CE = cholestoerol esters

TG
PL   essentially unchanged
GL
CE

TG
PL   + short and medium chain fatty acid
GL
CE

Stomach

Pancreas

Bile acids emulsify fats and pancreatic enzymes degrade dietary lipids.

Small intestine

To bloodstream

Primary products free fatty acids 2-monoglycerides cholesterol.

Chylomicrons via lymphatics

Remaining pcs of GL and PL

Figure 7-12. Notice that absorption of fats is complex and contingent on multiple factors. Lipids are split into fatty acids within the gastrointestinal tract, then absorbed in the intestinal lining, reformed into triglycerides and passed into the lymphatic system.

⁻COO that has an affinity for water. Ionized fatty acids are **amphipathic**—they have both a hydrophobic and a hydrophilic region. Very long chain fatty acids are nevertheless hydrophobic and must be esterified to be soluble in the plasma.

Saturated fats have no double bonds. If a fatty acid contains one double bond it is unsaturated. If it contains two or more unsaturated double bonds, it is a polyunsaturated fatty acid (PUFA). The basics used for naming fatty acids follows.

The COOH group is carbon number 1 and the next one is carbon 2 and so on, moving to the left of the COOH group. This is an easy system. The second carbon now is called an alpha carbon, or α and the third carbon is called a beta carbon or β the last carbon is called omega or ω. **Arachidonic acid** can be listed as 20:4 (5,8,11,14), which means that arachidonic acid is a 20 carbon fatty acid with 4 unsaturated bonds located a between carbons 5-6, 8-9, 11-12 and 14-15. Easy, right? Except the for the **omega** system.

The omega system counts the double bonds from the **omega carbon**. Example: linoleic has 18 carbons and 2 double bonds that normally would be called an 18:2 (9,12) fatty acid. The omega system calls it an ω-6 fatty acid because the first fatty acid is on the sixth carbon. So, it all depends on what end you start counting. See **Common Fatty Acids**.

Common Fatty Acids

Common Name	Number of Carbons	Significance
Formic acid	1	Formica, Latin for ant, the toxin in ant stings
Acetic acid	2	Vinegar, and basis for glycolic acid
Proprionic acid	3	Starting material for many products
Butyric acid	4	Found in butter and milk
Capric acid	10	Found in milk
Palmitic acid	16.0	Found in palm and coconut oils
Palmiticoleic acid	16:1 (1)	A very interesting fatty acid
Stearic acid	18.0	Found in vegetable and animal fats
Oleic acid	18:1 (9)	Helps skin penetration
Linoleic acid	18:2 (9, 12)	Essential fatty acid
Linolenic acid	18:3 (9, 12, 15)	Essential fatty acid
Arachidonic acid	20:4 (5, 8, 11, 14)	Precursor of inflammatory agents

Linoleic and linolenic acids must be in the diet since the body cannot make them. Most fatty acids are straight chain, but some foods, such as diary products, contain branched chain fatty acids. **Phytanic acid** is one such branched fatty acid found in milk. The inability to digest this acid leads to Refsum's disease, characterized by an accumulation of this fatty acid in the plasma.

Phospholipids

Phospholipids are compounds found throughout the body, but chiefly in cell membranes. These lipids are extremely important for cell functioning, for without the ability to form lipid cell membranes in an aqueous environment, life would be impossible. Phospholipids consist of an **alcohol** attached to **diacylglycerol**. The acyl group (RCO) is what remains of a carboxyl (RCOOH) when the -OH is removed. Their amphipathic nature allows them to span cell membranes by having their hydrophobic non-polar tail associate with other hydrophobic parts of the cell membrane and their hydrophilic polar head projecting into the aqueous extracellular space. This relationship is shown in **Figure 7-13**. The diacylglycerol is represented by the two carbons at the top and the third carbon has the phosphate group attached.

The alpha-2 carbon is the middle carbon and often is linked to **arachidonic acid**, a 20-carbon fatty acid with four unsaturated bonds. This is a key fatty acid in the inflammatory process. When an enzyme called **phospholipase A2** acts on this fatty acid it starts a reaction that produces the inflammatory reaction through two pathways, the **cyclooxygenase** and **lipoperoxidase**, both essential for normal life function as they

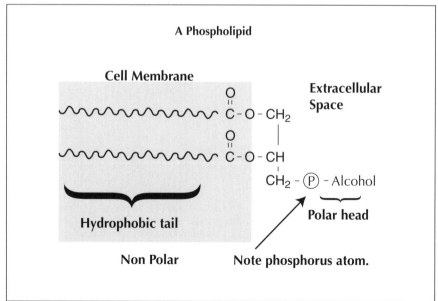

Figure 7-13. A phospholipid is not complex, just a triglyceride structure with a phosphate group on carbon 3.

make **prostaglandins** and **leukotrienes**, as well as other important biological compounds. These reactions are lipid-derived. Just knowing about the existence of the arachidonic acid cascade will give you a deeper appreciation of complex interaction between proteins, carbohydrates and lipids.

Glycolipids

Glycolipids are lipids joined with sugars or other carbohydrates. A key component in this series of compound is **sphingosine**, from the Greek *sphingo*, "to bind tightly." It forms the backbone of **ceramides**, the waxy components in the stratum corneum. The structure is much the same as a triglyceride but sphingosine starts with the amino acid **serine**.

Think of it as a cake. The first layer is a special chocolate mix, the sphingosine; the second layer is a plain vanilla mix, the fatty acid; stuck together with some icing, the peptide linkage. Add the galactose as the outer frosting and it's a **galactocerebroside**, a glycolipid belonging to the class of **glycosphingolipids**, collectively known as cerebrosides because they are found mainly in the cell membranes of brain cells, and also in peripheral nerves. They are the least complex of neutral glycolipids and function on the cell surface being found in the outer layer of the cell membrane where they interact with the extracellular environment. Cell interaction, cell growth and development, and cell surface receptors are a few of their functions. They also are powerful antigens since they make up part of the blood group antigens. Blood types A, B and O cause serious reaction if given to the wrong person. It is the **glycosphingolipid** component of the blood cell that causes this reaction. These compounds contain no phosphate groups.

Sphingomyelin is a phospholipid, not a glycolipid, but it is made up of a ceramide, a phosphate group and choline, a nitrogen-containing compound critical to the nervous system. It is the most abundant lipid in the nervous system including the brain and peripheral nerves. Think of it as consisting of the two-layer cake components, the ceramide, but instead of sugar a layer of phosphorus is added, then garnish with choline on the top. Unfortunately many diseases are associated with these complex lipids.

The sphinoglipidoses

These diseases are genetic and are due to lack of, or the malfunctioning of enzymes that metabolize the sphingolipids.

Tay-Sachs disease. Increased gangliosides. A fatal disease.
Ganglosidosis. Increased gangliosides and muco-polysaccharides. A fatal disease.
Gaucher's disease. Increased glucocerebrosides. Frequently fatal.
Metachromatic leukodystrophy. Increased sulfatides. Fatal in first decade.
Niemann-Picks disease. Increased sphingomyelin. Fatal in early life.

There are many more topics in lipid biochemistry, but we must tie together the proteins, the carbohydrates and the fats in the wonderful world of metabolism. You really are what you eat.

The three basic foods—proteins, carbohydrates and fats—have been discussed; now let's deal with **energetics**, or how the body stores and uses energy; and deoxyribonucleic acid (DNA) and the genetic code.

Metabolism

Where do you get the energy to live? Why must you eat to survive? How does the body turn food into energy without destroying itself? So many questions arise in discussion of food and energy, that one question leads to another until a Pandora's box of inquiries is opened. Let's start at the beginning of this story so all the pieces will fit together. It all starts with the sun.

Energy from the sun is taken up by plants in the form of **photons**, which are tiny particles of energy, and a process called **photosynthesis** is used to make foodstuff. Carbohydrates, fats and proteins are made from carbon dioxide, water, and nitrogen and minerals from the soil. Putting the complex compounds together requires an enormous amount of energy. Consider, for example, building a house. Laying bricks, hammering boards and pouring and finishing concrete uses up a great amount of manpower, which is energy. If the energy used in this process could be captured, an almost endless supply of stored energy would exist. Unfortunately, this is a violation of a basic physical law and cannot be done. Chemicals made by plants, however, can store the energy used to put them together, but need to be broken down to release the energy.

Sitting in front of a cozy fireplace on a cold winter's evening is an example of this process. Combustion, the burning of wood, releases two forms of energy-heat and light. Carbon dioxide and water also are released in the process. A very similar process goes on every minute of every day in the body, otherwise life would be impossible. When eaten, food is metabolized-converted to energy and heat to warm the body and run the metabolic machinery. This incredibly marvelous process will be revealed as the mystery of how the sun's energy is stored and used is unraveled.

Energy from glucose

In a nutshell, when glucose is broken down from a six-carbon molecule to two three-carbon molecules, a little energy is created. Then these three carbon molecules are broken down to carbon dioxide and water to produce no energy, but a lot of high-energy electrons. Next, almost all the energy from these electrons is pulled out and the result is lots of stored energy and some water-a neat process. In this three-step process, everything you learned before will be used in the explanation. Biochemical knowledge builds on itself. Some of the reactions will be condensed and this will begin with the glucose already in the bloodstream after the first phase of digestion.

Step 1. The Myerhoff cycle, or glycolysis. The sugar molecule is broken down into smaller units of three carbons in this first step. This process requires nine enzymes and two molecules of high-energy phosphate known as **adenosine triphosphate (ATP)**. In the process, four molecules of ATP are generated, leaving a net of two ATPs for the energy supply. This process takes place in the total absence of oxygen and is therefore **anaerobic**. Two **pyruvate** molecules are produced and if no oxygen is available, the pyruvate is converted to **lactate**, or **lactic acid**. This is diagrammed in **Figure 7-14**. While most college students are required to memorize these steps, you only need to know that *glucose goes in and two pyruvate, or two lactate molecules plus two ATPs, come out, and that the process occurs without oxygen.* Some cells, such as red and white blood cells, use glycolysis as a major source of energy. What happens to the pyruvate when oxygen is present? The answer is in the next step.

Step 2. The citric acid cycle-enter oxygen. Perhaps no single event in all evolutionary history is as important as the change from anaerobic to aerobic metabolism. The use of oxygen by cells to produce large quantities of energy required a new organelle in the existing cells, one that was able to handle the toxic effects of oxygen while simultaneously harnessing the power of oxygen—the power to combine with hydrogen to make water. While glycolysis takes place in the cytoplasm, the rest of the energy production occurs mainly in the **mitochondria**, tiny cigar-shaped organelles in the cell. The following chemical events occur in the mitochondria, beginning with the entrance of pyruvate generated by glycolysis.

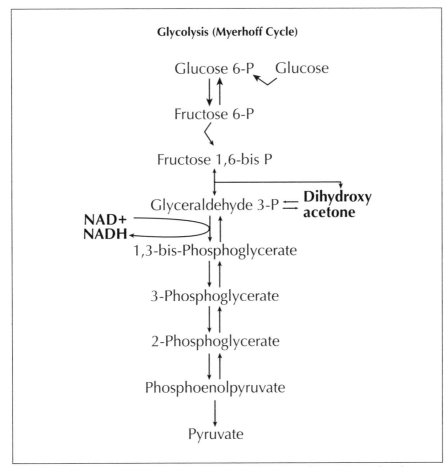

Figure 7-14. The pathway of glycolysis begins with a six-carbon sugar and ends up with two three-carbon molecules—lactic acid molecules if there is no oxygen and pyruvic acid in the presence of oxygen.

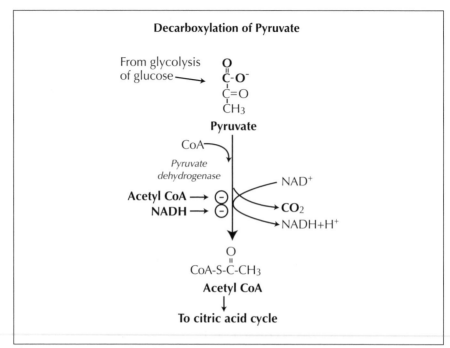

Figure 7-15. *Pyruvate decarboxylation simply means a carboxyl group COOH is taken off pyruvic acid and the remaining two-carbon molecule is combined with CoA to form acetyl CoA.*

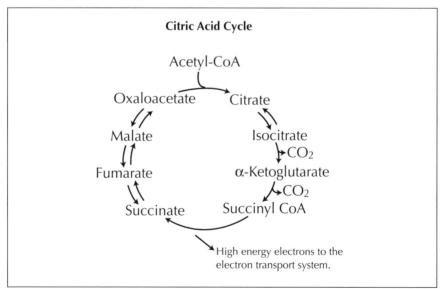

Figure 7-16. *The citric acid cycle takes the two-carbon molecule from glycolysis and converts it to two carbon dioxide molecules and high-energy electrons.*

The citric acid cycle can be simplified by dividing it into three phases:

1. Introduction of pyruvate into the mitochondria
2. Formation of acetyl coenzyme A (CoA)
3. Degradation of acetyl CoA and the regeneration of oxaloacetic acid.

Phase 1. Pyruvate crosses the mitochondria membrane. This process occurs in just about every cell in the body, every second of every day. Glycolysis occurs in the cytoplasm and produces pyruvate, if oxygen is present. The pyruvate must enter into the mitochondria to be metabolized by the citric acid cycle, and this occurs easily since it is of low molecular weight. Mitochondrial membranes can admit molecules up to 10,000 molecular weight (MW), but most of the molecules entering the mitochondria are under 5,000 MW. Having entered the membrane, the pyruvate passes to the matrix of the mitochondria for processing.

Phase 2. Formation of acetyl CoA. Pyruvate contains three carbons that must be cleaved to make a high-energy two-carbon molecule known as acetyl CoA. This is a complex molecule, but **pyruvate dehydrogenase**, the enzyme that is responsible for this action, is even more complex. It actually is an aggregate of three enzymes—**pyruvate decarboxylase**, **dehyrolipoyl transacetylasem** and **dehydrolipoyl dehydrogenase**. The lipoyl part is made from lipoic acid. It is the CoA part of acetyl CoA that makes it complex. The reaction is diagrammed in **Figure 7-15**.

Note the presence of nicotinamide adenine dinucleotide (NAD^+) and NADH in this reaction. These compounds are critical to the whole process of metabolism. Note, also, that as pyruvate is converted to acetyl CoA, one molecule of carbon dioxide is produced. A two-carbon molecule is ready to enter the citric acid cycle. Incidentally this cycle also is known as the **Krebs cycle** and the **tricarboxylic acid cycle**.

Phase 3. Degradation of acetyl CoA and the regeneration of oxaloacetic acid. The acetyl CoA enters the citric acid cycle and combines with oxaloacetic acid to form citric acid. Through a series of seven enzymatic processes, two additional carbon dioxide molecules are given off and oxaloacetic acid is regenerated in the process. Notice these steps in **Figure 7-16** as the cycle turns. Don't even try to remember all these steps. Just remember that multiple enzymes are involved, two carbon dioxides are produced and high-energy electrons in the form of NADH are produced. No ATP is produced in the citric acid cycle. It is essential that each component in the cycle regenerates to allow the cycle to continue. Two turns of the citric acid cycle are needed to metabolize one molecule of glucose.

At this stage, the two three-carbon units from glucose generated in glycolysis are gone. The high-energy electrons hooked to NADH remain. Now the energy from the NADH to make ATP needs to be extracted. This is done in the electron transport system (ETS).

Step 3. ETS. Before continuing discussion of the ETS, notice the structure of NADH, the key compound in this process. A **nucleotide** is a compound that contains an organic base, such as **adenine**, and a five-carbon sugar called a **pentose**. See **Figure 7-17** for diagrams of the two nucleotides. Note that only the top of the molecule undergoes oxidation and reduction. The bottom of the molecule contains a phosphate group that,

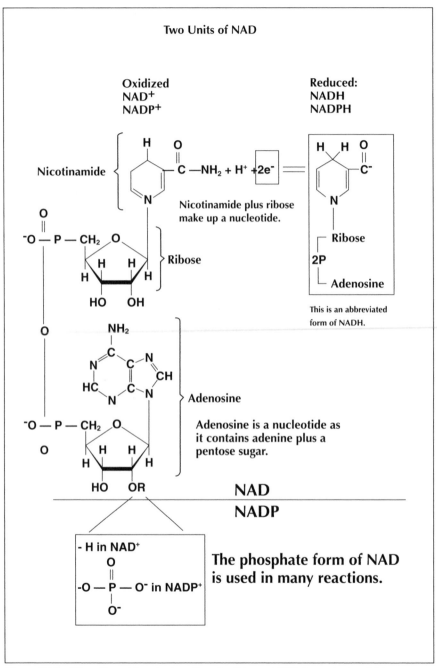

Figure 7-17. Nicontinamide adenine dinucleotide, or NAD, is made up of two units—adenosine nucleotide and nictinamide nucleotide. This is not so complex when broken down to smaller units. It is only the oxidation-reduction at the top that does the electron transfer.

when present, changes the molecule to a new compound called **NAD phosphate**, critical to many metabolic pathways.

Inside the mitochondrion

The mitochondrion contains an outer membrane, an inner membrane and a matrix. **Figure 7-18** diagrams these components. The ETS is found on the inner membrane and consists of five enzyme complexes, four that are active in the transport of electrons. The fifth one is used to form ATP. With the exception of **coenzyme Q**, all of the complexes are proteins. The core concept of the ETS is the passage of high-energy electrons along these four complexes, extracting energy from them, storing the energy, and the spent electrons then are bound as molecules of water. The concept is brilliant in its simplicity, but not fully understood even though a great deal is known about the ETS. Follow the diagram in **Figure 7-18** as you read the following description of the process and visualize this happening within the mitochondrion.

Electron passage

Remember that these are complexes—large molecular masses up to 800,000 MW—and that many things are going on in these complexes as the electrons pass through them.

Complex NAD dehydrogenase accepts electrons from NADH and passes them through a flavin, similar to NAD, and iron-sulfur centers to ubiquinone, or coenzyme Q, a small lipid-soluble compound that passes the electrons to the second respiratory chain complex.

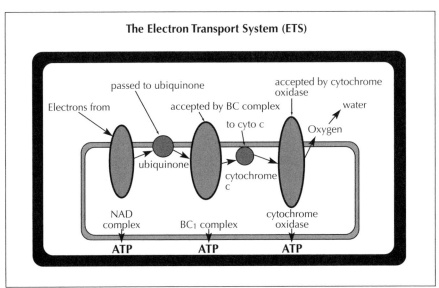

Figure 7-18. Much is left out to make it easier to see that electrons are passed from one complex to the other, each time transferring extracted energy to form ATP from ADP.

Complex B-C$_1$ accepts electrons from ubiquinone and passes them to cytochrome c$_1$ where they are passed to the cytochrome oxidase complex.

Cytochrome oxidase complex accepts the electrons from cytochome c$_1$ and passes them on to oxygen at which point water is formed.

Free energy is released as the electrons are transferred from complex to complex. These are oxidation-reduction reactions that always are associated with energy transfer. The strange thing about all this is that the electrons can be transferred in different forms. They can be transferred as a hydride ion[1]: **H$^-$** to **NAD$^+$**, as hydrogen atoms to **FMN**[2] or **coenzyme Q** and **FAD**[2], or as electrons to **cytochromes**. The free energy is collected and transferred to **adinosine diphospate (ADP)** to form ATP by an enzyme complex called **ATP synthetase** as the electrons flow through this complex. This process is called **oxidative phosphorylation**. One molecule of glucose will produce 36 ATP molecules by this system as compared to only two by glycolysis.

Mitchondrial effects

The mitochondria have their own deoxyribonucleic acid (DNA) inherited only from the mother. It is a circular DNA and has no repair system as found in nuclear DNA. There are more than 20 disorders associated with mitochondrial defects, most of which are characterized by loss of muscle power.

Within the ETS, certain systemic diseases can affect the process. For example, hyperthyroidism can prevent the transfer of energy to ADP to form ATP. This is called **uncoupled oxidative phophorylation** and is characterized by overall weakness and a hot feeling. It is one way the body can produce heat without producing energy to uncouple this reaction.

Which came first, the chicken or the egg?

How is information transferred from the DNA to be used by the cell? What is the genetic code and how does it work? These questions will be answered in the exploration of the mystery of life's most important molecule.

The discovery of DNA's structure by Watson and Crick[3] in 1952 opened the doors to a flood of research on the structure and function of this amazing molecule. So many research articles have been published since its discovery that no one can ever read all of them. What was so striking in this discovery was the simple structure of the DNA code. Only four bases accounted for the millions of bits of information contained in the structure of DNA. The sequence of these four bases spelled out all the genetic information needed to produce a rabbit, or a human—the fundamental model was the same for all animals and plants. A general description of DNA is a good starting point. Picture a very thin molecule about a yard long coiled up into a tiny package less than 1,400 nm thick and when uncoiled, is only 2 nm thick.[4] In **Figure 7-19**, the basic chromosome structure is diagrammed, but it is far more complex as it is unraveled. See **Figure 7-20** for the astonishing structure of a single chromosome. The DNA is packaged into chromosomes within the nucleus of every cell except end-cells such as red blood cells. There are 22 pairs of chromosome and two single chromosomes called x and y.

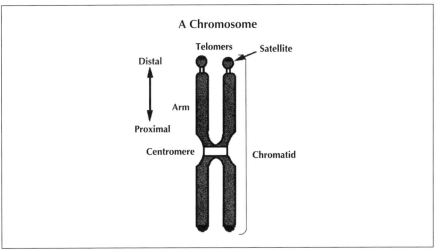

Figure 7-19. *Note the arms, the telomers and the centrosome of the chromosome. The entire structure is formed from tightly coiled DNA.*

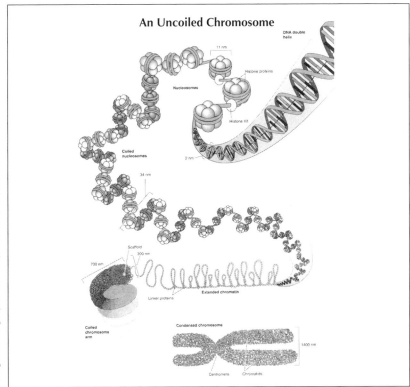

From *The Science of Genetics* by Alan G. Atherly, Jack R. Girton and John F. McDonald, © 1999 by Saunders College Publishing, reproduced with permission by the publisher.

Figure 7-20. *This illustration shows the bases forming the DNA code and the incredible complex structure of a chromosome.*

The base codes

When the chromosomes are uncoiled to reveal the DNA code, the four bases are seen. Two of these bases are **purines**—adenine and guanine, and two are **pyrimidines**—cytosine and thymine. A third pyrimidine occurs in ribonucleic acid (RNA) called **uracil**. The bases form complementary sequences along the DNA molecule that spell out proteins, amino acids and hormones. These bases are written as: **A=adenine**, **T=thymine**, **C=cytosine**, **G=guanine** and **U=uracil**. All of the amino acids are formed from three letters of this code, indicating a sequence of three bases. For example, serine is UCU or UCC, and leucine is CUA or CUG. With this information scientist have been able to make long sequences of amino acid using DNA. **Figure 7-21** shows the helix and the sequence of bases.

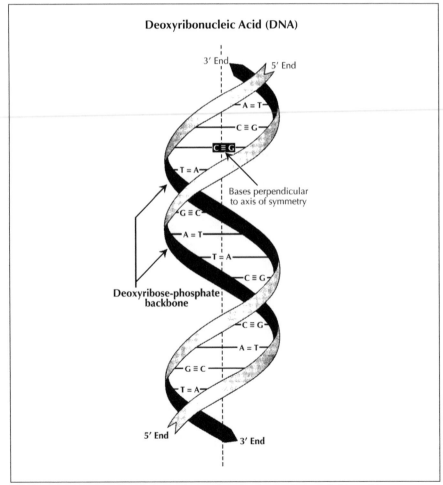

Figure 7-21. *A DNA double helix shows the winding and cross-linking of bases. Notice that each strand has a 3' and a 5' end.*

Some sequences for proteins can have hundreds or more bases. Since DNA is a double helix, two strands of DNA twisted in a helical spiral, they are joined together in a way that essentially reproduces the opposite strand but with purines replacing pyrimidines and pryrimidines replacing purines. The only way these strands can combine is by pairing A with T and C with G; or, in or ribonucleic acid (RNA), T is replaced by U to bind with A. These bases are illustrated in **Figure 7-22** showing, along with a diagram, how they combine to form a double strand of DNA in **Figure 7-23**.

Next problem: how do you get the information from the DNA to where it is usable in the cell?

This is a dual process called **transcription** and **translation** involving RNA. In transcription, the ATCG code is copied and carried to the cell for manufacturing a protein.

Transcription

Transcription is a biological code-breaking process that involves passing information from DNA to RNA. There are three types of RNA: **ribosomal RNA or rRNA, transfer RNA or tRNA,** and **messenger RNA or mRNA.** All these molecules are unbranched polymeric structures composed of mononucleotides joined with **phosphodiester** bonds. RNA differs from DNA in that it contains ribose instead of deoxyribose, and uracil instead of thymine.

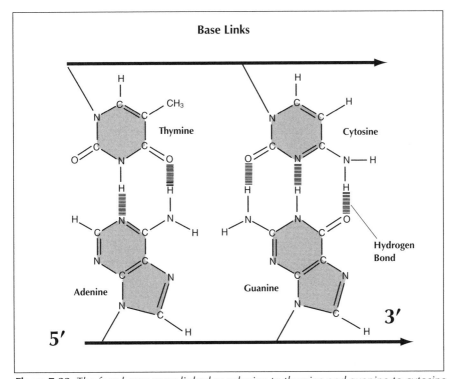

Figure 7-22. The four bases cross-linked as adenine to thymine and guanine to cytosine.

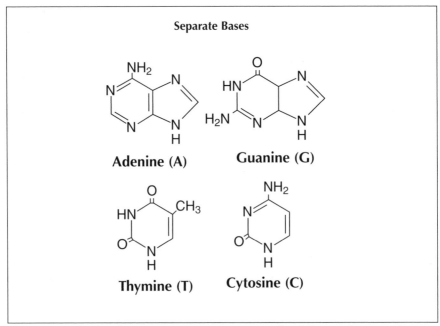

Figure 7-23. *The four bases as separate entities. Note the difference between the ring structures of purines and pyrimidines.*

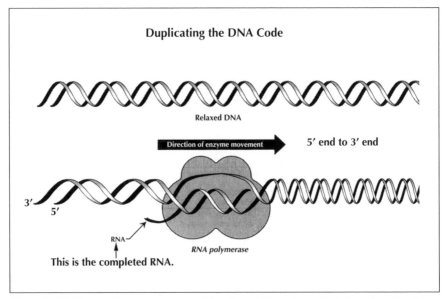

Figure 7-24. *RNA polymerase moves along the DNA, coil unwinds it and copies the code as an RNA molecule. The RNA molecule leaves the nucleus and is copied in ribosome to make a new protein.*

Transcription is less complex in bacterial cells called prokaryocytes. In bacterial transcription, RNA first must be made as a direct copy of DNA. RNA is synthesized using DNA as a template, just as dressmaker uses a pattern to cut out a dress. An enzyme called RNA polymerase, plus a second unit called the sigma, submit forms of RNA **polymerase holoenzyme**, which synthesize the RNA in two steps. The sigma unit is needed to recognize the promoter. The RNA polymerase binds to DNA, then the helix unwinds to allow recognition of the base pairs. In **Figure 7-24** the sequence begins at the 5' end and works to the 3' end. RNA polymerase recognizes the **promoter region** on the DNA that indicates the region to be transcribed and makes a complementary RNA copy of the DNA template. The process continues from the promoter to the **terminal end** where transcription stops.

Translation and protein production

The new RNA carrying the message for a protein leaves the nucleus as **mRNA**, or **messenger RNA**. The information is carried as words for amino acid, in three nucleotide base sequences called **codons**. There are 64 of these codons that code the amino acids, but three codons are used as stop or nonsense codons: UAG, UGA and UAA. When one of these codons appears, it signals the synthesis of that protein or peptide is complete. A **missense mutation** occurs when the codon is wrong, such as when a UCA is miscoded as UCU. This is an incorrect transcription and mutation can occur. A **nonsense mutation** occurs when a codon, such as serine UCA, is given a different base and becomes UAA, a stop codon. The synthesis is stopped and produces a meaningless molecule in the wrong place.

The proteins are synthesized in the ribosomes by ribosomal RNA after they are transferred to the ribosomes by transfer RNA.

The fundamentals

These are the basic bits of information needed for a fundamental understanding of the new molecular biochemistry. There is much more to learn, but this introduction provides a starting point. The references listed are good texts, detailed enough to give a strong background in biochemistry. As a skilled esthetician, you will need this information to keep abreast of the new developments, to choose treatment programs rationally and to enjoy the thrill of just knowing about the chemical basis of life.

References

1. Hyride ion is a negative hydrogen ion usually written as H⁻. It is formed only with reactive metals and decomposes on contact with water.

2. FMN and FAD are nucleotides formed from the vitamin riboflavin. FMN, the precursor of FAD, contains only phosphates plus riboflavin and is called flavin mononucleotide. The addition of a pentose sugar and adenine forms flavine adenine dinucleotide. These compounds accept electrons.

3. Watson, JD, *The Double Helix*, Atheneum (1968)

4. A nanometer is very small. A millimeter is 1/1,000 of a meter, about 30 inches; a micron is 1/1,000 of a millimeter; a nanometer is 1/1,000 of a micron or one billionth of a meter. It is written as 10^{-9} meters.

General References

Textbooks

Alters, S, Biology: *Understanding Life*, third edition, Boston: Jones and Bartlett Publishers (1999). Easy book to read, well illustrated with diagrams. A good first biology book or an excellent review.

Alberts B, Bray D, Lewis J, Raff M, Roberts K, and Watson JD, *Molecular Biology of the Cell*, New York: Garland Publishing {1989). Detailed and excellent.

Champe P and Harvey R, *Biochemistry*, Philadelphia: Lippincott (1994). This is an illustrated review of biochemistry, a good first book, or a refresher. Excellent.

Jones M, *Organic Chemistry*, New York: WW Norton (1997). A college-level textbook for reference or for the serious student of chemistry. Numerous illustrations and explanations.

Lodish H and co-authors, *Molecular Cell Biology*, New York: WH Freeman (2000). Has CD with excellent illustrations. Advanced, but easy to read; for a serious student.

Styer L, *Biochemistry*, New York: WH Freeman (1975). A classic biochemistry book with a different approach. Really a great book.

Zubay G, *Biochemistry*, Dubuque, IA: WC Brown (1993). A three-volume series, easy-to-read, very comprehensive.

Special References

Atherly A, Girton J and McDonald J, *The Science of Genetics*, Philadelphia: Sauders (1999). A great up-to-date reference or a college course in genetics. Easy reading and well illustrated.

Bolsover S and co-authors, *From Genes to Cells*, New York: John Wiley and Sons (1997). A good introduction for the new genetic student. Easy reading.

Sheffler IE, *Mitochondria*, New York: Wiley-Liss (1999). If you really want to get into mitochondria, this is a good start. Very comprehensive, not easy reading, but fairly up-to-date.

Chapter 8

Free Radicals and the Skin

What exactly are free radicals? What do they have to do with skin care? This chapter provides an introduction to free radicals—how they are created and relate to the body. Although it can seem to be overwhelmingly difficult to understand, read on. Then, read it again for a clearer understanding of free radicals.

Early history

Molecular oxygen, as it is known today, has not always been with us. About two billion years ago, oxygen was released into the atmosphere by water splitting microorganisms. As you might recall from your biology courses, during photosynthesis, plants produce molecular oxygen, or O_2. As the O_2 increases in concentration, some of it is converted to ozone. This ozone rises in the atmosphere and provides a protective layer against the high-energy ultraviolet (UV) radiation from the sun.

Throughout the years, new, more complex life forms arose that had to adjust to the oxygen in the environment. Many organisms took advantage of O_2 and used it to increase their metabolic efficiency. However, there was a danger associated with O_2 in biological systems. A complex array of positive and negative effects of O_2 had to be addressed by these organisms. One of the consequences of O_2 utilization was the generation of a chemical species called free radicals.

The oxygen story

When a person suffers a heart attack, the heart muscle undergoes changes due to lack of blood and oxygen in the tissues. This damaged tissue is called an **infarction**. As the muscle heals, new blood vessels again are supplied and oxygen is available. Only within the last decade has it been learned that as a person recovers from a heart attack, the inflow of oxygen-laden blood is dangerous to the heart muscle. This process is known as **reperfusion oxidation**.

The cause of this danger was found to be free radicals produced by the oxygen. This phenomenon is called **reperfusion**, or **reoxygenation injury**. Now it's known that more chronic diseases are associated with oxygen toxicity and are related to free radical mechanisms. To understand free radical chemistry requires some knowledge of the oxygen reactions. So, let's start with the chemistry of oxygen as this journey begins.

The chemistry of oxygen

There is a mystery about chemistry that causes some people to fear it, almost as something occult, grossly complex and forbidding. Even the word turns many people off. In reality, it isn't so bad. When taken in small bites, it easily is assimilated—in fact, it can be palatable. Take oxygen, for example.

Oxygen is one of the most abundant materials both on earth and in the atmosphere. While it is essential for life, it also is quite toxic to many life forms. Even plants must be protected against the very oxygen they generate by photosynthesis. The usefulness of oxygen and its harmful effects are related to the chemistry of oxygen, which in turn relates to the molecular structure of oxygen. To understand this molecular structure is to appreciate the role that oxygen plays in free radical mechanisms. A free radical will be defined later, but first, let's take a look inside the oxygen molecule.

All molecules are composed of atoms, which are made up of smaller particles called protons, neutrons and electrons. The protons and neutrons are located in the nucleus of the molecule while the electrons are found in the orbital that whirls around the nucleus. These orbitals are not discrete, neat circles or layers, but rather they are specific energy levels. These energy levels are very real even though they are hard to visualize, or even localize, without using complex mathematics. As rapidly as it moves, a single electron is easily located. It forms a veritable cloud of energy paths around the nucleus. While this can seem chaotic at first glance, there are very strict laws that the electrons must obey. These laws were discovered during this century by some very brilliant scientists, who eventually created **quantum mechanics**, a physics discipline that is used to describe this subatomic activity. Fortunately, to be able to understand how quantum mechanics relates to free radical chemistry and oxygen toxicity, little more than the name of this discipline needs to be known.

Inside the oxygen molecule

One of the quantum mechanical laws requires that electrons be paired when they react with other electrons in another molecule—paired in the sense that within a given molecule, each electron is harmonious with another electron to keep the molecule stable. The oxygen molecule has two unpaired electrons, which makes it quite unique in nature and at the same time limits its ability to react with other molecules. This limitation of oxygen makes it relatively inert as far as its reactivity. This is a blessing, for if molecular oxygen were slightly more reactive, life as it is known would be impossible.

This same limitation does, however, have another side. It is the reason that oxygen enters into free radical reaction. Since most molecular reaction involves two electrons, oxygen cannot enter into these reactions except under very special circumstances. Oxygen is forced to react with one electron at a time because of this molecular limitation. *This is a key concept in understanding free radical chemistry.*

Here is where a free radical is defined. *A free radical is any atom or molecule that has one or more unpaired electrons and is capable of independent existence.* Oxygen, then, is a free radical! In fact, oxygen is a **diradical**, which means it has two unpaired electrons.

Here, simplified, is the secret of the free radical—one or more unpaired electrons in a molecule or atom that can exist independently, and can react actively with other nearby molecules to alter or destroy them. An example will make this concept more graphic and easier to remember.

Water contains hydrogen and oxygen. It is a very simple molecule, and is written in chemical notation as either H_2O or HOH. The hydrogen atoms exactly balance the electronic charges in the oxygen atom to give us one molecule of water. If only one molecule of hydrogen would react with the oxygen molecule, a free radical would exist, the deadly hydroxyl radical ·OH. The little dot to the left of the "OH" formula means it is a free radical. This ·OH is called the hydroxyl radical and is a very nasty free radical because it reacts immediately with any molecule adjacent to it to alter or destroy it. It is a blessing that oxygen does not react with hydrogen in this manner to form hydroxyl radicals because life would be impossible if it did. It takes several steps and will be discussed later in the chapter. Let's move on to see how oxygen functions in the body and why oxygen is needed.

Oxygen and respiration

When we breathe, we take in molecular oxygen, or O_2. It passes into the lungs and then into the blood stream to bind a pigment called **hemoglobin** in the red blood cells. This action makes the hemoglobin turn red. When this hemoglobin reaches the many cells of the body, it releases the molecular oxygen that diffuses through the capillaries into the cells. The cells release carbon dioxide into the capillaries, then bind to the hemoglobin, turning it blue. This is a very neat arrangement and quite effective for transporting oxygen safely.

Once the oxygen is in the cell, it can be utilized in many ways. The most important use, the one that uses about 98–99% of the oxygen we breathe, is the neutralization of electrons. These electrons are carried over from the metabolism of foods. When sugar, for example, is metabolized, energy is produced in each cell while electrons are released in the process. The molecular oxygen combines with these electrons in a highly specialized enzyme system called the electron transport system. It is this enzyme system, located in tiny organelles in the cell called mitochondria, that adds electrons to the oxygen to produce water.

This process, called tetravalent reduction of oxygen to water, is a very special case for combining more than one electron with oxygen. Here oxygen will accept **four electrons** and produce two molecules of water, but only with the aid of these special enzymes. As these electrons are added to oxygen by the enzymes, a great deal of energy is produced with each step. This energy, in the form of adenosine triphosphate (ATP), is the energy source that runs the body. This is a very efficient system. Without it, multicellular organisms could not exist in great complexity.

However, about 1% of the oxygen we breathe is not used by this system, thus is available to wreak havoc with the rest of the body. This remaining oxygen can undergo several chemical changes that make it very unfriendly—in fact, quite dangerous. The changes in oxygen produce more reactive types of oxygen, which is called the reactive oxygen species.

The reactive oxygen species

The 1% of oxygen that does not enter the electron transport system is available to enter other reactions, mainly reactions that occur with oxygen accepting one electron. When a molecule or atom accepts an electron or hydrogen, this process is called **reduction**. On the other hand, when a molecule or atom loses an electron or hydrogen, this process is called **oxidation**.

These terms must be understood to appreciate the meaning of the one electron reduction of oxygen that results in forming **reactive oxygen species**, or ROS. The term reactive oxygen is used here because, as mentioned earlier in this chapter, normal oxygen is not very reactive. The **univalent reduction** of oxygen, or the addition of one electron at a time, produces these ROS. If a series of electrons is added to oxygen, four oxygen products with the formation of water as the fourth one is produced. Here is the scheme:

$$\text{Oxygen + one electron = Superoxide } (O_2\text{-})$$

$$\text{Superoxide + one more electron = Hydrogen peroxide } (H_2O_2)$$

$$\text{Hydrogen peroxide + one more electron = Hydroxyl radical } (\cdot OH)$$

$$\text{Hydroxyl radical + one more electron + hydrogen = Water } (H_2O)$$

Three reactive oxygen species, or ROS, are seen, but only two are free radicals. These are the superoxide and the hydroxyl radical. Hydrogen peroxide is an ROS, but not a free radical. Do not be confused by this, since not all free radicals involve oxygen, and not all reactive oxygen is in the form of free radicals. The fourth type of ROS, known as **singlet oxygen**, will be discussed later in the chapter. For the moment, keep this concept in mind: *adding one electron at a time to oxygen produces three types of ROS, all of which are reactive and dangerous*. Everything else will become clearer as you read on. Now, let's look carefully at each one of these ROS.

Let's return to the concept of oxidation and reduction, since they are critical concepts in what shall follow. Oxygen, under normal conditions, can only react with one electron at a time, so there must be other chemicals that can react with it. There are, and one you are familiar with is **iron**.

Rusty iron is seen all the time, but only because oxygen can react with it. Rusty gold isn't seen because oxygen cannot react with it. Iron is called a **transition metal** because it can go from one molecular state to another molecular state by adding or losing an electron. These two states of iron are called Fe^{II} and Fe^{III}, or Fe^{2+} or Fe^{3+}. Years ago, these two forms were called ferrous iron (Fe^{2+}) or ferric iron (Fe^{3+}), but this terminology has lost favor. These forms of iron are introduced for a number of reasons, and one of them is to help better understand the concept of oxidation-reduction, and how this concept fits into free radical chemistry. As a transition metal, iron can go backward and forward to form both types of iron in a reversible reaction. This reaction is written as follows:

$$Fe^{II} <===> Fe^{III}$$
One electron shuttles back and forth

It is reversible simply by adding or taking away an electron, but the ability of the iron in one form or the other to react with oxygen is quite different. To understand reversible and irreversible reaction a little better, consider two examples.

Water is liquid at room temperature. Add heat and it becomes steam. Take away the heat and it becomes water again. Take away a lot more heat and it becomes a solid called ice. While this is a physical change, it also is a chemical change that is completely reversible.

If, however, an egg is heated, the proteins in the egg coagulate into a solid mass. Cooling the egg has no effect on it. It remains changed forever. Heat produced a chemical change in the protein of the egg that caused the physical change to be irreversible.

Now look at the iron equation. By shifting one electron the chemical nature of iron is changed. The importance of this will become more evident later in the chapter. For now, remember the concept of oxidation-reduction and the shifting of electrons. With this added concept, you have all the basic chemistry you need to understand free radicals and oxidative stress in the skin. Now let's return to the superoxide radical.

By adding one electron to molecular oxygen, **superoxide** is produced. It is a molecule that is quite reactive since it has one more unpaired electron and tends to be unstable. Superoxide is formed by UV radiation and by certain enzyme reactions as a natural course of metabolism, so the body must be content with it. Superoxide can enter into a number of reactions with biomolecules, but it also can react with other superoxide molecules to produce hydrogen peroxide. Here is the reaction:

$$O_2\text{-} + O_2\text{-} + 4H ==> H_2O_2$$
This is an irreversible reaction

This is one way that hydrogen peroxide is formed. Other reactions with superoxide radical will be considered, but first, here is a description of the other ROS.

Hydrogen peroxide

The body uses hydrogen peroxide as a germicide, just as it is used in day-to-day living. Special cells make hydrogen peroxide partly on demand, but also as a byproduct of superoxide radical destruction. Hydrogen peroxide is destroyed by enzymes called **peroxidases**, which convert the hydrogen peroxide to oxygen and water. While hydrogen peroxide is not a powerful oxidant, it is quite dangerous because of two factors. The first is that it can diffuse rapidly, and cross both the cell membrane and the nuclear membrane. The second is that hydrogen peroxide can be converted to the hydroxyl radical quite easily in the presence of iron. Within the nucleus, the hydroxyl radical can react with the deoxyribonucleic acid (DNA) directly. The conversion of hydrogen peroxide to the hydroxyl radical can be written as an equation:

$$H_2O_2 + Fe^{II} ===> \cdot OH + \text{-}OH + Fe^{III}$$

One electron has been added to the H_2O_2 which **reduces** it to the hydroxyl radical and the harmless hydroxyl ion (-OH). Also notice that this is a one-way reaction by looking at the arrow between the two sides of the equation. The one electron transferred to H_2O_2 came from the Fe^{II} that was oxidized by losing an electron to become Fe^{III}. Now the hydroxyl radical can be discussed.

Hydroxyl radical

The hydroxyl radical produces most of the oxidative damage in our cells, particularly to the DNA in the nucleus. DNA makes up the chromosomes that contain the genetic material which directs all cellular operations. DNA is made up of components called **nucleotides** that consist of a base, a sugar and a phosphoric acid group. There are two kinds of bases known as purines and pyrimidines. When a hydroxyl radical reacts with one of these bases, it is denatured and becomes abnormal so the DNA cannot function. As a protective measure the cell will remove the damage base and replace it with a new normal base. Here is an example:

Purine (a base) + ·OH ===> Abnormal base

or

Thymine (a base) + ·OH ===> Thymine glycol

These two equations are the same reaction using different notations. Without the body's ability to remove these abnormal bases, life would not be possible. One more ROS needs to be covered—**singlet oxygen**—before the effects of oxidative stress on the body is discussed.

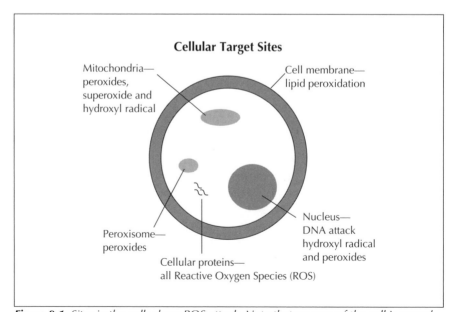

Figure 8-1. *Sites in the cell where ROS attack. Note that no area of the cell is spared.*

Singlet oxygen

As previously mentioned, oxygen in the normal state is not very reactive with other molecules. Oxygen prefers to react with free radicals because of its molecular restriction to single electron reactions. It is possible to remove this restriction on oxygen by changing the orbital configuration of the molecule.

When oxygen is irradiated with UV light, for example, it will absorb energy in the molecule and thereby change its molecular configuration. This is called **excited oxygen**, or **singlet oxygen**, because it is not in the triplet or ground state. This means that one of the unpaired electrons, which was mentioned previously in the chapter, now is elevated to a higher energy level, and most importantly, **its spin number is inverted**. Now, it can react like the villain it really is, rapidly attacking double bonds in fatty tissue. The skin, being exposed to UV light, constantly has to deal with singlet oxygen. With this last ROS discussed, oxidative stress finally can be discussed to see what it is and what can be done about it.

Oxidative stress

There is a constant inflow and use of oxygen in the body. ROS are generated continuously, but to a large measure they are quenched by the antioxidant defense system, and this will be discussed later in the chapter. Overall, there is an excess of ROS produced which results in oxidative stress. Any kind of stress indicates an unbalanced condition, be it physical, mental or chemical. Ideally, the body should be able to counteract the harmful effects of oxygen and in most cases it can do a very good job. There are conditions, however, which overwhelm the body's antioxidant defense mechanism and tissue damage results. This condition is called **oxidative stress**. (See **Human Diseases Associated with Oxidative Stress**.) What is the damage and what are the defenses against oxidative stress? (See **Figure 8-1**.)

The ROS that produces the damage has been covered; now the actual tissue damage that is produced will be outlined; and finally, the defense mechanism that operates to offset this damage will be discussed.

Superoxide radical damage

Superoxide is known to attack enzymes and cell membrane. It tends to attack unsaturated fatty acids in the cell membrane causing them to break down. You have seen this very same process occur in unrefrigerated butter. This process is called **rancidity**. Within the cell membrane, the fatty acids decompose and damage the integrity of the membrane that alters the control of materials in and out of the cells. Further decomposed products of the fatty acids form an amorphous yellow complex called **lipofuscin**. It is lipofuscin that gives the skin an ugly yellow hue as people grow older or if they smoke tobacco. The attack of superoxide on the fatty acid is a sequential process that produces a lipid peroxide. The process, therefore, is called **lipid peroxidation**. It requires one or more double bonds in the fatty acids. For example, the presence of three double bonds in linolenic acid makes it a prime candidate for peroxidation by superoxide.

The three major steps in lipid peroxidation can be diagrammed as follows:

(1) PUFA + Superoxide ====> Lipid free radical
(Polyunsaturated fatty acid)   (LFR)

(2) LFR + Oxygen ====> Peroxyl lipid radical

(3) Peroxy lipid radical + PUFA ====> Lipid hydroperoxide + LFR
                        (New)   (New)

Note that an actual chain reaction has started. Once superoxide reacts with a polyunsaturated fatty acid (PUFA), it produces a lipid radical that reacts in turn with molecular oxygen to form a peroxy lipid. This peroxy lipid is reactive and will react with an adjacent PUFA to steal a hydrogen atom and form a lipid hydroperoxide. The lipid hydroperoxide is then decomposed either by catalase or another enzyme, however, it will go on to decompose into more reactive components that can react with proteins to cross-link or otherwise denature them. One of these reactive byproducts is known as **malonyldialdehyde**, or MDA. MDA is used as a marker of lipid peroxidation. If we can stop this reaction before it starts, we have the best possible of all worlds. Vitamin E is one of the important antioxidants that can break this deadly chain reaction.

Superoxide radical defense. The most important aspect of superoxide is its ability to react with hydrogen peroxide and form the more reactive hydroxyl which attacks DNA. Superoxide can be destroyed by the enzyme superoxide dismutase before it can be converted to hydroxyl radical. This reaction is as follows:

superoxide + superoxide dismutase ===> water and hydrogen peroxide

Hydrogen peroxide has been produced, so the destruction it produces and how it is handled in the body must be addressed. (See **Figure 8-2.**)

Hydrogen peroxide

Hydrogen peroxide is produced not only by superoxide dismutase, but also by a variety of other enzymes called **oxidases**. As previously discussed, it is dangerous because it diffuses into cells, particularly into the nucleus of cells to react with DNA. It also reacts with proteins to cross-link and to denature them, making these compounds either nonfunctional or no longer able to function in a normal way. Inflammation from respiratory burst can produce reactive white blood cells, thus creating more superoxide and more hydrogen peroxide. The whole process of inflammation in the skin is attended with free radicals and hydrogen peroxide formation. For example, UV light produces superoxide and also can produce hydrogen peroxide. How does the body cope with this problem?

Peroxides in the body

Two major enzymes control the level of peroxides in the body. One is called **catalase** and the other is called **glutathione peroxidase**. Each of these enzymes destroys peroxides by converting them to water and oxygen. The reaction is simple:

$$H_2O_2 + \text{catalase or glutathione peroxidase} ===> H_2O + O_2$$

The importance of this enzymatic reaction cannot be over-emphasized, for it is critical in the defense against oxidative stress. Conversion of H_2O_2 to hydroxyl radical ·OH creates a serious problem for the oxidative defense system since this free radical will react as quickly as it is formed. An effective antioxidant would have to be at the site of ·OH formation to effectively quench and destroy it. Prevention of ·OH formation is the best protection against it.

The hydroxyl radical

The hydroxyl radical is one of the most potent oxidants known to science. Hydroxyl radical can react with almost any compound in the body such as enzymes, proteins, carbohydrates and lipids. It can attack lipids and produce lipid peroxides, and cross-link all kinds of proteins, but the attack of DNA is probably the most injurious to the body overall. Many scientists believe it to be one of the major causes of the changes we see in aging.

Hydroxyl radical defense. Vitamin E in the cell prevents hydroxyl radical action by quenching it, and it is able to stop chain reactions in cases of lipid peroxidation. Vitamin C enters into this reaction by regenerating active vitamin E. Again there is an oxidation-reduction,

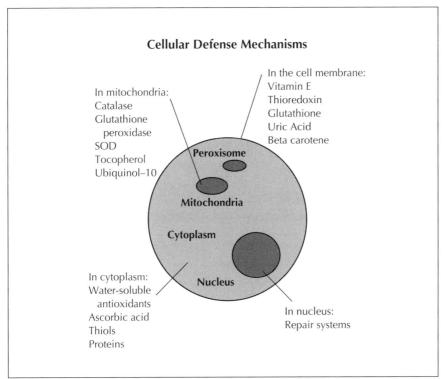

Figure 8-2. Antioxidant defense system in the cell. Note that multiple antioxidants are needed. If all else fails and the DNA is damaged, then a repair system is available to correct the damage. Unfortunately, this system is not 100% effective.

Human Diseases Associated with Oxidative Stress

Many diseases have been associated with oxidative stress in one manner or the other. To date, the role of free radicals and oxidative stress is not clear. The use of antioxidants is able to prevent many chronic diseases. To slow down the aging process, there is no true cause-and-effect relationship that most scientists demand. Antioxidant treatments benefit some chronic diseases, but prevention seems to be the major role of antioxidant use. Here is a list of diseases that have been associated with oxidative stress from oxygen radicals.

Inflammatory/Immune Injuries
Autoimmune diseases (such as lupus erythematosus)
Rheumatoid arthritis
Vasculitis (inflammation of blood vessels)
Renal diseases (kidney)

Ischemia-reperfusion
Myocardial infarction (heart attack)
Strokes
Organ transplants
Frostbite

Iron overload
Dietary iron (occurs in the Bantu tribe)
Thalassemia (a red blood cell disease) associated with
    multiple transfusions
Hemochromatosis

Alcoholism
Alcohol induces iron overload

Radiation injury
Nuclear explosions
Radiotherapy (X-ray)

Lung
Cigarette smoking
Emphysema
Asbestosis
Hyperoxia (too much oxygen)
Oxidant pollutants such as nitric oxide and ozone

Human Diseases Associated with Oxidative Stress, *continued*

Aging
   Disorders of premature aging (such as progeria)
   Aging changes in general (multiple chronic inflammatory changes)

Heart and cardiovascular system
   Alcohol cardiomopathy
   Arteriosclerosis
   Selenium deficiency (Keshan disease)

Brain and the neuromuscular system
   Hyperbaric oxygen
   Vitamin E deficiency
   Parkinson's disease
   Potentiation of traumatic injury
   Muscular dystrophy
   Multiple sclerosis
   Allergic encephalomyelitis and demylinating diseases (degeneration of nerves and brain tissue)

Eye
   Cataracts
   Ocular hemorrhage
   Degenerative retinal damage
   Photic retinopathy
   Retrolental fibroplasia

Skin
   Solar radiation (sunburn and aging)
   Thermal injury
   Porphyria
   Contact dermatitis
   Wrinkles

This is a long, although not exhaustive, list. It is constantly growing as more research is accomplished in this area. The reader should be aware that much of the damage due to oxidative stress appears to be preventable. Many cancers are believed to be related to free radical involvement and oxidative stress.

vitamin E loses a hydrogen to the hydroxyl radical and is thereby oxidized. Vitamin C reduces the vitamin E back to an active form by donating a hydrogen. The reaction is:

$$Vitamin\ E\text{-}OH\ +\ \cdot OH\ ===>\ Vitamin\ E\ =\ O + H_2O$$
$$(Natural\ vitamin\ E)\qquad\quad (Oxidized\ vitamin\ E,\ a\ quinone)$$

$$Vitamin\ E\ =\ O\ +\ Vitamin\ C\ ===>\ Vitamin\ E\text{-}OH\ +\ Oxidized\ vitamin\ C$$
$$(Dehydroascorbate)$$

This reaction is believed to be one of the major uses of vitamin C in the body. Other antioxidants are available to react with the hydroxyl radical, some of which include uric acid, vitamin C and glutathione. No antioxidant enzymes are included in this list because the reaction of the hydroxyl radical is too fast for enzymatic reaction.

Singlet oxygen

Singlet oxygen targets many tissue and cellular components, especially those in the skin. It can add on to molecules causing severe structural changes. Being an excited state of oxygen, it also can react with a biomolecule by transferring its high energy to the biomolecule. This results in an altered biomolecule and the returning of singlet oxygen to the less active or **ground state**. Singlet oxygen can react with proteins, carbohydrates and lipids, as well as a variety of other compounds. Fluorescent lighting in office buildings, classrooms and laboratories is sufficiently intense to cause singlet oxygen to be produced in the skin.

Singlet oxygen defense. Beta-carotene is a major pre-vitamin that protects us against singlet oxygen. Ubiquinone can scavenge singlet oxygen, along with uric acid and vitamin E.

Summary of ROS and antioxidants

Many new terms and concepts have been covered. Don't be frustrated if you have not grasped the concepts. It takes time to organize new data and to assimilate it. Refer to **Antioxidants/Reactive Oxygen Species** for help. As you review this chart, remember that some antioxidants can have more than one function.

The skin, free radicals and esthetics

What can you, as an esthetician or skin care specialist, do with this knowledge of free radicals? How will it help you in your business? If you have read this far, and I know it has not been an easy journey, you should be rewarded with some practical applications. There are some positive applications to skin care that arise from understanding free radicals and antioxidant mechanisms. Three areas will be discussed—skin inflammation, photo-damaged skin and aging skin.

Skin inflammation. Any inflammatory response will involve free radical formation—no ifs, ands or buts! If you see a red area that is tender and hot, it is inflamed and seething with free radical activity. Superoxide radical, hydrogen peroxide and hydroxyl radical will be there. Iron will react with superoxide and peroxide to form hydroxyl radicals, and produce great tissue destruction. Vitamin E, both orally and topically, will be beneficial; vitamin C will help, and superoxide desmutase in the form of gels or creams also will help. Do not use alpha hydroxy acids, or any of the new enzymes such as bromelain or papain, in any form on inflamed skin. Currently, highly effective creams are on the market which contain high levels of antioxidants in an effective delivery system. In Japan and Germany, there are superoxide dismutase-containing creams that appear to be effective.

Photo-damaged skin. It is now well-established that treatment of sunburn with vitamin E or superoxide dismutase shortly after the burn will reduce tissue damage greatly and increase the rate of healing. Chronic sun damage that is associated with solar elastosis does not need to continue to disfigure your client. Use vitamin A palmitate cream at 0.5%, making sure it is active vitamin A. If the product is heated above a certain temperature, it will degenerate.

Also, vitamin A will undergo oxidation and turn yellow in the jar. Make sure the product is not bright or dirty yellow. A slight tinge of yellow is normal for vitamin A

Antioxidants/Reactive Oxygen Species

The Antioxidant	Reactive Oxygen Species
Enzymes	
Superoxide dismutase	Converts superoxide to peroxide and oxygen
Catalase	Converts hydrogen peroxide to water and oxygen
Glutathione peroxidase	Converts hydrogen peroxide to water and oxygen
Non-Enzymes	
Lipid Soluble Group	
Tocopherol (Vitamin E)	Quenches hydroxyl radical
Beta carotene (Pre-vitamin A)	Quenches singlet oxygen
Ubiquinol, ubiquinone	Quenches hydroxyl radical and singlet oxygen
Water-soluble Group	
Ascorbid acid (Vitamin C)	Regenerates vitamin E, may react directly with other ROS
Glutathione	Reacts with hydroxyl radical, part of glutathione peroxidase system
Uric acid	Quenches singlet oxygen, hydroxyl radical inhibits xanthine oxidase which forms superoxide

products, but not a brown-yellow. Use anthocyanidins—grape seed or extracted bark—orally or in creams that contain them. They are expensive products, but well worth it. Tablets should contain 50 mg at least and your client will need two a day. The creams should contain anthocyanidins at 500 parts per million or more. That would be at least 0.005%. All of these items are nonprescription, and available at pharmacies and health food stores.

With everything known today, there really is no excuse for photo-damaged skin. Any individual who insists on sunbathing or tanning with UV light probably is not very health-conscious, or is misinformed regarding the damaging effects of the sun. Sunscreens without antioxidants are less effective than those with antioxidants. They should contain at least 1–2% of vitamin E, although some products that are well-formulated can deliver vitamin E at lower concentrations. Effective skin levels seem to be about 1,000 parts per million, that is 0.1% concentration in the skin.

Aging skin. Aging skin is treated the same as photo-damaged skin because usually there is a combination of both conditions. Aging skin shows only slight to moderate sagging, while photo-damaged skin shows the wrinkles and pigmented lesions. Any client with aging skin should be approached with the fact that treatment is lifelong. There are no easy fixes and no miracle products. It takes time to age, and time to restore the skin to normal. Good and effective anti-aging products address the free radical problem by containing antioxidants at levels that prove they work. Do not buy a product that has not been tested for antioxidant activity. Beware of products that have the antioxidants listed at the end of the ingredients; they are low in concentrations and are useless.

Use a product that contains beta glucan, vitamins A, E and C—however, it's tough to find one that is really active—panthenol, anthocyanidins, and, if possible, an iron chelator such as phytic acid. Rice bran oil, wheat germ oil, avocado oil and almond oil are good, but avoid mineral oil.

Oral products. A vitamin regimen cannot be suitable for all individuals, but it is one that I follow personally. Always recommend that clients consult their physicians before considering any oral medication.

This is the vitamin program that I recommend and follow each day. I recommend 600 mg of oral vitamin E per day and 500 mg of oral vitamin C twice a day. Vitamin C should be taken two to three times a day because it rapidly is used up or excreted if taken as a single dose in the morning. Avoid iron supplements or vitamins that contain them, unless there is a definite medical reason to be taking iron. Do not smoke cigarettes. Avoid sun exposure as much as is practical. Use sunscreens and advise UVA sunscreens be used if your client is indoors and working under fluorescent lighting. Increase the diet to include fruits and vegetables at least twice a day. Push oatmeal as a breakfast food and reduce fats to 30% of total calories.

I have listed the various vitamins and ingredients in the multiple vitamins that I take separately on a daily basis. Natural anti-aging products include 50–100 mg shark liver oil twice a day, 100 mg anthocyanidins, 1,200 mg calcium, 1,000 mg vitamin E, one aspirin every other day, 50 mg beta-carotene, 1,000 mg niacin, and a multiple vitamin complex in five tablets which contains:

Vitamin A (15,000 units)
Vitamin C (2,000 units)
Vitamin D (200 units)
Vitamin B-6 (75 mcg)
Vitamin B-12 (250 mcg)
Folic acid (50 mcg)
Magnesium (10 mg)
Manganese (10 mg)
Selenium (50 mcg)
Silicon (50 mcg)
Herbal complex—Hawthorn, yarrow, cayenne, red clover, chapparal, garlic (150 mg)

Exercise. Finally, I recommend an exercise program that will keep the free radicals at a low level. I do not recommend jogging, or strenuous exercise. The best exercise is walking a mile or two a day. Use a treadmill on rainy days or during inclement weather, but if you can walk outside, the physical and mental effect is terrific. Do calisthenics about 15 minutes a day, and if you have one, use a rowing machine or a stair climber. You really don't need any of these machines if you know some simple exercises, including push-ups.

Avoid stress. Stress produces many oxidants through the breakdown of adrenal products. It is important that you get in touch with yourself in order to stay young, and to help your clients stay young and healthy. You really must like yourself and have the self-confidence to know that other people will like you. Take a strong positive view of life. Any negative thoughts will work to shut down the body by having adverse effects on the tissues. Keep in mind that while time is relentless, the aging process is not. We can combat those nasty free radicals that age us by stopping them in their tracks.

What has been discussed in this chapter is only a brief introduction to the subject of oxidative stress. I have listed some recommended references for readers who wish to pursue the topic in depth. If you have a search system on your computer, search for free radicals or oxidative stress in Medline, available on Internet and also on Dialog, Compuserve and many other suppliers. You will have more references that you can read in a year. These references will provide a good second step into this subject.

General references

Fuchs J, *Oxidative Injury in Dermatopathology*, Springer-Velag: Berlin (1992). Easy to read with many references.

Halliwell B and Gutteridge JMC, *Free Radicals in Biology and Medicine*, second edition, Clarendon Press: Oxford, England (1993). A standard in the field. Well written, but quite scientific and very comprehensive.

William G, ed-in chief, *Antioxidants, Chemical, Physiological, Nutritional and Toxilogical Aspects*, Princeton Scientific Publishing: Princeton, NJ (1991). An excellent introduction to the subject.

Yu PB, *Free Radicals in Aging*, CRC Press: Boca Raton, FL (1993). Comprehensive overview of free radicals and aging. At times tough, but enjoyable.

Chapter 9

Sun's Effect
on the Skin

During Prohibition in the 1920s, alcohol was easily available only on the offshore islands of the United States. These islands were hot and sunny so the imbibers came home to the mainland with both a tan and contraband. Money and some connections were needed to make this run. It did not take very long for the out-group to notice that the in-group was tanned. Following the unerring law of monkey-see-monkey-do, these poor souls started to tan themselves to be identified with the in-group. Somehow this fad caught on and is perpetuated to this day. I should say perpetrated. I have heard that tanning began with Coco Chanel, but I like the story above better because I think it's closer to the truth.

The sun is the source of energy for all life on this planet. When the sun goes out, life on earth will cease. The sun and natural light have almost the same meaning, though by natural light visible light usually is meant. Both terms will be used interchangeably, but UV light will be stressed when needed. Many myths exist about the sun; religions and cults arose and some still exist in one form or another to worship the sun. The skin care specialist is faced with the difficult task of trying to separate facts from fiction about light and the sun. Sunbathing, sunscreen preparations, sun protection factors (SPFs), sun lamps, sun tanning booths, free radicals, oxidation, radiation, intensity and many other terms assail the ears and eyes of the skin care specialists, often in a bewildering and confusing array.

The purpose of this chapter is to help you through this maze and to attempt a presentation of current information that is both understandable and useful. To the serious student of skin care, it is essential to learn as much as possible about the use and effects of light. An irreducible amount of physical principles are required to understand light.

Magical qualities of light

While so much in science is fascinating beyond description, light can be the most fascinating of all. Light is a particle, and at the same time it is a wave; is stopped by most solids, yet it can pass through glass and plastic. It is the fastest thing in the universe. In fact, this is the basis of much of Einstein's science. It is never-ending. Light that was present at the creation of the universe is still here! All visual information comes from reflected light, for objects never are "seen," only the light reflected from the surface of objects. Red is considered a hot color and blue a cool color, yet blue is thousands of times hotter than red; is has more energetic photons. Now science is using light to heal and to communicate. With light communication devices and dimensions far beyond what could have been imagined ten years ago will be seen. Welcome to the world of light. Fiat lux! Let there be light!

The unit of energy in light

Photons are light particles that contain various energy levels. Consider a hammer. There are tack hammers, claw hammers, heavy hammers and sledge hammers. Each of these hammers will deliver a certain amount of energy depending on how they are applied to an object. You can drive a nail with a tack hammer or a sledge hammer, but more likely you would use a claw hammer. Photons come in packets of energy just like hammers. UVB, for example, has 1,000 times more energy per photon then does UVA. It is the interaction of the photon with living matter—the transfer of the energy in the photon to the living matter—that produces the biological effect, good or bad. This is the single most important concept to understanding how light affects us.

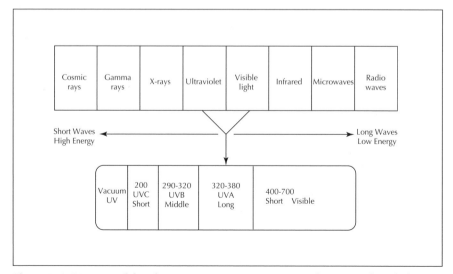

Figure 9-1. *Diagram of the electromagnetic spectrum. Note the range of UV light. Wavelengths are given in nanometers. Only 5% of the sun's energy is in the UV range, 35% is in the visible range and 60% is in the infrared range.*

Scattering and absorption of light

Light is both absorbed and scattered by matter. The photon, the fundamental unit of light, is a particle that behaves like a wave. It takes both particle and a wave action to effect absorption and scattering. The distinction is important because these two physical properties of matter have very different effects on light. When light is absorbed by matter, it disappears as light and is converted into energy, as heat. *The photon literally gives up its energy to a specific molecule in the material*. When sunlight falls on a green leaf, all the rays are absorbed except green, which is reflected, so the leaf is seen as green. Scattering of light occurs when sunlight is partially absorbed by the air and then is given out in new directions. Short waves are scattered more easily than long waves. Blue light is scattered ten times more than red light. This fact provides us with blue skies and inspiring sunsets.

As the sunlight travels through the atmosphere to earth, the short waves are scattered about in all directions. These short waves create a blue sky. In the evening as the sunlight travels a greater distance all the blue is absorbed by air along with the yellow and the orange light. This leaves only the a longer wavelength of red light, which produces the color of the sunset, but all of the color changes are visible as the evening progresses. On a clear day the sunset is not very beautiful, for a little dust and smoke is needed to scatter the sunlight. While this phenomenon is all very beautiful and poetic, it has a very elegant scientific basis.

Light and energy

Sunlight is a small part of radiant energy classified as electromagnetic radiation. This radiation ranges from very short cosmic rays to very long radio waves. (See **Figure 9-1**.) This range of rays is called the electromagnetic spectrum. Only a very small part of the spectrum, called visible light, is seen. The range of the total spectrum with corresponding wavelengths for the ultraviolet (UV) section is diagrammed in **Figure 9-1**.

Sunlight is made up of many different levels of energy. These various levels of energy collectively are called the spectrum of light. A rainbow, for example, essentially is a partial spectrum of white light that has been dispersed or split into the various color components of white light by a raindrop. The spectrum of sunlight covers the entire span of energy from ionizing radiation, or cosmic rays, to radio waves.

The two terms related to light and energy are the wavelength and frequency of light. The speed of light is a universal constant: it is related to wavelength and frequency by the following equation:

$$\text{Speed of light} = \text{Wavelength} \times \text{Frequency} \qquad \text{(I)}$$

The energy in light is related to the frequency by the following equation:

$$\text{Energy} = \text{Planck's constant (h)} \times \text{Frequency} \qquad \text{(II)}$$
Planck's constant is 6.6×10^{-34} joules[a]/sec

---

[a] Joule, pronounced "jewel," is a scientific unit of energy equal to the energy required to lift one kilogram, about 2.2 pounds, a distance of 10.2 centimeters. An inch equals 2.54 centimeters.

Because of the constant in equation II, the higher the frequency, the higher the energy. Also in equation I, in order to keep the speed of light constant, the higher the frequency, the lower, or shorter, the wavelength. So, these two powerful equations illustrate that the shorter the wavelength, the more energy there is in the light.

Basic photobiology

The science of the interaction of light and living matter is called **photobiology**. The fundamental, or first law of photobiology is that a substance must absorb light to produce a chemical or physical change in that substance. No absorption; no change. When a particular substance absorbs light, energy is transferred to that substance and in some manner the substance undergoes a change, that is, an activated particle will be formed. These activated particles can be molecules, atoms or free radicals. Free radicals are very reactive chemical species. The activated particle that now has more energy must release this energy to return to stable form. It releases energy as heat, light at a longer wavelength or it can transfer its energy to other molecules. (See Figure **9-2**.)

The sun and the skin

The major interest is the skin and how the sun affects the skin. Most organic molecules will absorb some UV light at very short wavelengths. Water, which is not an organic molecule, will absorb light below 150 nanometers (nm) [b], however, most of the sunlight

---

[b] The measurement of nanometers (nm) is used to quantitate wavelength of visible and UV light. A nanometer is 1/1,000 of a micron, 1/1,000 of a millimeter, which is 1/1,000 of a meter.

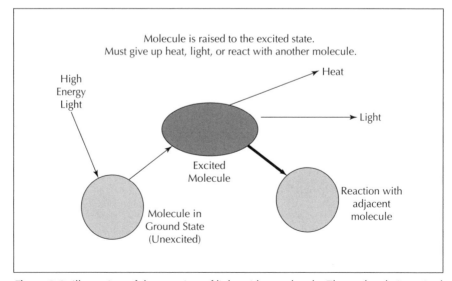

Figure 9-2. *Illustration of the reaction of light with a molecule. The molecule is excited and raised to a higher energy level and now is unstable. To become stable, it must give up the new energy as heat, light or reaction with another molecule.*

in this region is absorbed in the ozone layer of the atmosphere. Consider that only 5% of the sun's energy is in the UV range; 35% is in the visible range; and the rest, about 60%, is in the infrared (IR) range, that is, more than 700 nm.

Within living cells, visible light is absorbed only slightly unless the cells are pigmented, such as melanin cells in the skin and corpuscles in the blood stream. Infrared light can pass completely through parts of the body, though it will have some affect on the tissues. This chapter's focus is on the effects of UV light in the UVB range of 280–320 nm, the UVA range of 320–380 nm, and the effects of visible light, that which our eyes can detect, from 400–700 nm because these three energy levels are the most damaging.[c]

Proteins make up the bulk of most solid matter in the cells. Water makes up 70%+. These are the prime targets of UV in the range of 260–280 nm, though absorption occurs both below and above this range (230–300 nm). The prime target molecule in the cell is deoxyribonucleic acid (DNA). It is the deleterious effects on DNA that account for many of the problems associated with sun-damaged skin, including cancer. While it is important to know the energy levels in the various rays of the sun, *it is even more important to know the total amount of the sun's energy that is absorbed during an exposure to sunlight*. This is called dosage. The dosage relates to the intensity of the sun and the time of exposure.

$$\text{Dosage} = \text{Intensity} \times \text{Time} \qquad \text{(III)}$$

It does not matter how short a time you are exposed if the intensity is high. This is particularly important with artificial sunlight such as sun lamps. The term watts per square centimeter is used for UVA energy and milliwatts per square centimeter is used for UVB energy since it has 1,000 times the energy of UVA. Simply multiplying the watts by the time you are in the sun, in seconds, will give the total energy you receive in joules. Normally this measurement is given in terms of square centimeters of skin because it helps to standardize measurements for scientific comparison. Here is the equation:

$$\text{Joules} = \text{watts per unit area} \times \text{seconds} \qquad \text{(IV)}$$

And of the UV and visible rays, the lower wavelengths are more damaging because if you refer to the equations, lower wavelengths mean higher frequency in Equation I; and the higher the frequency, the higher the energy in Equation II. The higher the energy, the greater the effect on the molecules and consequently there is more damage.

Optical properties of the skin

Since the skin is a complex structure one would expect the interaction of sunlight and skin also to be complex, and so it is. When light strikes the skin, it is reflected, then it penetrates into the lower layers. The amount of reflection and the amount of penetration obviously are related. The stratum corneum produces the greatest amount

---

[c] *Author's note:* Although there have been preliminary reports that IR rays also can be damaging to the skin, there are few specifics that can be reported. None of the other rays, although they are very damaging, reach the earth's surface.

of reflection of the sunlight since it is the outermost layer of skin. The amount of reflected light depends on the condition of the stratum corneum and certain optical principles.

Light rays will change direction when they encounter different media through which they pass. **Figure 9-3** shows this phenomenon with skin. The light is further scattered by the various components of the skin: cells, molecules and fibers. The light rays are bent and enter the skin at a different angle than that which struck the stratum corneum. Now the rays are further scattered and absorbed as they pass into the epidermis proper by the various cell components that include the proteins, DNA and ribonucleic acid (RNA), melanin and amino acids. If the light rays are not all absorbed by the epidermis, they will pass down into the dermis where they will be scattered further, refracted and then reflected out again if they are not totally absorbed or transmitted by dermal components. (See **Figure 9-4**.)

Melanin is a skin pigment that is the first physiochemical defense against the sun's damaging rays. The structure of melanin absorbs both UV and visible light. It is not only the quantity of melanin pigment, but also where and how it is dispersed in the skin. The exposure to the sun stimulates the production of melanin with the resulting suntan. Tanning is stimulated by UVA radiation and UVB radiation, but it is unknown if the mechanism is the same for both types of radiation.

Wavelengths of less than 320 nm are absorbed mostly by the stratum corneum and the epidermis, while rays of more than 320 nm pass into the dermis. Do not think of these numbers as sharp cut-off points for there are too many variables in skin to allocate such defined numbers for any layer of the skin. From a practical point of view, shiny wet skin absorbs more light than dry, dull skin since the index of refraction is closer to air. There is less scattering and more penetration. ***Using oil on the skin, such as mineral oil, before sunbathing greatly increases the amount of sunlight absorbed by the skin without any benefit of protection***. The use of these products on the skin is very much like using a frying oil to transfer the heat from the stove to the meat one is cooking. This is very bad business for the skin.

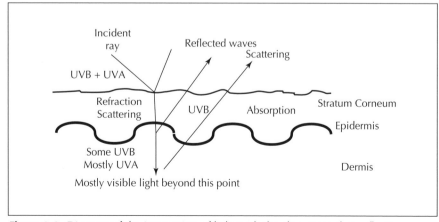

Figure 9-3. *Diagram of the interaction of light with the skin. Note that reflection, scattering, refraction and absorption can occur at all levels of the skin.*

Immediate changes in the skin

The first changes produced in the skin by UVB and UVA are in the altered biochemistry of DNA, cell membrane disorders, effects on enzymes and other proteins and amino acids. The breaking and repair of DNA is quite rapid, generally being completed within a day at a low radiation dosage, while at higher doses of radiation the actual repair process may be inhibited.

Products from damaged cells are released and these can cause both immediate and delayed effects. These compounds are part of the inflammatory response in the skin and are designed to meet the challenge and affect a repair of tissue. This acute response is associated with enzyme-release and cell-breakdown products. These changes can be seen microscopically, occurring hours and days after the radiation.

Sunburn cells and gene p53

The body has a mechanism to destroy cells that are altered by UV rays if they are beyond repair. The gene that is responsible for this action is called the p53 gene. The destruction method is called **apoptosis**, pronounced *apó-toe-sis*. Apoptosis is the systematic destruction of the nucleus and cytoskeleton of a cell. It has been found that moderate exposure to UV light can damage the DNA to a point that the p53 gene is destroyed and cannot function to destroy a damaged cell. A second exposure to UV radiation could produce severely injured, but not fatally damaged cells that become abnormal. Without the protection of the p53 gene, these cells can continue to grow and eventually become malignant. This may be one of the major reasons that so many cases of skin cancer in sun-exposed areas are seen.

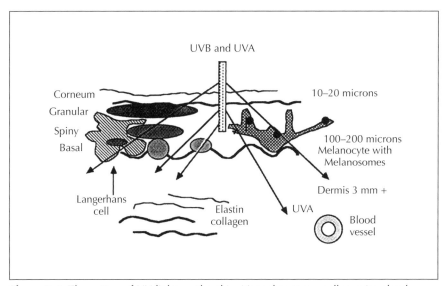

Figure 9-4. The action of UV light on the skin. Note that many cells are involved and that many structures are affected by both UVA and UVB.

Intermediate responses

One of the first visible signs of sunlight radiation damage is **erythema,** or redness of the skin. Erythema results from dilation of blood vessels in the dermis as a response to by-products of cell damage. Depending on the wavelength of the light, erythema appears two to six hours after irradiation with a peak at 12–20 hours later. It is possible for the erythema to last from a few hours up to several days; again this is a function of the total energy received in the exposure.

The intensity, or degree, of erythema is a good indication of the severity of the damage to the skin inflicted by the sun. This redness is used as a measure of the effectiveness of sunscreens. The term minimal erythematous dose, or MED, is established for each individual used in a panel to test sunscreens when the sun protective factor, or SPF, is determined. There are six types of skin currently classified by the amount of pigmentation and ease of burning and resistance to tanning. They are shown in **Skin Type Classifications**.

Much remains to be learned about the effects of both UVA and UVB regarding damage and tanning. The most effective wavelength for erythema production is at 297 nm. For UVA exposure at 365 nm, it requires 1,800 times more energy to produce erythema than at 297 nm.

Action on the keratinocytes. Between 8 and 24 hours after irradiation, a damaged cell that has been termed a "sunburn cell" appears in the epidermis. How and why they appear is unknown, but these cells have a characteristic appearance that is diagnostic of sun-induced damage. They are shrunken cells with a condensed nucleus and eosinophilic, or reddish, cytoplasm. Within the cell, clumped filaments,

Skin Type Classifications

Skin Type	Working Classification	Physical Characteristics
I	Always burns easily, never tans, extremely sun sensitive skin	Red-haired, freckles, Celtic, Irish-Scots
II	Always burns easily, tans minimally, very sun sensitive skin	Fair-skinned, fair-haired blue-eyed, Caucasian
III	Sometimes burns, tans gradually to light brown, sun sensitive skin	Average skin
IV	Burns minimally, always tans to moderate brown, minimally sun sensitive	Mediterranean-type Caucasian
V	Rarely burns, tans well, sun insensitive skin	Middle Eastern, some Hispanics, some Blacks
VI	Never burns, deeply pigmented, sun insensitive skin	Blacks

melanin granules and intact lysosomes can be seen. It is not known why only certain cells show this sunburn phenomenon. It only is known that these cells appear to have sustained heavier nuclear damage probably because of increased DNA synthesis at the time of exposure.

After irradiation, cells decrease DNA production for up to 12 hours, but then increase production to normal levels after 24 hours. This is followed by a much faster rate, six or seven times faster, of DNA synthesis up to 48 hours. What is even more impressive is that the mitotic rate in the epidermis increases and stays elevated for up to four weeks.

Immune effects. While some of the effects of the sun on the immune system are only beginning to be known, it is known that there is an effect on the Langerhans cell. These special cells lose certain membrane markers that are essential for information processing. It is possible that the ability to repair and to detect abnormal changes within the epidermis is altered or lost by Langerhans cells. Tumors of the skin and other adverse conditions arise as a result of this alteration. The delayed hypersensitivity reaction in the elderly is impaired and certain sensitivity reactions to known allergens also are reduced or eliminated.

The action of melanin. Melanin previously has been discussed, but since it is the main defense against the sun it is necessary to look more deeply at this substance and its role as a skin protectant. Melanin arises from cells called **melanocytes** that reside in the epidermis, usually about one melanocyte to every 36 keratinocytes. They are characterized by long filaments that contain melanosomes, dark pigment bodies. The melanosomes are introduced into the keratinocytes to provide the protective effects of melanin. The stratum corneum cells contain melanin pigments which they received while they were young cells deep down in the epidermis.

The chemistry of melanin is complex but follows a pathway from tyrosine, an amino acid, to a compound called indole 5, 6 quinone and then to eumelanin, which is the true melanin in cells of mammals. You do not need to learn the pathway unless you want to study skin pigmentation in depth. It is known how the melanin granules move from the melanocyte to the keratinocyte, but some investigators believe this is a phagocytic process, that is, the keratinocytes engulf the particles presented to their surfaces.

Tanning and melanin. There is an immediate effect on the melanin granules occurring within a few minutes after irradiation. This is a photo-oxidation effect on the melanin and may be a trigger signal. Within two hours melanosomes have moved to the branching processes of the melanocyte and then to the keratinocyte.

Two to three days later there is a delayed effect that is manifested by an increase in melanogenesis and an increase in melanocytes and keratinocytes. The skin becomes darker as a result of this activity, which is tanning. Tanning occurs with both UVA and UVB. It seems to require about the same time to appear, but higher doses are needed with UVA. There is an amount of radiation with which the cells proliferate at a maximum rate and no further stimulation can produce more melanin. It is believed currently that the melanocyte and the keratinocyte are dependent on each other with regards to proliferative activity and light exposure.

Sun-tanning booths. There are many sun tanning salons in the world using UVA stimulation. There is yet insufficient information to say if these units are safe. UVA is harmful to skin in many ways, probably the most serious of which is depressing certain immune functions. In addition, photochemical reactions with certain medications take place with UVA in the skin, producing unwanted and harmful results. At best one should use a sunscreen with these units, the dosage must be controlled carefully and the clients screened for contraindications to tanning. The dangers of the tanning process must be explained to the client, for beyond the client's presumed cosmetic benefit from the tan, there is no scientific basis for a tanning benefit.

Long-term effects on skin

The major effects of chronic sunlight exposure are divided into aging effects and carcinogenic effects. Since the non-medical skin care specialist does not treat skin cancers, aging effects will be discussed.

At least 90% of the age-associated cosmetic problems, known as photo-aging of the skin, are due to excessive sun exposure. These changes are wrinkling of the skin, sagging of the skin, discoloration and the presence of multiple unsightly pigmented spots. Atrophy, or thin skin; telangiectasia, a web of dilated vessels or spider veins; and hypo-pigmentation, or lack of color, also can be seen as part of the sun-aged skin. Photo-aging also is called actinic damage, from the Greek word *aktis* meaning "ray," a term frequently used in medical literature.

When the skin is examined microscopically, only minor changes in the epidermis manifested by a flattened dermal-epidermal junction and some thinning of the spiny layer is seen. In the dermis, there are more pronounced changes. The papillary dermis is thin and fairly homogeneous, blood vessels are dilated and there are amorphous, fragmented, fibrotic areas called solar elastosis present throughout the dermis. These effects are related to both severity and frequency of exposure. Only by unwise, unfortunate, or foolish exposure to sunlight can such skin be produced.

Conclusions

With the present knowledge about biology, the only known benefit from UV light on the skin is the conversion of 7-dehydrocholesterol to pre-vitamin D, which becomes vitamin D3. No harm is done by protecting ourselves from harmful UV radiation.

Work has been done for the approval of UVA screens by the U.S. Food and Drug Administration, and one product that has been approved for use as a UVA sunscreen called Parsol 1789. Benzophenones also absorbs UVA up to 360 nm and UVB. Here are a few chemical names of UVA absorbers seen on the labels of sunscreens:

2-hydroxy-4 methoxybenzophenone
2-ethylexl-4-phenylbenzophenone-2-carboxylate
2-hydroxy-4-methoxybenzophenone-5-sulfonic acid
4-isopropyl dibenzoyl methane
4-tert.butyl-4-methoxy-dibenzoyl-methane
2-ethyl-hexyl-p-methoxycinnamate
benzophenone-3(2-hydroxy-4-methoxybenzophenone)

Sun blocks should be used where total sunlight must be eliminated. These agents effectively scatter and reflect the sun, preventing penetration and absorption. They include talc, kaolin, clay, starch, zinc oxide, titanium dioxide and ferric chloride. They have limited use because they are not very acceptable cosmetically. Oral agents are not yet approved, but two substances have been tried that are effective against certain deleterious aspects of the sun exposure. They should not be used without topical sunscreens. These substances are beta-carotene and aspirin, both taken before sunbathing.

There is much to learn about photobiology. The action of light and the skin is a complex phenomenon that has some little benefit but more detriment.

Once the harm is done, is there anything that can be done to reverse the damage? Yes, there is. The body can repair the DNA damage. Singlet oxygen can be quenched and free radicals can be stopped. Collagen and elastin can be repaired and new circulation established. Much of the ravages of photo-aging are reversible if the continuous insult from the sun is stopped. The use of vitamin E and beta-carotene and vitamin A will help prevent, and to some measure, restore the skin. In severe cases the client will need the expert help of a dermatologist or a reconstructive surgeon. In any event, this is a problem that requires a multi-disciplined approach, a team of skilled and dedicated professionals working to one common goal—the benefit of the client.

Chapter 10

Herpes-type Viral Infections

As a skin care specialist, sooner or later you will come into contact with a client carrying a viral rash. Any time you see a group of vesicles, or blisters, you are looking at a viral disease. Some of these conditions are benign while others are quite serious.

Frequent questions you can have to answer are, "What is herpes?" or "Why is herpes important in facial peeling or laser surgery?" You need to understand the basics of viral infections; how to recognize them; and when referring a client to a physician, what can be done to control and to treat them. This article stresses the herpes infection, but the basics are applicable to most viral infections.

What is a virus?

A virus is a nonliving segment of deoxyribonucleic acid (DNA) or ribonucleic acid (RNA) that can be reproduced in a living cell. Both DNA and RNA make up the genetic material in the cell. Each virus consists of a coat covering a nucleic acid, and this complete virus is called a **virion**. The covering is called the **capsid**. Often, the complete virus is referred to as a **virus particle** or simply a **particle**. To understand the concept of a viral infection, it is necessary to know that a virus can multiply within a living cell by using the cell's genetic mechanism. In this article, these systems only can be reviewed briefly, but there are enough basic facts to understand the replication of a virus.

The basics

Within the nucleus of a normal cell are strands of material called **chromosomes** that contain all of the information necessary to reproduce and maintain the cell. This information is coded in a sequential manner on chemical compounds called **bases**.

The four bases are adenine, thymine, guanine and cytosine. How these bases are arranged determines both the structure and function of any particular sequence.

For example, the segment that determines blue eyes will have a different base sequence than the brown eyes segment. To make a protein, a particular segment of the chromosome will expose a portion of its DNA, which then is copied, or transcribed, into a new segment called RNA. The RNA then is used as a template on which the protein is constructed. (See **Figure 10-1**.)

Viral reproduction and infection

All viruses that are infectious follow a life cycle that includes:

Absorption of the organism. The virus enters the cell. Most viruses are cell-specific; that is they can infect only certain types of cells in certain types of organisms. This is called tissue tropism and host specificity, and is the hallmark of a viral infection. For example, the polio virus infects only the neurons of nerves, while human papilloma virus infects only epithelial tissue. These cells that allow a virus to replicate are called permissive cells. (See **Figure 10-2**.)

Entry of the viral nucleic acid into the cell. Once in the cell, the capsid must be removed by enzymes within the cell. This releases the DNA or RNA in the virus.

The **nucleic acid** is reproduced in the cell by the genetic mechanism and how this is done largely depends on the type of virus. It can be single- or double-strand DNA, or single- or double-strand RNA. The amount of information carried on these nucleic acids will vary tremendously from virus to virus. All viral nucleic acids, however, contain a particular sequence that serves for replication origin that overrides the host cell DNA.

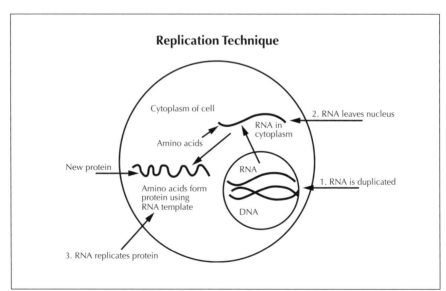

Figure 10-1. *Basic replication technique of first-forming RNA, then building proteins on RNA with amino acids.*

In the case of RNA-type viruses, they first must copy their own RNA molecules using a special type of polymerase enzyme that is carried on their nucleic acids. This is the most complex part of the replication process. It is not necessary to go into detail at this point, except to appreciate the complexity of this system as it changes for specific types of viral infections.

Transcription, translation and replication. The codes on the viral DNA first must be transcribed into RNA, which then is translated into components of the cell capsid. The DNA can be replicated by the normal genetic enzymes within the cell.

Maturation of particles. The viral DNA and capsid are assembled in the cytoplasm of the cell.

Release of particles. The virus is released from the cell and infects other cells. In some cases, the virus is not released and remains dormant until reactivated. A common example of this type is herpes simplex, the common fever blister.

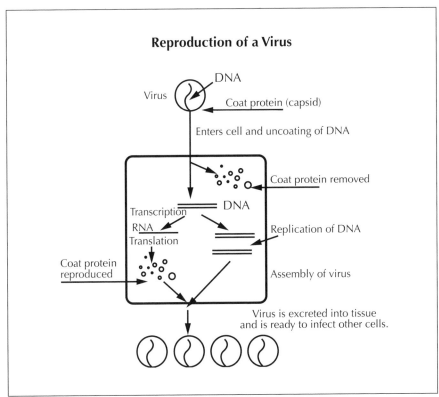

Reproduction of a Virus

Figure 10-2. The virus enters the cell and the capsid is removed. The viral DNA makes an RNA copy to reproduce the capsid. This is called transcription. The actual formation of the capsid is called translation. The viral DNA is then reproduced and joined with the capsid. Finally, the completed virus is excreted.

Major Skin Lesions

Type of Rash	Viral Infections Seen
Macule (flat red spot)	Rubella (German measles) Echovirus Coxsackie A and Coxsackie B EBV (infectious mononucleosis) Human herpes virus 6 (roseola)
Maculopapular (raised Macule)	Echovirus 6 and 9 Measles Human parvovirus
Maculpapular-vesicular (raised macules and blisters)	Coxsackie and Echo types
Urticarial (hives)	Coxsackie and Hepatitis B
Vesicular (blisters)	Herpes simplex virus Hand, foot and mouth group of coxsackie A, and vesicular stomatitis (inflamed mouth)
Vesiculopustular	Varicella and herpes zoster
Papulovesiculopustular	Vaccinia, variola, cowpox
Papulovesicular	Orf nodes and milker's nodes
Papular	Molluscum contagiosum Warts

This is not a complete list. Orf is a disease seen mainly in sheepherders; milker's nodes are seen mainly in dairy farmers; and molluscum contagiosum frequently is seen in children and young adults. The coxsackie virus group is quite large—more than 24 group A types and six group B types. They are associated with painful conditions with a rash and usually are self-limiting, requiring only symptomatic treatment.

Classifications

Viral diseases of the skin can be classified in several ways, either from type of virus, or from the type of rash that it produces. (See **Major Skin Lesions**.) However, in this article, the focus is on the herpes-type infections.

The word *herpes* is from the Greek word for "snake or reptile." This name was chosen since some of the skin manifestation of these infections are associated with a twisting, serpentine appearance. Herpes is a DNA-type virus that mainly replicates itself in the nucleus. A major feature of this virus is that it is not eliminated from the body following manifestation and recovery. It persists in the cells for which the strain is specific for an individual's lifetime. Six types of herpes infections will be examined in this chapter.

Herpes simplex

Herpes simplex is the common cold sore. The most common viral infections, caused by *herpes virus hominis*, is expressed by two types. Type 1 is the common **facial type** and Type 2 is the **genital type**. While they are separate antigens—specific proteins that have characteristic immune properties used to identify them—there is considerable overlap. The lesion appears as a painful vesicle in groups or singularly. It infects nerve tissue, which is one reason it is so painful. Oral lesions can last for a week or more, while genital lesions can last for two to three weeks. The most common site for facial herpes is the lip. In genital herpes, the penis in the male and the labia in the female are the sites affected most frequently. In the female, the vagina and cervix also can be involved. With both sexes, painful urination is common.

In the United States, there about 100 million reported cases of Type 1 herpes simplex every year, mostly in children. Type 2 herpes simplex has increased 15-fold over the last 25 years. The risk of a woman who is exposed to a male infected with Type 2 herpes and developing herpes genitalia is 80–90%. Recurrent attacks of herpes genitalia occur in 60% of cases and these infections can occur anywhere on the skin.

Contraction. Herpes simplex is transmitted by direct contact with droplets or secretion from infected areas. The virus can be spread by saliva or genital secretion, especially days or weeks after an acute episode, from individuals who have no clinical signs of herpes. However, the amount of virus shed from an active lesion is 100–1,000 times greater.

In poor or underdeveloped countries, most children are infected with the facial type by the time they are 5. The infection rate is less in upper socioeconomic groups. Type 2 occurs after puberty and is transmitted by sexual contact. In cases of infection with Type 2 in pre-pubescent children, one must suspect child abuse or transmission through pregnancy.

Any part of the skin can be infected with this virus, particularly broken areas of the skin. An infected person commonly will spread the condition by finger contact, such as in the case of nail biters or thumb suckers. In pregnancy, primary herpes genitalia can be transmitted to the infant about 50% of the time, if the mother's immune response has not taken place. Severe and at times fatal infections have occurred in the newborn. In cases where the mother has had a previous infection, called a non-primary infection, the infection rate of the newborn is very low and less serious, presumably due to the antibodies that exist in the mother's system.

Complications. The complications of herpes infections usually are quite serious. Here are a few:

Keratoconjunctivitis—a primary herpes infection of the eye that starts with a severe conjunctivitis and a pus discharge, often associated with opacity and ulceration of the cornea. The eyelids markedly are swollen and at times vesicles can be seen on the surrounding skin.

Inoculation herpes simplex—this condition is important to consider because it can be mistaken for several other skin infections. It occurs by direct inoculation in an abraded area or even normal skin by direct contact, usually with the fingers. Large blisters, called **bullae**, can appear along with scattered smaller vesicles. It usually takes five to seven days to develop after inoculation, so there may not be an association with the original infection. This condition can be confused with bacterial infections such as impetigo or folliculitis since the lesion can occur on the face or the scalp. Look for vesicles as the diagnostic sign since vesicles do not occur in bacterial infections as a rule.

Systemic infections with herpes include **pharyngitis**, a painful spread of the infection to the throat. **Radiculoneuropathy**, a condition that involves the nerves in the lower spine, can result in temporary loss of feeling, urinary retention and impotency, and often is seen in homosexuals.

Recurrent infections are a common problem and occur about 50% of the time with Type 1 herpes and about 95% of the time with Type 2. They can be triggered by such events as minor trauma, upper respiratory infections, ultraviolet light, intra-cranial operations, dental surgery, dermabrasion and laser surgery, premenstrual time, emotional stress, other infections and unknown causes.

Treatment. Almost all cases of herpes will resolve over time and require only symptomatic treatment for relief of pain. There are a number of over-the-counter products that work quite well. Most preparations are designed to coagulate the protein of the virus. Tannic acid gel in alcohol works well, as do solutions of zinc sulfate from 0.0025–0.1%. In serious or recurrent cases, refer to a physician as internal treatment can be needed. Acyclovir, an antiviral agent, is used by physicians to treat serious infection and as prophylactic in cases of elective surgery. The drug interferes with the DNA polymerase of the virus so that it cannot replicate. A 5% ointment is available by prescription and can be used topically to treat both Type 1 and Type 2 herpes.

Also, upon a physician's recommendation, the use of dietary measures is helpful. Lysine, an amino acid, has been shown to inhibit the herpes virus if arginine, another amino acid, is reduced. Up to two grams of lysine may be needed if arginine foods are eaten. The foods highest in arginine are chocolate, then nuts—such as peanuts, Brazil nuts and hazel nuts. High lysine foods include fish and cheddar cheese. Two grams of vitamin C per day in divided doses in addition to one gram of bioflavanoids, 25–50 milligrams of beta-carotene and 400–600 milligrams of vitamin E also may be recommended. Licorice root, which contains glycyrrhizic acid, is known to inhibit growth and cell-damaging effects of the herpes virus.

Herpes and cosmetic surgery. When skin is traumatized as in cosmetic surgical procedures such as peels and laser ablation, the latent virus can become active. Once activated, it can spread over the entire face and produce a horrendous infection. There is no effective treatment for this condition, so prevention is the only means to control it. Surgeons routinely prescribe the drug acyclovir. Before working on pre- or post-cosmetic surgery treatments with clients, ask them about their history of herpes, and particularly about recurrent herpes infection. Record this information on their client history charts.

Herpes virus varicella

Varicella, also known as chickenpox or zoster, is caused by the same virus. The primary infection is chickenpox, which infects nerves and then remains in the sensory nerve ganglion. Zoster, or shingles, is the result of the reactivation of this latent virus.

Contraction of chickenpox. The highest incidence of chickenpox is in children between 2–10. It is spread by droplets from the nasopharynx from a cough, sneeze or runny nose. This is not a serious infection and the dry scabs of chickenpox are not infectious. The incubation period is 14–17 days, with a low-grade fever and malaise as the first symptoms. A scarlet rash appears, followed by papules that rapidly become clear vesicles. In a few hours, they appear turbid and pustular surrounded by a red areola. In two to four days, they crust over; then the crust separates, leaving a shallow pink depression. Unless a secondary infection occurs, these depressions heal without scarring.

The vesicles appear in three to five crops over two to four days beginning on the trunk and spreading to the face and scalp, then to the legs and arms. The spread is centripetal. The characteristic of this disease is that the lesions appear at different stages, so that at any one-time papules, vesicles and pustules are seen together.

Complications with chickenpox. Complications with chickenpox are rare, but serious when they occur. Encephalitis, or inflammation of the brain, occurs in only 1 of every 1,000 cases with 80% of the cases having complete recovery. Secondary infection is serious in some climates, particularly tropical areas, as it can lead to the infection spreading to the bloodstream. Arthritis also is a rare complication.

About 10–20% of adults will get herpes zoster during their lifetime. Two-thirds of these individuals will be 50 or older, with the highest incidence happening between 80–89.

Seeing a case of shingles for the first time can be a frightful experience, especially if it is on the face. The disease always follows a nerve root, so it is quite characteristic in appearance, almost never crossing the body's midline. When the infection occurs on the face, near the eye, it is a problem that requires prompt referral to an eye specialist.

Contraction of shingles. Only those who have had chickenpox at some time can get shingles. They represent a specific type of recurrence of this infection many years later.

The first symptom is pain at the site where the lesions will appear. On the face, the pain comes about a day and a half before the eruption, while on the chest, pain can be felt for three to four days before the eruption. Papules appear first, followed by vesicles and then pustules. Usually one dermatome is involved, at times two are involved and rarely, three are involved. A **dermatome** is a segment of skin that is innervated by one dorsal nerve foot. (See **Figure 10-3**.) For example, the three-part, or trigeminal, branch of the facial nerve covers a specific area of the face involving the skin over the eye, down the cheek and over the mouth. (See **Figure 10-4**.) Any area of the body can be involved, depending on the nerve that is infected. While this is a description of a classic case, it is more common to see many variations of the disease. Forms of abdominal pain to electrocardiographic abnormalities are possible.

Complications of shingles. Ophthalmic nerve zoster is one of the most serious types of complications and can involve many complications to the eye. While most cases of herpes zoster infect sensory nerves, often motor nerves are involved, resulting in paralysis of the muscles supplied by the nerve. In ophthalmic nerve zoster, 13% of patients have ocular paralysis and 7% have facial paralysis. Complete recovery is expected in most cases.

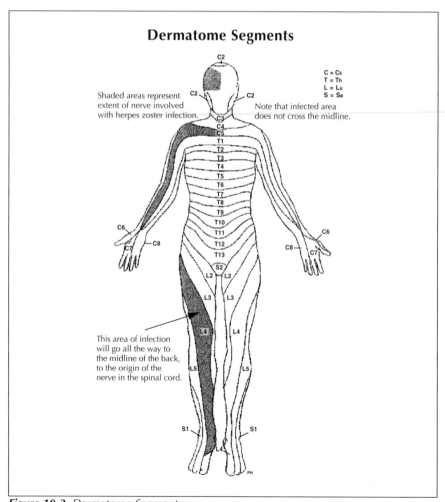

Figure 10-3. Dermatome Segments

Post-herptic neuralgia unfortunately is a common sequel of herpes zoster. It is a very persistent and painful area that follows the same nerve pattern about one month after the zoster lesions have disappeared. It occurs in about 30% of patients over 40, and the pain is described as a mild, dull pain to a continuous burning pain. The trigeminal area most often is associated with post-herptic neuralgia.

Treatment. As in herpes simplex, acyclovir has been shown to be helpful in cases of herpes zoster. Not all cases respond well, however. In some, steroids, or corticosteroids, have been used successfully. Herpes zoster is a condition that always must be treated by a physician. However, a client with post-herptic neuralgia can be seen by a skin care professional and would perhaps benefit from topical applications of soothing herbal lotions, or herbal compresses. Generally, anti-inflammatory types, such as chamomile, linden and mallow, can be helpful. Capsaicin, as a topical, has been used medically to treat post-herptic neuralgia. Cream and ointment at a concentration of 0.025–0.0075% have been used with success. There are some commercial preparations available.

Cytomegalovirus

The cytomegalovirus (CMV) infection is common around the world, yet surprisingly, few people have heard of it. Adults are infected at a 40–100% rate, depending

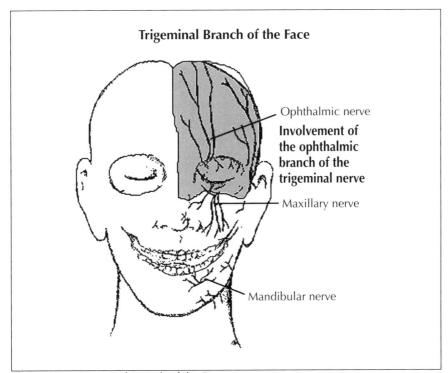

Trigeminal Branch of the Face

Ophthalmic nerve
Involvement of the ophthalmic branch of the trigeminal nerve
Maxillary nerve
Mandibular nerve

Figure 10-4. Trigeminal Branch of the Face

on the community. It is important to the skin care specialist only because it has skin manifestation at times. It can appear as follicular, maculpapular or a rubelliform rash that looks like rubella or German measles. The clinical picture closely resembles infectious mononucleosis. It's noteworthy that, like infectious mononucleosis, ampicillin will trigger a widespread eruption. The most severe form of congenital CMV is with newborns, who rarely will live more than two months, and those who survive have severe neurological damage.

Contraction. The infection can be transmitted during pregnancy and at birth from cervical secretions. Children can be infected from oral secretions and from urine contamination. As adults, transmission is mainly sexual, but blood transfusions and organ transplants also can transmit the disease.

Treatment. Generally, no treatment is needed. In rare cases, it can produce a life-threatening situation that requires heroic medical treatment.

Epstein-Barr virus

The Epstein-Barr virus (EBV) causes infectious mononucleosis. The clinical picture of infectious mononucleosis is well known to most adults. Just about everyone knows someone who has had this virus. Symptoms include fever, sore throat with exudative pharyngitis that produces seepage of a yellowish discharge, swollen glands or lymphadenopathy. A swollen spleen occurs in some cases, and about 4% of cases experience liver involvement with jaundice. In 10% of the cases, there is a rash at about the fourth or sixth day, starting as a macular or maculopapular lesion on the trunk and upper arms. In some cases, the face and legs also can be involved, but this is not frequent.

A distinctive feature of infectious mononucleosis is the dark blue hemorrhagic spots that appear in the mouth on the junction of the hard and soft palate on the second or third day. These spots are called **petechiae** and represent small hemorrhages in the skin.

The rash also can appear as scarlatiniform, with small papules that do not touch; or morbilliform, with irregularly shaped measles-type papules that can run together; with urticaria, hives, sometimes as the initial rash. The lesions disappear after a few days. As noted above, if ampicillin is given, about 90% of patients experience a diffuse rash that is maculopapular and appears seven to ten days after treatment begins. Penicillin and tetracycline can produce a similar effect.

Contraction. The disease is spread in lower economic conditions mainly from saliva on fingers; or common utensils, such as glasses, cups and silverware. It is common in young children in this group and can be spread from droplets in the air, such as in coughing or sneezing. In more advantaged socioeconomic groups, the disease occurs later, in young adults, and is spread mainly by kissing. Fully 40% of college entrants in the United States are tested positive for the disease. The disease is milder in children and more severe in young adults. While infected individuals recover, aren't contagious and no longer manifest symptoms of the disease, the virus remains with them the rest of their lives.

Complications. While no specific complication is associated with infectious mononucleosis, the virus has been implicated in other, more serious, conditions such as nasopharygeal cancers and B-cell lymphomas. Burkett's lymphoma, seen in Africa and New Guinea, is associated with this virus as well. In human immunodeficiency virus (HIV), both Burkett's lymphoma and large cell lymphoma are common.

Treatment. The treatment for infectious mononucleosis is mainly symptomatic. Bed rest and adequate nutrition are the mainstay of therapy.

Human herpes virus 6

Human herpes virus 6 is a newly isolated virus that causes roseola infantum, or exanthem subitum. It is a rose-pink maculopapular rash that occurs on the neck and the trunk, and spreads to the arms, face and legs. The rash appears after a fever, which will not be very high but persists for three to five days. As the fever goes down, the rash will appear. This disease goes by many names, but often is called the three-day measles, or fifth disease. If a child is exposed it will take at least 10–15 days of incubation before the fever will appear.

Sub-clinical infection is common. Only 30% of cases develop clinical signs of the disease. It is rare to see a case in a child older than 3, and almost nonexistent in adults.

Complications and treatment. Convulsions from the fever are a primary complication, but other complications are very rare. The disease is benign and doesn't need treatment.

AIDS and viral infections

Acquired Immune Deficiency Syndrome (AIDS), caused by the HIV virus, still is very much a problem in the world. HIV-infected individuals are more prone to viral infections, so the skin care specialist needs to be more alert to this possibility. The HIV patient also is highly susceptible to bacterial infection, such as staphylococcus and mycobacteria.

The common viral infections seen with HIV include herpes simplex, herpes zoster, genital warts and molluscum contagiosum. The presence of oral hairy leukoplakia, a condition that can be recognized by white plaques on the sides of the tongue with a hairy appearance, suggests HIV because 83% of these patients develop HIV within three years. There are other relatively benign forms of leukoplakia that are distinguishable from this type. The important thing to remember is that any white plaque on the tongue, lips or inside the cheeks represents dysplasia, or abnormal tissue, and signals a problem that should be looked at by a physician.

General guidelines

If unsure about the treatment or cause of a skin condition, or if it appears to be a chronic one, refer the client to a physician. There are, however, some general guidelines that can be followed by a skin care professional who sees a client with a herpes simplex infection. Since most clients use self-medications for these types of infections, an esthetician can recommend treatment products. Over-the-counter medicines, self-mixed astringent botanicals, or any product with tannic acid and alcohol usually are effective.

If there are only one or two lesions on the face or elsewhere, it usually is safe to treat with simple remedies. Do not attempt to treat profuse or widespread herpes anywhere on the body. This type of infection most often is associated with fever and other serious symptoms. Also, do not treat herpes infections near or in the eyes. These lesions always are serious and the client must be referred to a physician.

A physician can ask an esthetician to assist in the treatment of a patient with shingles. The first step in this process is to discuss with the physician what esthetically can be offered to the patient, and be sure that there is an agreement on a treatment program.

General References

The following contain many specific detailed references for the interested reader:

Cano RJ and Colome JS, "Viruses and Viral Infections," *Microbiology Biology of Viruses*, Minneapolis: West Publishing, 17: 389 (1986). This is an excellent general textbook in microbiology and the chapter on viral infections is quite comprehensive.

Champion RH, Burton JL and Ebling FJG, *Textbook of Dermatology*, London: Blackwell Scientific Publications, 22: 867 (1992). A comprehensive treatment of viral skin infections, including non-herpes types.

Conant MA, "Genital Herpes, An Integrated Approach to Management," *Journal of the American Academy of Dermatology*, 35: 601–605 (1996). A current management program for genital herpes.

Harrison GA, Tanner JM, Pilbeam DR and Baker PT, "Part IV Human Adaptability," *Oxford Science Publications in Human Biology*, Oxford, England: Oxford Press, 459–543 (1993.) A good review of the mechanisms of disease and the adaptability of both infectious agent and host. This book helps one to appreciate the complexity of infections that affect humans, while providing an understanding of the ecological factors involved.

Lookingbill DP and Marks JK, *Principles of Dermatology*, Philadelphia: W.B. Saunders 11: 160 (1993). This chapter is a good summary of vesicular lesions, while the book is a good review of skin disorders.

Murray M and Pizzorno J, "Herpes Simplex," *Encyclopedia of Natural Medicine*, Rocklin, CA: Prima Publishing 45: 356 (1991). An excellent source for treatment using natural materials.

Pereira FA, "Herpes Simplex: Evolving Concepts," *Journal of the American Academy of Dermatology*, 35: 503–520 (1996). Extensive review with many excellent references.

Wood J, *Capsaicin in the Study of Pain*, New York: Academic Press 12: 255 (1993). This chapter is excellent if you are interested in using capsaicin in the treatment of pain. The book is a comprehensive, current coverage of the capsaicin.

Chapter 11

Elastin:
The Youth Protein

Although all proteins in the body are essential for life, there probably is no single protein that has as much to do with a person's appearance and well-being as the protein elastin. This protein is found in many tissues and organs, but particularly in blood vessels and skin. Elastin gives both the snap to the skin and the attractive, smooth lines to the figure. Yet, this marvelous protein makes up only a very small part of the body structure.

I was introduced to the wonders of elastin when asked to photograph the changes in the skin as it moved against gravitational forces. I started with a simple television camera that was able to capture 1,000 frames per second. In science, this is called a millisecond exposure, or 1/1,000 of a second. To my astonishment, I was not able to capture the motion of young skin with that camera. The skin of those 30 or younger, when deformed by a pinch, would snap back to normal shape in less than a millisecond! To do this experiment, it was necessary to obtain a camera capable of a one microsecond exposure, which is one millionth of a second. The cost of this special equipment was prohibitive at the time, so the project was discontinued. However, I was impressed with the functional capacity of elastin.

Since then, elastin has held a fascination for me, as it has for many scientists. Elastin has guarded its secrets tightly, so that even today there are many mysteries and unknowns about it. Understanding the importance of maintaining elastic tissue, however, is a major part of a skin care specialist's job. This article will review the basic chemistry, physiology and pathology of elastin, and will provide an appreciation and a working knowledge of this gift-giving protein.

Myths about elastin

To begin, let's dispel some of the myths about topical elastin.

Can elastin get into the skin? Elastin is a big molecule that contains many ionic charges. Elastin cannot pass through the skin, but it binds to it just as most proteins do. Consider this—if elastin could pass into the skin, what would keep the native elastin in your skin from seeping out of it?

Can topical elastin become part of the native elastin? Topical elastin, since it cannot get into the skin, works as a smoothing agent on the surface, just as many other non-protein polymers. Expecting topical elastin to replace native elastin is about the same as expecting a load of bricks dumped on a lawn to spontaneously form into a house. The same is true of topical collagen and deoxyribonucleic acid (DNA). They only have surface effects on the skin.

Can natural elastin be derived from plants? Elastin is an animal protein derived from ligaments of animals. In most cases, it is a by-product of the meat packing industry. Until there are plants with lungs that move about on legs, elastin will not be derived from plants.

Chemical components

It almost is impossible to separate a discussion of the chemistry of elastin without some discussion of the **fibroblast**, a large, oval cell found in connective tissue and responsible for the formation of fibers. Newly made elastin is a protein that has a molecular weight of approximately 72,000 and, although it can be reported as 140,000, this value most likely represents a **dimer**, or two molecules of elastin linked together. There are some very unique aspects to the elastin fibers, one being the ability of the molecule to be stretched to 100% of its length and return to the original size. Only very special chemistry would allow such action to take place in a solid material.[1]

Amino acids and polypeptides

The basic unit of elastin is a linear polypeptide chain of 72,000 molecular weight, often referred to as **tropoelastin**. There are several unique aspects of this molecule. First, the composition of elastin is high in non-polar amino acids, alanine, proline, phenylalanine, leucine, valine and glycine, which make elastin hydrophobic and not water-soluble when cross-linked. The glycine amino acid is distributed in the molecule randomly, unlike collagen, which has a glycine molecule as every third amino acid.

Comparing elastin to collagen again, there are very few hydroxyproline molecules in elastin and no hydroxylysine at all. There are no histidine, methionine or tryptophan amino acids present in elastin either. The total number of amino acids in the elastin polypeptide is 800+. Elastin also contains a unique amino acid called desmosine, which will be discussed later.

Elastin, however, does not consist only of the polypeptide chains. There are **microfibrils** present that are an essential part of the whole elastin molecule. Little actually is known about the microfibrils except that they always are found with elastin as an integral part of the structure.

The elastin molecule

Desmosine as a molecule is a very interesting structure. (See **Figure 11-1**.) The desmosine molecule is formed in the extracellular space by changes in the lysine molecules of the individual polypeptides of elastin. It is not necessary to know exactly how this is done, except that the desmosine molecule is formed from the peptide chains and links the molecule together. The critical enzyme for this reaction is **lysyl oxidase**.[1]

In looking at the desmosine molecule in **Figure 11-2**, notice that the four side chains are linked to the polypeptides forming almost a complete square. Also notice that there are both positive NH_2 groups and negative COOH chemical groups at the ends of the peptide chains. These groups are capable of linking and forming strong peptide bonds. A peptide bond forms when NH_2 groups link with COOH as pictured to the right.

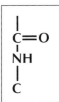

Here is the most interesting part of the elastin molecule—the random arrangement of the peptide linkages. As the molecule expands through the water environment of the tissues, it will be forced to contract again, and since it is hydrophobic, the water will repel it. (See **Figure 11-3**.)

The hydrophobic charges in the water are the energy sources that force the molecule to contract to its original shape. It's really a neat, tidy and conservative arrangement.

Elastin and the skin

Elastin is found in the skin, liver, aorta, lungs, Achilles tendons and ligaments of the neck. In the skin it is only about 0.6% by dry weight, which is almost nothing compared to collagen, which makes up 72% of the dry weight of the skin.[2]

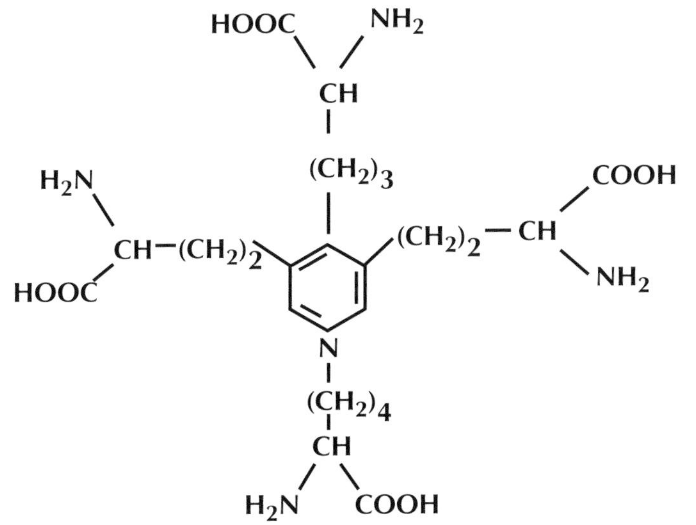

Figure 11-1. Model of Elastin Molecule

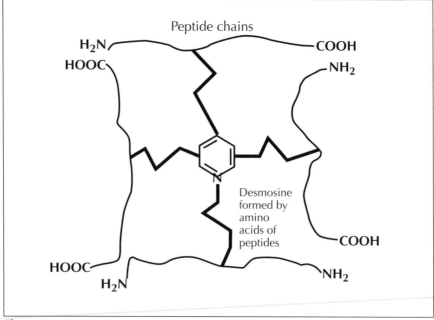

Figure 11-2. Desmosine

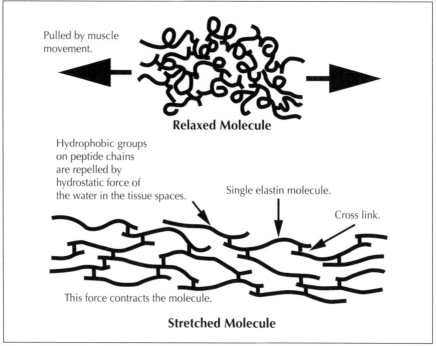

Figure 11-3. Relaxed/Stretched Molecule

It is remarkable that such tiny amounts of tissue can cause such joy or havoc. Elastin undergoes continuous degradation with replacement of new elastin, even though the turnover rate of elastin is slow.

A certain number of diseases are associated with a more rapid degradation of elastin, and in studying these diseases it was apparent that a proteolytic enzyme had to be the cause of this degradation. Proteolytic enzymes first break down proteins to peptides and then break them down even further to amino acids. Only those conditions that are genetic will be discussed so that you can be familiar with the names, although they are quite rare. Two aspects of elastin degradation that affect your clients most frequently—aging and sun damage—will be discussed in depth.

Genetic diseases

Elastosis perforans serpiginosa. This is an example of a genetic disease associated with molecular defects of elastic fibers. It is a genetic defect in the cross-linking of collagen and elastin.

Buschke-Ollendorf syndrome. This syndrome is characterized by small, yellowish papules that form on the skin and an associated bone disease. It is not known why these two conditions are associated, but some scientists feel it can relate to elastin producing fibroblasts in the bones.

Cutis laxa. Easily recognized because the skin becomes pendulous and very stretchable, this is a genetic condition. It occasionally is seen in carnival sideshow performers billed as "rubber men." Patients with this disease look quite old due to gravitational changes, even when they are young. One of the interesting aspects of this disease is broken or fragmented elastic fibers that also are seen in stretch marks.

Aging, the skin and elastin

In the 1980s, dermatologist Albert Kligman, MD, and scientist Robert Lavker turned their attention to the histological appearances of wrinkles. Their purpose was to determine if a wrinkle could be described in terms of classical histology, more accurately termed classical histopathology.[3] They were unable to detect a single defect beyond a deterioration of the elastic network. All of the papers written about wrinkle formation arrive at the same conclusion.

For skin care specialists interested in treating the signs of aging skin, it means that one target must be elastin fibers. It's necessary, however, to briefly take a look at the anatomy of skin and wrinkles.

The skin is composed of the epidermis and dermis, and the dermis is divided into two major layers. The top layer is the **papillary layer** and the lower layer is known as the **reticular layer**. Both of these layers contain collagen and elastin, but the collagen mainly is in the lower layer of the dermis while the elastin mainly is in the upper layer of the dermis.

Whatever the cause—be it sun or free radicals within the skin—the elastin undergoes degradation from the enzyme **elastase**. The specific action of elastase is to break down elastic fibers. In addition, new elastin is produced that is nonfunctional, called **elastotic elastin**. The result is a loss of retraction in the skin. As the skin is pulled by gravity, the elastin fibers stretch and there is no return, so that the skin droops and stays droopy. The feeling is one of a doughy consistency.

There is a relatively common condition called **anetoderma** that illustrates this quite well. Anetoderma is a cutaneous disorder characterized by a localized flaccid skin that can lead to herniation, or protrusion of the subcutaneous tissue. These lesions can be seen on the upper arm and upper trunk, and usually in young adults as raised, soft areas almost appearing as a small sack. There frequently is a history of some inflammatory condition preceding the lesion, but in some cases it occurs without a history of inflammation. In any case, no treatment currently is available.

If these patients were to be studied by a skin biopsy and the skin stained with a routine stain such as hematoxylin and eosin (H&E), nothing remarkable would be seen when compared to adjacent normal skin. However, when the skin is stained for elastin with a specific stain such as Luna's stain, a remarkable reduction in the amount of elastin fibers of the anetoderma skin compared to the normal skin would be seen.[4] Chemical analysis of the skin would show a very low level of desmosine in the affected areas.

Stages of aging skin

Skin laxity is one major sign in aging seen before wrinkles. There is so-called normal, or gravitational aging, as contrasted with sun-damaged skin. Usually there is a noticeable discoloration of the skin before other changes are seen, and the skin has a reddish-brown, almost leather-like appearance. Now real wrinkles are seen, starting first around the eyes and mouth, progressing to the middle and lower face and then onto the neck. The neck can show changes before the eyes. This skin shows histological changes that are described as **elastosis**—thick fibers of elastin in the reticular dermis and less in the papillary dermis.

As the process continues, the wrinkles become deeper and longer. If the individual is a smoker and drinker, besides being a sunbather, the progress is very fast after the 37–40 age range. The underlying cause is not fully known, although increased production of abnormal elastin and destruction of normal elastin are two processes known to be happening.

A very interesting paper[5] discusses findings on sun-protected skin and unprotected skin in an effort to separate the changes seen in sun damage versus those seen in chronological, or normal, aging.

Unprotected skin shows two types of elastic fiber damage present in the skin, the first is typical solar elastosis and the second is a degenerative process of the elastic fibers. In unexposed skin from the buttocks only the degenerative process was present. Subjects between the ages of 30–70 were examined, and it was found that a minority of the elastic fiber exhibited degeneration, but after 70, the majority of fibers showed this slow degeneration. While younger elastic fibers are compacted tightly, or associated, the fibers from age 50–93 were more loosely associated. It was proposed that cutaneous aging "is a slow, spontaneous, progressive degradable process inherent in the elastic fiber that can be enzymatically accelerated from decades to hours by elastase and chymotrypsin."[5]

Chymotrypsin is another proteolytic enzyme found in skin. The spectacular thing here is the great difference in time span—from ten years down to hours. This is an incredible difference due to enzymatic degradation, and is good evidence that aging is not an intrinsic or inevitable consequence of life. (*Author's note:* Even though the paper's authors say the process in inherent in elastic fibers, I do not think that is correct.)

The versatile fibroblast

I believe that the **fibroblast** is the key to many of the aging changes. It may not be the initial cause, but certainly is a major culprit. A fibroblast is not a fibrocyte. A fibrocyte is a well-differentiated cell, but a fibroblast can differentiate into other cell types, such as a fat cell, a muscle cell or a bone cell.

Fibroblasts that are wandering in the dermis, not quite differentiated, easily could be damaged and converted into abnormal producers of elastin. It is not known if each fibroblast is programmed to produce only collagen, elastin, both proteins or the proteins making up **glycosoaminoglycans**, complex proteins in the dermis that bind, release water, and are responsible for the turgor in the skin.

It is possible that, as an early cell, the fibroblast could make all three components, but after differentiation will make only one compound. This still is unknown. Consider, however, that the fibroblast and the differentiated fibrocytes are key elements in the story of aging and of health in general.

Part of the key to the behavior of the fibroblast can be the amount of UVA radiation that reaches the dermis. Unlike UVB, which has a thousand times more energy than UVA, UVA has a much slower and subtler effect on cells than UVB. UVB often kills cells, or so severely damages their DNA, that they never recover and become cancerous cells. I think we need more effective UVA blockers for protection. A great deal more work remains to be done on the fibroblasts before the answers are known.

Restoring elastin

Everyone needs help in restoring elastin. If skin sags, it needs help; if skin wrinkles, it needs help. Use the back of the hand to perform a very simple test for the condition of elastin. Hold the hand in a neutral position with the fingers only slightly bent, as if you were feeling an infant's head. Then pinch the skin together in the middle of the back of the hand by putting your index finger on the knuckle side and the thumb on the wrist side, pinch tight and let go. The skin should snap back so fast that you couldn't see the movement. If it does, this is good skin. If the movement is slow, you have elastin that needs help. Positive and negative controls can be established by doing the test on anyone under 30 without sun damage and anyone over 60. The position of the hand is critical. If it is too straight, you will get a false bad reading. If it is too curved, you will get a false good reading.

It is known that elastin is produced during our lifetime continuously. It constantly is being degraded and the structure of elastin can be affected by sunlight. From the age of 30 onward, elastin begins to degrade faster so that after 70, much of the elastin is degraded. Why is this so? There really is no answer. All that can be done at this stage is to either try to prevent the damage from occurring, or at least try to slow down the rate of degradation.

Help for aging skin

First and foremost, prevention is needed. Reduction of sun exposure is a must, as well as the elimination of smoking and heavy drinking. These measures will ensure a minimal amount of damage to the body. Next, the internal endogenous free radical damage that occurs from normal respiration and metabolism must be prevented. This translates into reduction of food intake.

These measures are extremely important in any aggressive treatment program. Such a treatment program actually is a defensive measure against the insidious erosion of the cells. In this article, discussion will be confined to elastin and how to prevent the breakdown of elastic fibers. All of this hinges on the control of the enzyme elastase. Elastase is important in stimulating new elastin formation for the construction of new blood vessels, in building connective tissues and in providing snap or resiliency to the skin. The action of elastase is quite complex, however.

The body functions by a series of checks and balances to maintain the internal composition of the body chemistry, a process known as homeostasis. If elastin is broken down, a signal is given to the fibrocytes to produce new elastin. In order to protect the body from excessive breakdown of elastin fibers, there are other proteins that function to decrease the action of elastase, known as elastase inhibitors. One of these is alpha 1 anti-trypsin, which is found in large quantities in the lungs. When this protein is missing or low, such as with cystic fibrosis, the elastin in the lungs is broken down at a fast rate resulting in emphysema. This is a physical condition that is characterized by an inability to take deep breaths and to exhale fully, resulting in poor aeration of the lungs. The tubes that carry the air into the lungs are called bronchioles, and are surrounded with elastic fibers that allow them to contract and to expand. When these elastic fibers are broken down by unopposed elastase, they can no longer contract, so the bronchioles enlarge, fill with mucous and cease to function as air carriers. One all too common example of this condition in adults is smoker's lungs, which is characterized by chronic bronchitis and emphysema, due to the inhibition of alpha 1 anti-trypsin by the tobacco tars.

Stretch marks

Once stretch marks have occurred, about the only procedure that can eliminate them completely is surgery. Stretch marks vary in severity from very mild to quite severe, and they are related to many complex metabolic conditions. Generally, they are worse in fair-skinned individuals and less problematic in dark-skinned individuals.

There is a link between stretch marks and blood sugar levels. Most often, the higher the blood sugar level, the greater the severity of stretch marks.

Estheticians can recommend the use of Retin-A[a] immediately after pregnancy to help lessen the appearance of stretch marks. This won't eliminate them completely, however. The use of alternating electrical current, ranging between 1,500–4,000 cycles

---

[a] A registered trademark of Ortho-McNeil Pharmaceuticals, Raritan, NJ

per second, can be somewhat effective as well. Also, laser surgery by a physician can help diminish the appearance of stretch marks, but this technology is relatively new.

Preventive approach

The preventive approach is to attack the action of elastase, primarily by encouraging the inhibition of elastase through natural means. There are many pharmaceutical companies working on synthetic elastase inhibitors, but there are some very effective ones right now from nature. Help your clients maintain good skin tone by recommending the following courses of action:

1. Use soybean-based cleansing oil—not soap. Soybean oil contains natural inhibitors of elastase.

2. Develop a reasonable exercise program that prevents unnecessary elastin breakdown. Don't jog—walk, sprint, lift weights or do calisthenics instead. Get off your duff and move about more!

3. Increase your intake of proanthanols. You will find these in blueberries, strawberries, spinach and many other foods. Take supplemental proanthanols at a level of 100 mgs a day. Proanthanols bind to elastin fibers and inhibit the action of elastase.[6]

4. Have some type of beans at least two to three times a week. Beans contain elastase inhibitors and are excellent anti-aging foods.

5. Seek immediate help for any inflammatory reaction of the skin, even mild sunburn. Every inflammation will produce an influx of white blood cells to the skin, and white cells are major producers of elastase.

6. Encourage lymphatic drainage on a regular basis. This will produce less inflammation, less venous stasis and less accumulation of intracellular toxins.

7. Use facial products that contain antioxidants and anti-inflammatory agents, such as vitamins E and C, as well as proanthanols. You need a stable source of proanthanol for both topical and oral use. The only one I know is OPC-85,[b] developed in France.

8. Avoid excess iron and copper in the diet. Both are needed, but they should be used carefully.

9. Take an elastin stimulator. There are two new products available that I have tested which work quite well. One is Sincera Tablets[c] and the other is Forever Young[d]. Take two tablets a day. They contain ingredients from marine sources,

---

[b] A trade name of Life Plus, Inc., Batesville, AK
[c] A trade name of Scandinavian Natural Products, Perkasie, PA
[d] A trade name of Life Plus, Inc., Batesville, AK

though the mechanism of action of these products has not been determined. They are classified as food supplements, and are the only substances of this type that I have tested clinically.

10. Finally, if you really are brave and serious, I suggest you shave your face once a month with a razor, just as men do. This will stimulate epidermal growth factor that will then stimulate elastin production. Contrary to conventional wisdom, shaving does not grow hair, as any male who is bald well knows!

Keep up with the literature on elastin and elastase. The number being written is expanding rapidly. Besides the research being carried out on free radicals and mitochondria, I believe elastin research is one of the most important areas for increasing both life span and productivity in later years.

References

1. Ryhanen L and Uitto J, Elastic Fibers of the Connective Tissue, Vol 1 in *Biochemistry and Physiology of the Skin*, Oxford, England: Oxford Press 433 (1983)

2. Grant MF and Prockop DJ, The biosynthesis of collagen, *New Eng J of Med* 286: 174–179, 241–249, 291–300 (1972)

3. Kligman AM, Zheng P and Lavker RM, The anatomy and pathogenesis of wrinkles, *British J of Derm* 113: 37–42 (1985)

4. Kligman LH, Luna's technique, Vol 3 in *J of Dermat* 2: 199–200 (1981)

5. Braverman IW and Fonferro E, Studies in Cutaneous Aging: 1. The Elastic Fiber Network, *J of Invest Dermat* 78: 434–443 (1982)

6. Tixier JM, et al., Evidence by in vivo and in vitro studies that binding of pycnogenols to elastin affects its rate of degradation by elastases, *Biochem Pharm* 33: 3933–3939 (1984)

Chapter 12

The Biological Role of Oxygen

The opportunity to provide a factual account of the role of oxygen in the biological processes is welcomed and the prospect that a great deal of emotional fallout can arise from the subject has been considered. The truth must be told; however, and it is my firm belief that ignorance is the only real danger.

Understanding the role of oxygen is not easy, for its actions encompass several scientific disciplines, most of which are formidable. The rewards, however, are worth the effort because it is a fundamental life process, one that holds the key not only to life in general, but to the aging process. Estheticians are concerned mainly with the health and appearance of the skin, and while the needs and utilization of oxygen by the skin will be discussed, the effects of oxygen on the total body will be covered as well.

Chemistry of oxygen

Molecular oxygen is symbolized by the designation O_2. The "little two" means that two atoms of oxygen form a molecule of oxygen. There is a second form of oxygen called ozone, and it is designated O_3. An **atom** is the smallest unit of any element, and elements are made up of **protons**, **electrons** and **neutrons**. The protons and neutrons are in the nucleus of the atom, and the electrons fly about in orbits around the nucleus.

These orbits actually are energy levels of the electrons, and electrons occupy these orbits according to strict rules of quantum mechanics. A **molecule** consists of two or more atoms.

Whenever the term oxygen is used, unless stated otherwise, it refers to molecular oxygen. While the molecular structure of oxygen is relatively simple, understanding sub-molecular structure is a great deal more complex. The critical fact to know about the structure of oxygen is that the outer orbits contain two unpaired electrons. This property of oxygen makes life on earth possible, but also is the cause of most of the human race's ills. This quality of oxygen makes it a **diradical**, a free radical with two opportunities to create havoc.

Origin of molecular oxygen

In the early days of this planet's formation, there was no molecular oxygen in the earth's atmosphere. Oxygen did not appear in the atmosphere until about two billion years ago when it was formed as a consequence of **photosynthesis**, a process used by plants to convert the sun's energy into food molecules. Using the energy from the sun and carbon dioxide in the air, plants produce carbohydrates. At the same time, photosynthesis splits water and releases oxygen into the air. It is extremely complex and all of the steps involved in this life-giving chemical process still have not been unlocked. Over the millions of ensuing years, the level of oxygen in the atmosphere increased until it reached the present concentration of 20%. Most of the atmosphere is nitrogen, which makes up 70%+ of the air we breathe.

The ultraviolet (UV) energy of the sun can split water as well. The process is called **photolysis**. This takes place when the same high energy of the sun acts on the newly formed oxygen and converts it to ozone. Ozone also can absorb high-energy UV light, which is a good thing, because it protects us from the deadly UV rays of the sun. All ozone comes from the action of UV light on oxygen.

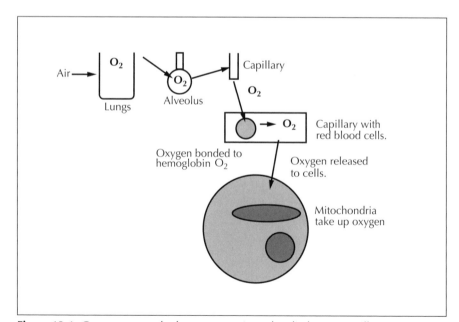

Figure 12-1. Oxygen enters the lungs, passes into alveoli, then to capillaries, is dissolved in the plasma, diffuses into red cells and is bonded to hemoglobin. At the level of the cells, the oxygen dissociates from the hemoglobin and diffuses into the cell where it enters the mitochondria.

Unpaired electrons

Most chemical compounds have two paired electrons in their outer orbit that allow them to react with other compounds in two electron reactions. Since oxygen cannot react with other compounds in this manner, it must react with one electron at a time. The unpaired electrons in an atom or molecule create a chemical compound known as a **free radical**.

The word radical comes from the Latin word *radix*, which means "root." The word radish comes from this same Latin word, and radish is a root. Roots are only part of a plant, not the complete plant. So it is with the free radical; it is not a complete atom or molecule. Something must be added to make it complete. What usually is added is a hydrogen ion or electron.

The breath of life

When oxygen appeared in the atmosphere, most simple life forms died. Oxygen reacted with these life forms and killed them, but some life forms such as bacteria were able to adjust to the presence of oxygen. How this happened is of course unknown, but it was incredibly important for all other life forms that followed the evolutionary trail.

For life to happen, energy must be available in unlimited amounts. All the energy on earth comes from the sun, blazing away 93 million miles in space. Animals can't convert the sun's energy to food—only plants can. We eat the plants, or eat other animals that eat the plants, and then extract the energy locked into the protein, carbohydrates or fats that make up whatever we eat.

This is the starting point of the journey into the metabolism of food and how oxygen plays a critical role in converting food into energy. Oxygen enters the body when we breathe and it is the first step on a long journey.

Biology of respiration

Oxygen is taken into the body with each breath of air. The number of liters of air breathed per minute depends on the size of the lungs and the activity. A liter is a bit more than a quart, and that amount of air contains 20% oxygen. The oxygen passes through the bronchial tubes into the parenchyma tissue of the lungs and then into little sacs called **alveoli**. In these little sacs, the oxygen passes through the thin tissue and enters the bloodstream by way of the capillaries.

Once in the bloodstream, the oxygen combines with the red corpuscle cells and is bonded to a carrier pigment in the red cells. This process turns the blood bright red by forming a compound called oxyhemoglobin. This is diagramed in **Figure 12-1**.

When the oxygen reaches the other tissues of the body, it is released from the hemoglobin and enters the cells of these tissues. Now carbon dioxide, a byproduct of the metabolism of food, is released from the tissue cell, captured by the red cell, and hooked onto the hemoglobin, turning it blue. At this stage it is called carboxyhemoglobin, a blue pigment that accounts for the color of veins. All of this is just the transport system for oxygen going from the air to the cell where it will be utilized to make energy. The easy part is over.

Energy-producing cycle

New biochemistry students usually gasp when they first see the tricarboxylic cycle of Krebs. It is called the **Krebs Cycle**, named after Hans Krebs, a brilliant chemist who unraveled this mystery. The process is diagramed in **Figure 12-2**.

Unfortunately, oxygen has nothing to do with the Krebs Cycle since the Krebs Cycle merely generates a little energy and a lot of electrons to be used later. But look at Figure 11-2 to see that sugar is broken down into two three-carbon molecules by the first metabolic step and these three-carbon molecules are broken down into carbon dioxide and electrons with some adenosine triphosphate (ATP) being produced. Now it's time to enter the real purpose of this chapter—the electron transport system, otherwise known as **oxidative phosphorylation**.

Briefly, this is the mechanism of extracting energy from food. During photosynthesis, the energy obtained from the sun is used to bind atoms together to form molecules. Just as it takes energy to hammer two boards together, it takes energy such as heat, light or in some other form to bind the molecules. Burning wood is an example. When oxygen is added rapidly to the wood, heat and light are the outcome, as well as some water, carbon dioxide and ash. This is a simple example of oxidation or combustion, which is the same process that occurs in the body except that it is under highly regulated controls.

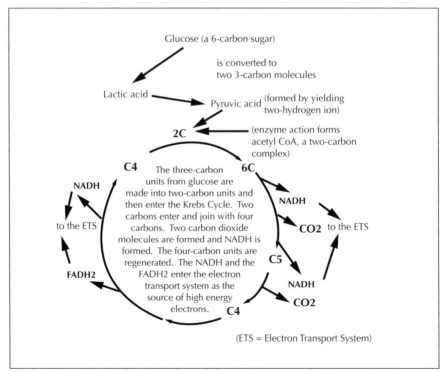

Figure 12-2. Krebs Cycle.

In the final analysis, oxygen is used to burn up food intake and convert it to energy. Again, oxygen is needed to make energy for the cells, and thus for the whole body. One basic fact exists—oxygen is utilized by the cell, specifically the mitochondria of the cell, in a complex procedure to process ATP, the body's energy source. The production of ATP by the combining of electrons with oxygen is the end result of both breathing and eating.

A great mystery

Oxidative phosphorylation and the mitochondria are a great mystery. One of the appeals of mystery stories is the thrill of finding the murderer. The thrill of discovery is the driving force in scientific research. Gossip is related to discovery, and while at the bottom of the pile but still related, its main appeal is in learning something bad about someone else. One never gossips about good things. We are going to raise the hem on the production of energy and learn the very secret of oxygen, deep in the cell.

First, a couple of terms need to be explained. **Oxidation** is a chemical process that involves the loss of an electron, the combination of a compound with oxygen or the loss of hydrogen. Any one of these three is oxidation. **Reduction** is just the opposite process of oxidation. It is the gain of an electron, the loss of oxygen or the gain of hydrogen.

Look at this process as batting a tennis ball back and forth over a net. You hit the ball over the net, losing one tennis ball—you are oxidized. Your opponent receives the ball and is reduced; she hits it back and is oxidized; and when you receive it, you are reduced. Oxidation-reduction goes on constantly in biology, but it needs carriers for the electron and hydrogen. The carriers are called **cofactors** and they work with the enzymes, although they are not enzymes themselves.

Here is an example. Symbolize ethanol, a common drinking alcohol with the notation R-OH. In a shorthand method used by chemists, the R means any other chemical structure. When a person has a few cocktails, the body oxidizes the alcohol and converts it to an aldehyde, which is written as R=O. A hydrogen has been removed. The body does this with an enzyme called **alcohol dehydrogenase**, or hydrogen remover. The hydrogen is transferred to a cofactor called nicotinamide adenine dinucleotide (NAD). The addition of hydrogen converts the cofactor to NADH, the so-called reduced form of NAD. Big deal! One little hydrogen has been transferred from alcohol to NAD and ethyl aldehyde, a compound that gives a person a hangover, was made. Congratulations—you have made a biological oxidation-reduction reaction for the first time.

In essence, this is all there is to it. Perhaps it is a bit more complicated, but really it's just electrons going back and forth. One more bit of information and then the mitochondria will be discussed. Electrons have specific amounts of energy and the molecular orbits are just energy fields. When electrons move from one compound to another, they can lose or gain energy. This is very important to keep in mind. The various energies of electrons can be compared to a series of metal balls at the top of a hill. One ball is two-inches in diameter, another is ten-inches in diameter and a third is two-feet in diameter. If all these balls went rolling down the hillside, which one would you want to clobber you?

Mysterious mitochondria

No one has yet solved the mysterious origin of the mitochondria. These complex organelles in the cellular cytoplasm look like little sausage links. Somehow they entered the cells two billion years ago and changed life's basic processes. It is the mitochondria that supply the energy for the body by making ATP. Food is eaten and broken down into small molecules that are sent to the mitochondria to produce energy and water. See **Figure 12-3** for a summary of these steps. At this point the steps should be described in a bit more detail.

Step 1: Electrons leave the Krebs citric acid cycle. The key point to remember is that electrons are generated in the Krebs Cycle. As the three-carbon molecules resulting from the first stage of sugar metabolism enter the Krebs Cycle, they are metabolized to three molecules of carbon dioxide—just plain old CO_2. Some ATP is generated in the process, but the bookkeeping begins as those electrons that also were generated in the cycle are taken into account. The body can't tolerate electrons flying around without a purpose. The major reason you breathe oxygen is to capture these electrons and at the same time wring from them every bit of energy possible. Step 2 details how this is done.

Step 2: Over the waterfall and in the cytochrome system. In high school physics you probably were bored to tears with kinetic and potential energy studies; you have not escaped it, because here it is again. Consider a waterfall—lovely to look at, yet a powerhouse of energy. As the water falls, it gives up energy until finally hitting the ground level when it has little or no energy left. Some electrons have high energy that can be extracted as they move down an energy gradient, much like the waterfall.

Within the mitochondria there is an oxidation and reduction gradient composed of enzymes called **cytochromes**. When the electrons leave the Krebs Cycle, they first pass to a compound called NADH dehydrogenase complex. This is **Complex I**, which

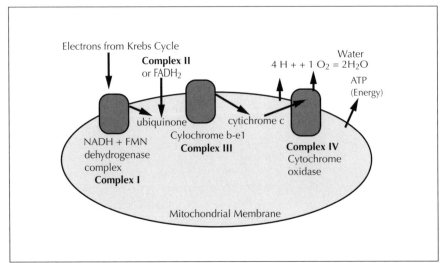

Figure 12-3. Energy and water are produced in the mitochondria.

accepts electrons from NADH produced in the Krebs Cycle. The electrons enter the respiratory chain through a second pathway via a flavin compound. Flavin is a yellow compound found in many plants and in the compound **riboflavin**, a vitamin. The flavin compound is called FADH, which stands for flavin adenine dinucleotide reduced, or $FADH_2$. The $FADH_2$ is called **Complex II**. These electrons are of a lower energy than those that enter at NADH. Regardless of the entry pathway, the next compound to pass is ubiquinone, an electron carrier.

Step 3: In the ubiquinone-cytochrome shuttle. Ubiquinone transfers the electrons to the next major compound in the mitochondria, the cytochrome complex known as the **b-c1 Complex**, or **Complex III**. Here the electrons are passed to another cytochrome known as **cytochrome c**, which is an electron carrier like ubiquinone.

Step 4: The formation of water. Finally, the electrons are passed to cytochrome oxidase, or **Complex IV**, the last complex in the mitochondria, and they combine with oxygen to form water. If all this sounds terribly complex, it is. If you do not understand it you are in good company because no one fully does.

Protons, which are H^+ ions, are pumped out of the mitochondria during this process and as of yet, no one truly understands this process. When the electrons reach oxygen, they have given up 1.4 volts of energy. In the process, the lost energy is converted to ATP. This is the least understood area of the respiratory chain. A theory known as the Chemiosmotic Theory offers a good explanation.[1]

The process of oxidative phosphorylation is diagrammed in **Figure 12-4**.

Different names have been used in literature, as well as in this chapter, for the same process. For example, the **electron transport system**, the **respiratory chain** and **oxidative phosphorylation** mean essentially the same process. The concept of oxidative phosphorylation is more directly referred to as the formation of ATP from adenosine diphosphate (ADP).

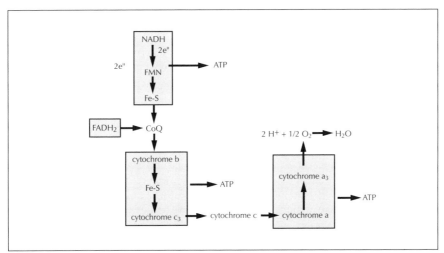

Figure 12-4. The electrons are transported from the Krebs Cycle to mitochondria via NADH. They are transferred to the cytochromes and then to oxygen.

The final use of oxygen, about 95% of what is breathed, is used in this system to produce ATP. The other uses of oxygen are rather small and involve even more complex reactions. Nevertheless, when you say oxygen and energy, you are talking about the electron transport system and oxidative phosphorylation and nothing else. Period. This is the key to understanding oxygen use in life. If anyone offers you an explanation of oxygen use without talking about the electron transport system, or free radical activity, real science is not being discussed.

Recap of the steps

Let's review these concepts to make them a little clearer. Energy comes from the sun, and plants convert this energy into complex carbohydrates and proteins. The energy used to form these compounds is locked into the structure of the molecules. To release the energy, the molecular bonds must be broken. In burning gasoline or wood, the same thing is done to obtain energy for cars or to heat a room. In the body, the safer, but more sophisticated, method to release the energy is a process called **metabolism**.

In metabolism, the complex molecules are systematically broken down and released energy is captured in the ATP molecule. The ATP is made from ADP by transferring high energy from electrons produced in the metabolic process to the ADP. The energy actually is transferred as a high-energy phosphate atom to ADP. Electrons gain energy through a process called the electron transfer chain in the mitochondria. At the bottom of the chain, the electrons have lost most of their energy and are combined with oxygen to produce water.

Think of this process as combustion, the burning of organic matter releasing energy and heat, which requires oxygen. The rest is just complicated biochemistry, but the end result is the same—oxygen combines with the electrons and makes water. You breathe oxygen mainly for this purpose. No oxygen—no energy.

Oxygen utilization

Gases usually are measured in terms of pressure. A mixed gas such as air is measured in terms of absolute and partial pressure. The partial pressure is that part of the total pressure contributed by a particular gas. For example, air has an atmospheric pressure at sea level of 760 mm of mercury. This means it will support a column of Hg, which is the chemical symbol for mercury, 760 mm high in a tube 1 mm in diameter.

Oxygen makes up 20% of the air, so 20% of 760 mm Hg is 152 mm Hg. This is the partial pressure of oxygen in the air. It is written as **PO2**. Why is this important? All of the oxygen you receive is at this pressure and all of the delivery systems of oxygen to the tissues also are based on this pressure. The higher up you go in the mountains or in a plane, the lower the partial pressure becomes and the less oxygen gets into the cells.

The diffusion of oxygen into tissue depends on the health of the tissue, the solubility of oxygen in the body fluids and on the partial pressure of oxygen. In the lungs, the partial pressure of oxygen is 100 mm Hg, and at rest the diffusion rate is 25 ml/min/mm. This means 25 milliliters, about an ounce, will travel one millimeter in a minute. During exercise it will increase to 65 ml/min/mm.

Insects, on the other hand, having no lungs, receive oxygen through their exoskeleton. The exoskeleton is the hard shell on an insect that gives support to the tiny bodies. Small openings in the exoskeleton permit oxygen to diffuse to the tissues, but the diffusion distance is limited to only about 12 mm based on the partial pressure of oxygen in the air. This is why you never see insects larger than one inch in one of three dimensions. They could be a foot long, but never more than one-inch thick or one-inch wide. Oxygen limits many characteristics of life on earth.

Oxygen uses

The major non-biological use of oxygen is in chemical manufacturing. A fair amount still is used in medical therapy, mainly for pulmonary diseases. Since oxygen is a toxic substance, especially when used by untrained personnel, a whole new specialty has arisen in pulmonary disease just to provide inhalation therapy. Oxygen only is used in some cases of hypoxia, which means low oxygen in the blood. Other than in carbon monoxide poisoning, there are four types of hypoxia:

Anemic hypoxia. This condition is characterized by low red blood cells. The patient feels fine at rest, but any exertion brings on difficulty because of the inability of the red blood cells to supply oxygen. Supplemental oxygen does not benefit this condition. It requires the prognosis of anemia and must be treated.

Stagnant hypoxia. This condition is seen mainly in shock due to slow circulation. Again, the cause of the condition must be found and treated. Temporary oxygen treatment is given on occasion.

Histotoxic anoxia. This is a condition seen in poisoning with cyanide. Specific treatments are used and at times, hyperbaric oxygen can be used.

Hypoxic hypoxia. This common condition is caused by a reduction of oxygen in the blood due to pulmonary disease. It is the major indication for inhalation of oxygen. Oxygen usually is given at less than 100% concentration and can be used for several years. It is important that 100% oxygen not be given, which could produce a sore throat, nasal congestion and chest pain in less than eight hours.

Oxygen toxicity

While oxygen is essential for life, it also is toxic. No organism—bacteria, fungi, plants or cultured cells—escapes this toxicity. The parameters for life's use of oxygen has been set down for millions of years and those parameters are narrow. The toxic effects of oxygen are attributed to the production of a superoxide radical, which is a free radical derived from oxygen by the addition of an electron. Superoxide can be converted into a hydroxyl radical, a powerful free radical responsible for most of the cellular damage from free radicals.

Before understanding the free radical concept, oxygen was given freely in clinical medicine for all types of conditions. In distressed newborns, particularly premature infants, oxygen was given as a routine procedure. This proved to be a disaster in many cases, as retinopathy of prematurity, also called retrolental fibropasia, resulted from the oxygen. This condition is characterized by opaque blood vessels forming in the retina, causing serious visual defects and even blindness.

Many studies have shown that life span relates inversely to the amount of oxygen you breathe. High intake of oxygen produces more free radicals, creates more tissue destruction and thus more disorders in the functional capacity of the body. Increasing oxygen beyond the capacity of the body to handle excess oxygen increases the free radicals produced in the body. Free radical production by excess oxygen already surpasses the antioxidant capacity to contain the damage. Many diseases are associated with free radical formation. Here is some information on oxygen and the skin.

Oxygen as a skin treatment

To my knowledge, there are only two uses of oxygen in the treatment of skin disorders. The first is post-operative care in which the skin is pulled tightly enough to decrease the blood supply to the edges of the skin. Supplemental oxygen then can be given by inhalation. The other indication is for hyperbaric oxygen therapy. This requires some discussion.

Hyperbaric oxygen therapy

Administration of oxygen at pressures higher than atmospheric pressure is called hyperbaric oxygen therapy. A special chamber is required to contain the high pressure of oxygen that will vary with the medical condition. High pressure is needed to force the oxygen to dissolve in the plasma, which forces it into the tissues. At 4 atmospheres—four times the normal partial pressure of oxygen—toxicity develops in 30 minutes or less. The symptoms are twitching, ringing in the ears, dizziness, convulsion and coma. With 6 atmospheres, toxicity develops in less than three minutes. Keep in mind that this still is administered through the lungs. Now let's talk about using oxygen as skin treatment in esthetics.

Non-medical uses of oxygen

The skin uses very little oxygen. In fact, it uses only 12.8 milliliters per minute, just a tad over two teaspoons of oxygen, which is only 4.8% of the oxygen taken into the lungs each minute. Every 100 grams of skin uses only 0.3 ml/min. One hundred grams of skin is a lot if you consider only the epidermis, because the dermis uses almost no oxygen.

Let's figure out the size of 100 grams of skin surface. The total weight of the skin in an average human is about 4 kilograms or 4,000 grams, and the surface area is about 1.5 square meters, so 4,000 grams divided by 1.5 m^2 is 2,666 gm/m^2. Since each square meter contains 10,000 square centimeters, 2,666 grams divided by 10,000 equals 0.26 grams per square centimeter. Divide 0.26 into 100 grams and it equals 384 square centimeters (cm^2). How big is that in inches? Roughly, to make it easier, it can be rounded off to 400 cm^2, which is a 20 cm x 20 cm piece of skin. Divide 20 by 2.54 and you get about 8 inches, giving us a skin section 8 inches by 8 inches, or a good part of the upper back, or most of an anterior thigh. This area of skin uses only 0.3 ml of oxygen a minute.

Such a small amount of oxygen does not require the blood supply found in the skin. This tells us that the skin is not an oxygen-using tissue. In fact, it prefers to metabolize without oxygen. Remember that the skin is subject to pressure from many sources, such as sitting or lying down. Pressure reduces the blood flow to the skin, as well as reducing the oxygen supply.

The process of supplying energy without oxygen use is inefficient, but necessary, for the survival of the skin. Terrence Ryan, MD, at Oxford University, observed that the capillary loops supplying the epidermis are rather far from the papillary projections. The significance of this finding is very important. Tissues that are metabolically active, or require large quantities of oxygen and nutrients, have the capillary loops quite close to the cells they serve. Muscle cells are an example of highly active cells. From this it can be concluded that the oxygenation of the skin is of less importance in regards to the blood supply of the skin. The lymphatic flow and the interstitial pressure force appear to be of more importance.[2]

Oxygen therapy

Peroxides. There are two forms of oxygen therapy used by estheticians. One form is peroxides of some type—hydrogen peroxide, zinc peroxide or other basic elements such as calcium. All of these compounds decompose to release oxygen and the hydroxide of the base element. In the case of hydrogen peroxide, the most commonly found oxygen source in cosmetics, water and oxygen are produced. As the oxygen is released, it reacts on the skin surface with anything that it can oxidize. It becomes an effective bleaching agent and a weak germicide on the surface of the skin. But that is all. It cannot penetrate the skin.

Oxygen is a gas, and gas will diffuse into other gases before it will dissolve in anything else. You can't affect anything other than the outer stratum corneum with these topical products. Any claim that oxygen penetrates the epidermis, or goes to the deeper layers of the epidermis, must be highly suspect. It will require substantiation that would stand up under peer review. I have not seen any data of this type to date. All other benefits from so-called oxygen generating products are not based on true science. (See **Figure 12-5**.)

Oxygen as a gas. This form of oxygen therapy is a waste of time and money. Here is why. One molecule weight of oxygen will fill 22.4 liters of atmospheric pressure. No matter how much pressure is in the tank, what comes out will be at atmospheric pressure when it hits the air.

If you spray this oxygen over a face that is dry, what will happen? Nothing. It immediately will go into the air, as oxygen does not diffuse into dry protein. OK, so wet the face. How much will dissolve in water, or whatever fluid used? Under atmospheric pressure, or 152 mm Hg, 5 micro liters of oxygen will dissolve per milliliter of water, written as 5 ul/ml of water. Think about this for a minute; the water you are using consists of 1,000 ml of oxygen in the air or 1 million micro liters of oxygen. How much water can you get on the face at one time? Maybe an ounce, or even two ounces if a cotton cloth was used. Now you have 60 ml of water in which 3 x 60 or 180 ul of oxygen at a maximum can be dissolved.

Of the one liter of oxygen that you have used, you have, at the very best, an opportunity to have 0.180 ml dissolve in the solution on the face. You have wasted 500 times more oxygen. Now here is the sad part. None of that oxygen gets into the skin to do any good. Even if it did, by some unknown law, it still would be of no benefit to the skin because of the skin's physiological makeup.

Summary

Oxygen is an essential element for life. It is maintained in the atmosphere at 152 mm Hg partial pressure. All life on earth has adjusted to this pressure of oxygen and has adapted a use of oxygen to create large amounts of energy. This process, known as **oxidative phosphorylation**, is the major use of oxygen by all life forms. Mitochondria are the organelles in the cells that convert energy stored in food to ATP, the energy source for the body. Using high-energy electrons, the mitochondria transfer the electrons down an electrochemical chain extracting the energy, linking it to ATP and finally passing the electrons to oxygen to form water. As a tradeoff, the benefits of oxygen are counter-balanced by a tendency for oxygen to interact as a free radical and to create other free radicals. A complex system of antioxidants protects the body from these damaging free radicals.

The skin uses very little oxygen since 90% of the metabolic process in the skin is anaerobic, or does not require oxygen. Oxygen does not penetrate the skin at atmospheric pressure or in a solution. The action of oxygen is mainly a surface action; as an oxidant it is an effective bleaching agent and a weak germicide. Gaseous oxygen

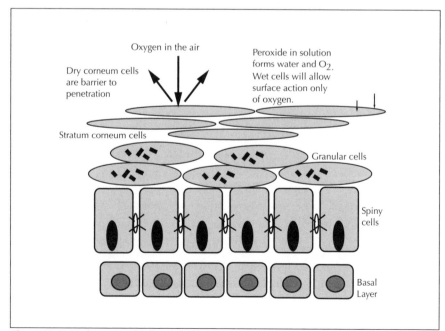

Figure12-5. To have any biological effect, oxygen must reach the living basal layer.

has no basis of use in a topical system since it does not penetrate dry skin and has very limited solubility on wet skin. The medical application of gaseous oxygen is limited and difficult to use. No data exists to support the use of topical oxygen for any non-medical application.

References

1. Mitchell P, Coupling of Phosphorylation to Electrons and Hydrogen by a Chemiosmotic Mechanism. *Nature* 191:144–148 (1961)
2. Ryan T, Exchange and the mechanical properties of the skin: Oncotic and hydrostatic forces control by blood supply and lymphatic drainage, *Wound Repair and Regeneration* 3: 258–264 (1995)

General References

Ackermann U, *Essentials of Human Physiology*, Boston, MA: Mosby Year Book (1992). A good general reference in human physiology and easy to read.

Cadenas E, Biochemistry of Oxygen Toxicity, *Ann. Rev Biochem* 58: 79–110 (1989)

Evans PFD and Naylor NTS, Steady states of oxygen in the human dermis, *Respir Physiol* 2:61–72 (1966/67)

Fridovich I, The Biology of Oxygen Radicals, *Science* 201: 875–889 (1978)

Ganong WF, Respiratory Adjustments in Health and Disease, 18th edition, *Review of Medical Physiology*, Stanford: CT: Appleton and Lange, 638–651 (1997). Medically oriented, but full of useful data.

Stryer L, Metabolic Energy: Generation and Storage, Part III, *Biochemistry*, 4th edition, New York, NY: Freeman, 441 (1995). Excellent, but advanced.

Chapter 13

Immunology and the Skin Care Specialist

Why should a skin care specialist know anything about immunology? As you will learn in this chapter, the immune system is one of the most important defense systems in the body. This chapter introduces the foundation of immunology and a few of its basic concepts.

What is immunology?

The word immune comes from a Latin word meaning "exempt." If you are immune, you are exempt, or free, from something. For example, to immunize a child from a certain disease, such as measles, diphtheria or polio, a procedure called **immunization** is used, which is a series of injections or dosages with a vaccine. The science of immunology is the study of how this process occurs in the body. It is not necessary that you know all the details of this process to appreciate and understand the immune system any more than you need to be a mechanic to drive a car.

Consider that everything outside your body is a potential threat or enemy. The skin barrier prevents the entrance of invaders; the immune system forms a secondary internal backup system to handle invaders that break through the skin. An internal system is needed that provides protection from these enemies. First, it must be able to recognize or identify the enemy; second, it must remember that enemy; and third, it must be able to do something about the enemy when it appears. There are many enemies out there— bacteria, viruses, fungi, bugs, grasses and a host of others. Biologically, these things are called foreign matter. The immune system provides protection from all these things.

The immune system can be defined as a group of special cells in the body that recognize, remember, and react or respond to foreign matter. (See **Figure 13-1**.) These are the three key words needed to understand basic immunology: recognition, remembrance and response.

Recognition

Cells called **macrophages** recognize the foreign matter called bacteria and viruses. The macrophage is important when the foreign invader enters the body. It is the macrophage that engulfs or takes the foreign particle within the interior of the cell and begins to process it. (See **Figures 13-2A** and **13-2B**.)

This cellular processing is very complex, but eventually ends in the particle being placed on the surface of the macrophage cell in combination with another cellular protein substance called a class II Major Histocompatibility Complex (II MHC). II MHC antigens are present on macrophages, B cells and Langerhans cells. They are "recognition molecules" on the surface of the cells.

It is important to appreciate the role of the MHC in the process of cell-to-cell recognition. The MHC is a special type of protein that is specific for each individual. Every cell in the body will have an MHC class I antigen on the cell surface to identify that cell as belonging to that individual. This permits the T cells in the body to separate foreign cells from native cells. *The MHC antigen is responsible for the rejection of organ grafts from person to person unless there is a perfect match of organs*.

The other MHC, known as MHC class II, is found only on the macrophages, lymphocytes and Langerhans cells. The role of the MHC class II is to process and present antigens to other immune cells. Consider the MHC as a badge, or signal of identity among cells to understand the role of the MHC in the immune system.

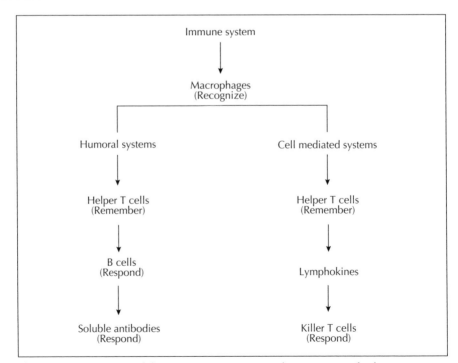

Figure 13-1. Overview of the immune system. Note the two types of sub-systems—the humoral system and the cell mediated system.

The next cell in the recognition process, the helper T cell, now enters the picture. The helper T cell has a special spot on the cell membrane that reacts with the processed particle on the membrane surface of the macrophage. Information is transferred to the helper T cell. (See **Figure 13-3**.) The recognition step is complete.

(*Note:* Somehow the cancer cell escapes the recognition process, and is allowed to go almost anywhere in the body, though it is not known why. If a liver cell, for example, passed into the lungs via the blood stream, it would be destroyed immediately by the immune cells. Cancer cells move about with impunity in a process called **metastasis**, that is, cells gone beyond their normal place in the body. Somehow cancer cells have become a wolf in sheep's clothing.)

Remembrance

Now a new set of B cells must be activated to record a permanent memory of this foreign particle. B cells produce a special protein, called an antibody, that will react to the foreign particle and destroy it. (See **Figure 13-3**.) There are hundreds of thousands of antibodies in the body. The B cells produce very specific antibodies to fight against every foreign particle, or as it is otherwise known, an **antigen**. An antigen is any substance that can produce an immune response. The term antigen will be used, but you must understand the basic concept that the B cell produces antibodies against specific antigens when they are present in the body.

In the immunization procedure, a child receives a vaccine and a low dosage of the virus is introduced into the body. The macrophages ingest or take in the virus. The virus is processed and recognized as an antigen or foreign particle. The processed antigen is presented to helper T cells that further process it and present it to B cells. Now the B cells start to make antibodies against the virus.

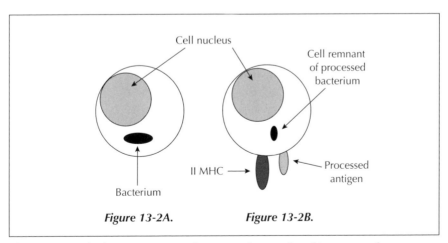

Figure 13-2A.   *Figure 13-2B.*

Figure 13-2A. The bacterium enters the macrophage cell and is processed.
Figure 13-2B. Following processing, the bacterial antigen moves to the macrophage cell surface now connected to II MHC. (They usually are attached, but separated here for clarity.)

The next time the child gets the same vaccine, the B cell remembers this virus so it immediately can go into action and produce more antibodies. In fact, the B cell now divides into many cells of this type just for making antibodies against the virus. This is known as cloning. If a third dosage is required, many more cells and antibodies are made against the virus. Upon completion of the procedure, if the child comes into contact with the virus from the air, the body will be able to destroy the virus and be free from the disease. The child now is immunized.

Response

Every antigen that invades the body causes an antibody to be produced as long as the immune system is functioning. The reaction described above with the immunization is called a **humoral immune response**. This means that only antibodies are produced which attack the invading antigen. These antibodies are called **immunoglobulins** because they fall into a group of proteins in the bloodstream called globulins. They circulate in the bloodstream, are found on the surface of B cells or on the surface of body orifices, and react with any antigens for which they are specific, i.e., produced to fight against.

Immunoglobulins are Ig for short. B cells produce them and there are five types: IgG, IgA, IgM, IgE and IgD. Each of these immunoglobulins has a specific function. IgG is the major serum antibody of the immune system. It can pass through the placenta to the baby and transfer immunity from the mother to the baby. IgM is the first antibody that appears

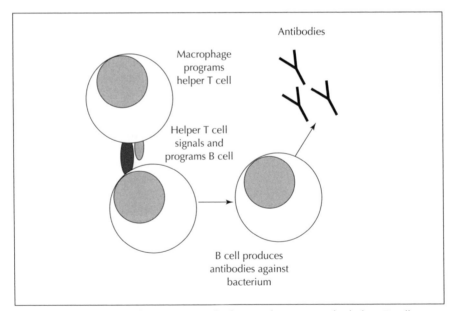

Figure 13-3. *The macrophage presents the bacterial antigen to the helper T cell which in turn "signals" the B cell to produce antibodies against the bacteria. An important concept to remember is each antigen causes one specific antibody to be produced by one selected group of B cells. This is what is meant by the term "antigen specific."*

in response to an antigen. One of its important functions is to activate complement, which is a very complex group of proteins that bind to cells and kill them. IgA is found on many body surfaces and is a first line of defense against many organisms. It is the only antibody in secretions, including mother's milk, tears, saliva and gastric juices. It protects against infection by destroying the bacteria at the surface of the mucous membranes, thus keeping the infection at the initial site, or localizing the infection.

Next, we must look at the **cell mediated (defense) system** which also uses the recognize, remember and respond sequence. This system is called CMI for cell-mediated immunity. (See **Figure 13-1**.)

Helper T Cells have already been discussed. Killer T cells also play a role in this system. The T cells are so named because they come from the thymus gland. These cells are selectively labeled with markers that determine whether they become helper T or killer T cells. The II MHC antigens also have been explained. In this system, I MHC antigens play a role. I MHC antigens are present on all cells in the body and are recognized by killer T cells.

Killer T cells seek out and destroy infected or abnormal body cells that bear specific markers. The process is regulated highly to prevent indiscriminant destruction of normal body cells by killer T cells. Among the requirements are: the killer T cell and the target cell must be of the same genetic type, the target cell must be infected or have some

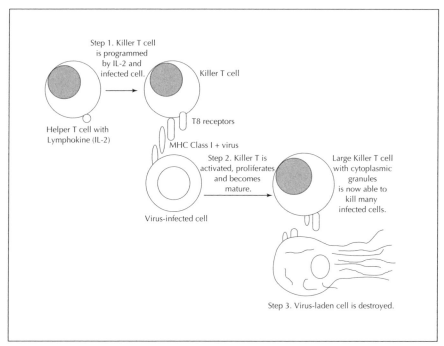

Figure 13-4. In order to destroy a virus-laden cell, the killer T cell must be activated by material lymphokine IL-2 from the helper T cell. Then it must undergo signaling from the virus laden cell. Finally, the killer T cell enlarges, proliferates and destroys the infected cell. The killing step involves cell-to-cell contact.

recognizable antigen on its surface. Finally the killer T cell must be stimulated to act by lymphokine IL-2 from a helper T cell. (See Figure **13-4**.) Without all these conditions, the killer T cell cannot destroy the target cell.

The key role helper T cells play in the immune system has been outlined above. One of the major problems in Acquired Immunodeficiency Syndrome (AIDS) is that the helper T cell is destroyed by the AIDS virus and can no longer function in the immune system.

The skin and immunology

The epidermis of the skin forms a natural defense against the invasion by antigens. It is believed to contain half of the circulating T cells. First there is the stratum corneum, next the lipid layers, the low hostile pH[a] and the Langerhans cell (LC). The reader is familiar with the physical barriers, so we shall concentrate on the LC and immune reactions/responses.

The LC is known as a **dendritic cell** in that it has many spidery projections called dendrites. The second characteristic is the indented nucleus. The third is the Birbeck granule that looks like a tiny tennis racket. This cell also is known as a macrophage since it can ingest and process antigens. Some investigators believe that the LC controls the division of the epidermal cells and is responsible for all types of complex cellular growth.

Once the LC is stimulated, it in turn can activate macrophages in the dermis. The activated macrophages then release a series of compounds that can produce, among other responses, the stimulation of fibroblasts to produce collagen or elastin. These substances are important structural elements of the skin. When the immune system is not functioning well, the effect on collagen and elastin is seen as a delay in wound healing.

In older individuals there is a decreased response in many of the immune functions, and perhaps signs of aging skin is related to this phenomenon.

Future signs

One new approach to skin care is based on the observation that use of a safe immune stimulant known as beta 1,3 glucan is capable of stimulating wounds to heal faster. The application of certain glucans topically has been shown to improve the skin in aging individuals.[b] The process takes four to six months to show a significant change, but appears to be both effective and safe.

Beta glucan works because there is a specific receptor on the dendrites of the LC that stimulates the LC to activate dermal macrophages. Once the macrophages are activated, they set into motion a natural process by activating both fibroblasts and the cells in the blood vessels. This causes new tissue to be generated to replace older and damaged tissue. How this is accomplished is not yet completely understood. This is not a miracle substance, but rather one that takes advantage of the body's natural immune mechanism.

Many new products have come into use over the last few years and there will be many more. It's been learned that many different substances are produced by the

---

[a] Bacteria live best in a high pH environment.
[b] Unpublished work by Peter T. Pugliese, MD

macrophages that stimulate many different types of cells that produce the ultimate result of tissue repair and regeneration.

Recently a derivative of thymus gland has become widely used in the treatment of cancer and immune diseases. A special isolate of thymus gland known as Fraction V is used in injection form but has been used topically with great success as a healing agent and as an anti-aging agent. Many references relate to the use of this substance as having effective anti-aging properties.

Summary

The immune system primarily is a defense system against outside invaders. It also functions as a repair or restorative system when activated by certain immune stimulant agents. This system promises to be an exciting new means of maintaining healthy skin.

General References

Benjamini E, Leskwitz S, *Immunology—A Short Course,* Alan R Liss, Inc., New York (1988)

Bier OG, et al, *Fundamentals of Immunology,* Springer-Verlag, Berlin, Heidelberg (1986)

Christensen OB, Nickel Dermatitis: An Update, edited by Adams RM and Nethercott JR, *Dermatologic Clinics,* Philadelphia, WB Saunders Company, Jan 1990, p 37

Engleman EG, Grumet FC, *Influence of the JLA System on Disease Susceptibility in Dermatology in General Medicine,* 3rd ed, edited by TB Fitzpatrick, et al, McGraw Hill

Holness DL, Nethercott JR, Dermatitis in Hairdressers, edited by Adams RM and Nethercott JR, *Dermatologic Clinics,* Philadelphia, WB Saunders Company, Jan 1990, p 119

Lawley T, Immunoglobulins and Immune Complexes, *Dermatology in General Medicine,* 3rd ed, edited by Fitzpatrick TB, et al, McGraw Hill

Romain PL, Schlossman SF, T and B Lymphoctyes, *Dermatology in General Medicine,* 3rd ed, edited by TB Fitzpatrick, et al, McGraw Hill

Stingl G, Wolff K, Langerhans Cells and Their Relation to Other Dendritic Cells and Mononuclear Phagocytes, *Dermatology in General Medicine,* 3rd ed, edited by Fitzpatrick TB, et al, McGraw Hill

Chapter 14

How Wrinkles Develop

To a large measure, wrinkles were ignored as a serious subject by most scientists until about 35 years ago when scientific articles began to appear on the nature and origin of wrinkles.[1, 2] Since that time there has been some confusion about the definition of a wrinkle. Much like the doughnut hole, do wrinkles really exist?

Recent work has explained much of this confusion. First, consider the definition: "Wrinkles are configuration changes in the skin as a result of mechanical stresses acting on lax and excessive skin ... "[3] This chapter will cover the structure of wrinkles, how they form, what can be done to help prevent them, and finally, explore some current treatment methods for wrinkles.

Skin aging pattern

To form a wrinkle you need loose skin. The process we call "aging" can contribute to laxity of the skin and over time certain physical changes are manifested. At 25, the eyebrows move down over the superorbital ridge of the eye, resulting in a sagging, droopy appearance. There is some intraorbital fat that herniates, or falls down, into the eyelids causing the baggy look of the aged face. The culprit in this process is lax, or loose skin.

At about 30, the nasolabial folds become more prominent as they deepen. At 40, forehead wrinkles appear and crow's-feet are etched at the outer canthus of the eyes. By 50, the outer canthus starts to slope downwards and the nose starts to droop. This is accompanied by the appearance of wrinkles about the mouth and neck. Around this time, the cheeks start to sink in due to loss of fat.

At 60, the eyes seem smaller because of the folded skin around them; there is more fat absorbed in the cheeks and in the chin area. During this period the bones of the skull begin to shrink and more loose skin is produced. From here on, it is a continuing process of fat absorption and elastic reduction that produce the sagging skin associated with many people over 70.

The most obvious place to look for wrinkles is on the face. Here they begin and here they stay, and oh, how we wish they would go away. Consider the anatomy of the facial muscles. Here a clue to the behavior and nature of the wrinkle becomes apparent. **Figure 14-1** shows a complex group of muscles, all of which relate in some manner to facial expressions. Now if the wrinkle pattern is superimposed over these muscles, it is easy to see that the **wrinkles form perpendicular to the long axis of the muscle**. In the case of the circular muscles about the eyes and the mouth, the wrinkle line is perpendicular to a tangent drawn to the curved area. (See **Figure 14-2**.)

At this point it is important to distinguish between a wrinkle and a crease. **Creases are normal folds in the skin that occur at joints and other areas of the body associated with movement and lax skin.** Normal folds occur at all ages and are necessary for normal functions. Wrinkles occur only on sun-damaged skin or aged skin.

Histopathology of wrinkles

Histology is a department of anatomy that deals with the minute structure, composition and function of tissues. It is also called microscopic anatomy. Frequently certain stains or dyes are used to visualize the tissues. Histopathology is the study of

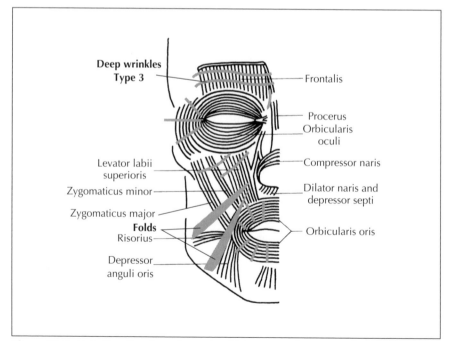

Figure 14-1. Note the direction of muscle. All these muscles are used in facial expressions. The gray shows the direction of wrinkles across the muscles. Normal folds run parallel to muscles.

abnormal tissues using the techniques of histology. When a small piece of skin with a wrinkle is examined under the microscope very little is seen.

In 1969, Wright and Shellow published their results of the histological examination of wrinkled skin and could not distinguish wrinkled skin from normal skin.[2] This finding was confirmed by Montagna and Carlisle in 1979.[4] Recently Kligman and co-workers, in an extensive study of wrinkled skin, were able to find only fine changes in the structure of elastin in wrinkled skin. This finding was so small that it required an electron microscope to detect it. However, the finding was consistent and implicates the elastin fiber as the major culprit in wrinkle formation.

In 1999, a new study by French scientists[5] involving 157 biopsies of 46 subjects between 57–98 confirmed the previous results and shed new light on the pathogenesis of wrinkles in that biochemical studies as well as histological studies were performed. Their findings indicated that significant biochemical changes contributed to the formation of wrinkles. In particular markers of cell differentiation were significantly decreased. Fliaggran, keratohylan granules and the enzyme transglutamase I all were decreased also. These components are essential for the maturation of corneocytes, so there decreased resulted in a thinner epidermis, water loss and defects in desquammation.

At the dermoepidermal junction there was a decrease in collagens IV and VII and a loss of oxytalan fibers, all of which contributed to weakening the interface between these two structures. In the dermis, glycosoaminoglycans were noted to vary in distribution around the wrinkled area, while a marked decrease in chondroitin sulfate

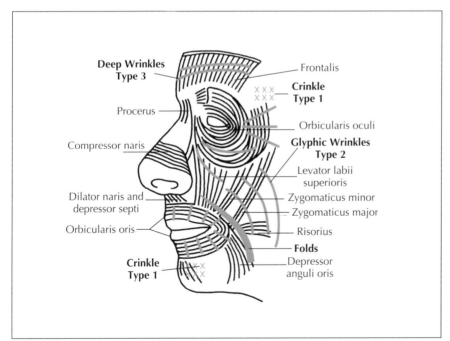

Figure 14-2. Side view of facial muscles used in expression. The gray shows the direction of wrinkles. Crinkles may occur anywhere on the skin.

was noted in the papillary dermis. Taken all of these finding together suggests a primary defect in the fibroblast that make these components. How and why this occurs is another question.

In the first chapter of this book, the basic structure of the epidermis and the dermis was reviewed.[a] Two major components of the dermis—collagen and elastin—were discussed as important fibers that provide strength and resiliency to the skin.

The wrinkle seems to start in the dermis as a change in the elastin structure that causes the elastin to lose its snap, and thus allows the skin to become lax and loose. Skin care specialists who work with aging skin see this as the fundamental problem to be solved before aged skin can be restored and later prevented from becoming flaccid as aging progresses.

Classification of wrinkles

For a body of knowledge to be called a science, it must be arranged in a systematic form called **classification**. So we must classify the types of wrinkles seen in skin. The classification in this chapter is slightly modified from Kligman and co-workers. There are three major groups of wrinkles.

1. *Crinkling-type wrinkle.* These are fine wrinkles formed from folded skin. They usually are seen in persons around 75, and in sun-damaged individuals with post-inflammatory changes in the skin called elastosis.
2. *The glyphic wrinkle.* From the Greek word *glyphein*, which means "to carve," this wrinkle has a crisscross pattern and frequently is seen on the cheeks and the neck.
3. *The deep wrinkle.* This wrinkle forms a major line or deep groove that is long and straight. This is the most troublesome wrinkle because it is so visible and so difficult to eliminate.

Development of a wrinkle

The structure of wrinkles has been discussed and they have been classified. Now let's look at the why and how of wrinkles, and then explore what can be done to help eliminate them.

In **Figure 14-3**, a half face of a young woman and a half face of an 85-year-old woman is shown. The greatest change is in the presence of wrinkles. It can be noted that these wrinkles follow the pattern in **Figure 14-1**. The underlying muscles of the face are attached to the skin by the superficial fascia that sends fibers to the dermis. Both elastin and collagen fibers are present in the superficial fascia and in the dermis. Within the mid-portion of the dermis, the elastin fibers become weak with age, abuse or sun damage, and are no longer able to resist the pull of gravity and the underlying muscles. **Figure 14-4** shows these basic structures and their relationship to each other as well as the connective tissue in these compartments. Finally, **Figure 14-5** shows how the muscle contraction under the skin draws the skin into folds that produce the wrinkles. If all the connections to the muscles were removed, the skin would not form deep wrinkles but would hang loosely from the face. However, crinkling-type wrinkles would remain.

---

[a] A detailed explanation of keratins can be found in Chapter 1, "Behavior of Normal Skin."

Let's put all this information together and pull the bits and pieces into a complete picture. Skin is a composite tissue, consisting of a fibrous matrix containing elastin and collagen. Collagen provides strength to the skin structure and elastin provides the snap or resiliency, allowing the skin to move about and assume conformational changes as required. When the elastin fibers undergo changes that cause them to lose their resiliency or snap, the skin no longer is able to return to its original state. As a result sagging and crinkling occur in a pattern that is called wrinkles.

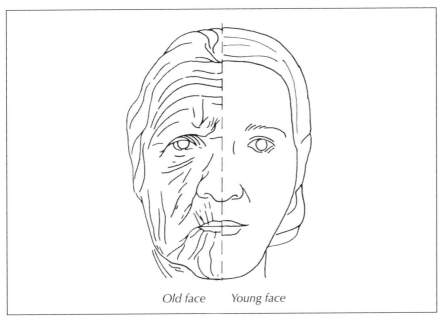

Old face   Young face

Figure 14-3. A comparison.

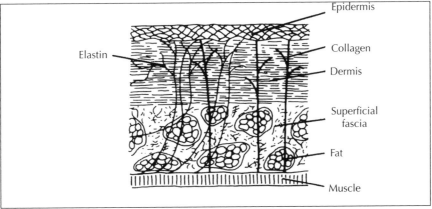

Figure 14-4. Major planes of the skin down to the muscle layer including fibrous components. They are not shown in true anatomical position but this illustrates the connection between dermis and muscle.

There can be crinkle-type wrinkles without muscle involvement, but glyphic wrinkles and deep wrinkles require muscle involvement. This process is accelerated by basking in the sun, by smoking tobacco and other toxins, by drinking alcohol and by being exposed to harmful topical agents.

Causes of wrinkles

Sun exposure. Always the number one bad guy, sun tops the list of causes of damaged skin. The skin must be protected from both UVB and UVA irradiation (that is 280-400 nanometers). The sun's rays denature protein and enzymes, affect deoxyribonucleic acid (DNA) and the total cellular structure which results in profound abnormal structures.

Protective clothing and sunscreens are effective. The use of the proper SPF is important. When in doubt go higher in SPF value. A simple rule—the lighter the skin, the higher the SPF needed. Celtic skin prefers cloudy, wet days, so avoid the sun unless well-protected. Just one really good sunburn is needed to produce the wrinkles seen on the sun lovers, though it will take 15–20 years to show itself.

Smoking cigarettes. One of the best theories on aging is the free radical concept. There is growing evidence that free radicals are one of the major causes of abnormal proteins in the body. The resultant abnormal proteins produce the signs of aging in the various body tissues. Within a single puff of cigarette smoke, there are 1×10^{17} free radicals, that is, one hundred quadrillion, which in turn is ten thousand trillion free radicals—many more than one for every cell in the body. These free radicals bind to our proteins and fats, and cause tissue damage.

Notice that smokers have a yellow hue to their skin and that luminescence is reduced to a dull gray-yellow. Even young girls of 16 and 17 show these signs after six months of smoking. The skin is slow to react to other toxins and as a result, ages faster. If you want to look old at 35, smoking is an excellent way to accomplish this goal. Trying to treat the wrinkles of an individual who smokes is a waste of time and money.

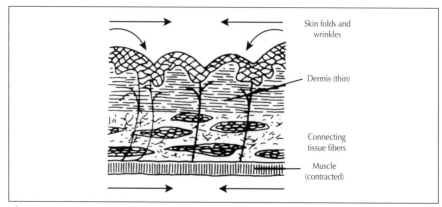

Figure 14-5. Contraction of muscle pulls dermal and epidermal components into folds. Note the reduced elastin content in aging skin allows the dermis to "fall into folds" by modest muscle contraction.

Alcoholic beverages. The effects of alcohol in beer, wine and whiskey are complex and many. Without going into detail it can be said that at a certain level, alcohol is toxic to the body. Alcoholics and habitual drinkers have a very dry, dull yellow skin that shows the ravages of the underlying tissues.

A good, healthy liver can burn up about an ounce of alcohol per hour depending on a number of variables. You can recommend to your client that the limit of one-ounce of alcohol per day is not likely to have adverse effects on the skin. One 16-ounce beer containing 5% alcohol introduces about .08 ounces of alcohol to the system. Above this amount alcohol can be quite deleterious and will obviate most efforts to treat or prevent wrinkles.

Soap-based products. The use of soap has some side effects on the skin. This is true for all skin lotions or creams that are soap-based emulsions. The most common emulsion system used of this type is stearic acid and triethanolamine. This system is used because it is inexpensive and because it forms very stable emulsions. The pH of these emulsions is often above neutrality, often higher than pH 8, which is one hundred times the pH of the skin, approximately 5.5. The pH measurement is a logarithmic expression, so that an increase from pH 5.5 to pH 6.5 is a tenfold increase in acidity, an increase from pH 5.5 to pH 7.5 is a hundredfold increase in acidity.

Soap must remove oil and dirt to clean. Unfortunately it removes lipids, the natural skin oils, at the same time. In addition soap reacts with the keratins[a] of the skin, denatures them and causes them to lose function. This produces the dry, tight feeling associated with soap use. Using soap as the major facial cleansing agent has serious drawbacks. To what extent it adds to wrinkle formation has not been determined exactly, but there is no doubt that it is a contributing agent.

Essential lipids such as linoleic acid and perhaps cholesterol and ceramides will help to protect and restore the epidermis. This action, in turn, provides for a healthier dermis. These agents will help to decrease the size of wrinkles already formed if the continuing damage is stopped. For a deep wrinkle, more heroic measures are needed, but such treatment should be followed with a regimen as outlined.

Physical treatments

Reconstructive surgery is best for deep wrinkles. This should be done early by the best surgeon available. Obtain references from satisfied patients if possible, but make sure in any event that a qualified physician will be performing this procedure. Face lifting is the term commonly used for this procedure, and it is most effective for the repair the sagging skin of the lower face, somewhat less effective for the middle face and not effective for the upper face. This is a subject in itself, so it only can be discussed briefly here. After the surgery a face peel, either by chemical or by dermabrasion, may be helpful.

Facial peels may be deep or superficial. They particularly are helpful around the mouth. Healing takes 10 days or longer, with redness and crust formation. Patients must avoid the sun. Light-skinned individuals are better subjects for this type of procedure than are darker-skinned people.

---

[a] A detailed explanation of keratins can be found in Chapter 1, "Behavior in Normal Skin."

Nutritional support

It's been known that nutrition is important for healthy skin. A diet high in protein and rich with vitamin C is the basis of a good skin care program. Obviously the avoidance of smoking and alcohol are important as well. Calcium and other minerals, along with a balanced B vitamin intake, also is essential to maintain skin. An adequate intake of antioxidants also is helpful, and this includes vitamin E, 250 units/day; beta-carotene, 5 mg/day; and vitamin C, 500 mg/day. In addition 100 mg of niacin can be added three times daily, and 600 mg of calcium at bedtime for people over 40.[6]

Topical treatment and prevention

As people age, changes in the skin are perceived—acne at puberty, hair growth in early adult life and finally the wrinkles of aging skin. However, there are great variations among individuals. Some of these differences are due to genetic causes and others to environmental causes.

With all due respect to manufacturers of skin care products, there is no really adequate line of products for all the skin's problems. Wrinkles are best *prevented* and this requires sunscreen use with added anti-inflammatory and antioxidant agents.

Next those agents that are capable of restoring collagen and elastin by building new tissue should be considered. Here vitamin C is helpful along with bioflavonoids. Bioflavonoids are the unsung heroes of skin care. Vitamin A is essential in very small amounts along with panthenol.

Superficial peels can be done by a trained esthetician using appropriate agents. Superficial peels are most effective on fine wrinkles such as crinkle-type or the glyphic type. They always should be done first on a small area to see the effect on the client. The eye area must be avoided. The agents used most frequently by estheticians for this procedure are resorcinol and salicylic acid in various combinations and concentrations. Proper training in the use of these agents must be completed before using them on clients.

Retinoids. The use of retinoic acid is limited to physicians at this time as the product remains somewhat experimental for the treatment of aging. Retinoic acid is a metabolite of vitamin A which is retinol. Do not confuse retinol with retinyl palmitate and retinyl acetate, which are esters of retinol. (Esters are compounds formed from acids and an alcohol.) You can use retinol in your products and it will give similar, but not exact results as does retinoic acids. The esters of vitamin A are not as strong as retinol on a weight for weight basis.

There are other agents that are being developed that appear to be equally as effective as retinoic acid without its side effects. These products will be available soon for use by professional skin care specialists.

Subdermal and intradermal injections. The use of injectable collagen and silicone placed into the soft tissue by hypodermic needles is a current practice that offers some temporary improvement in small wrinkles and moderately deep wrinkles. The major problem with these techniques is that the collagen is degraded by collagenase and the silicone tends to migrate from the site of injection. These still are viable methods in selected cases and should be explored.

Moisturizers. The use of agents that add moisture to the skin has a long history. Superficial lines will be eliminated briefly with the application of most moisturizers. It is unrealistic to think that permanent improvement can be achieved with these agents. Materials such as hyaluronic acid, elastin and collagen in creams do no more than provide surface moisture and texture changes. There is no direct effect on the dermis by these materials.

Superhydration of the dermis can plump up the skin, but this again is a transient phenomenon. Remember that water flows, evaporates and constantly is in a state of flux in skin. It is not possible to have water immobilized, unless it is strongly fixed to another molecule. However, in this state it does not function as a moisturizer. Current research is being conducted to develop agents that will restore the ground substance[b] in the dermis in an attempt to replenish the water-holding capacity of older skin.

Alpha hydroxy acids. These agents appear to be effective anti-aging and anti-wrinkle products. At present, to my knowledge, there is no completely effective product on the market. This is an extremely exciting area and one that has been explored by many companies.

Summary

I would like to leave the reader with hope. Yes, there is something that can be done about wrinkles; yes, there is much more to learn. Each client must be seen as a unique challenge to our skills and our knowledge; there is no single answer, no single remedy. An accurate assessment of the client's condition, with appropriate referral if needed, followed by a plan of management, usually will result in a satisfied client. Understanding the origin and nature of wrinkles, and what can and cannot be done, must provide the basis for the approach to each individual client.

References

1. Wells GC, Senile changes in the skin, *J Amer Geront Society* 2:535 (1954)

2. Wright ET and Shellow WR, The histopathology of wrinkles, *J Soc Cosmet Chem* 24:81 (1965)

3. Kligman AM, Zheng P and Lavker RM, The anatomy and pathogenesis of wrinkles, *Brit J Dermatol* 113:37–42 (1985)

4. Montagna W and Carlisle K, Structural changes in aging human skin, *J Invest Dermatol* 73 47 (1979)

5. Contet-Audonneau JL, Jeanmaire C and Pauly G, A histological study of human wrinkle structure and comparison between sun-exposed areas of the face, with and without wrinkles, and sun-protected areas. *British J Dermatol* 140:1038–1047 (1999)

6. Ruberg RL, The role of nutrition in plastic surgical practice; a review, *Plast Reconst Surgery* 65:363–370 (1980)

---

[b] A detailed explanation of ground substance can be found in Chapter 1, "Behavior in Normal Skin."

Chapter 15

Biology of Acneic Skin

Acne is a chronic inflammatory disease of the pilosebaceous characterized by macules, papules, pustules and, at times, nodules, cysts and scars. The primary lesion of acne is the comedo. Acne starts most frequently in early adolescence, with females starting earlier than males. Comedones, however, can appear as early as age 8 or 9.[1, 2]

The peak acne years are 14–17 in females and 16–19 years in males. As many as 40% of females and 35% of males are affected during these years. A slow resolution occurs during the 20s, but at least 5% of females and 1% of males still are affected at age 40.[1, 3]

A genetic factor is evident in that identical twins, monozygotic or one-egg twins, are equally affected with the same type of acne while fraternal, dizygotic or two-egg twins, are not.[4] Racial differences indicate Blacks are less affected than Caucasians, and Chinese are more affected than Japanese. Interestingly, when Japanese change to an American-type diet, their incidence of acne increases.

Common wisdom sees acne as a plugged duct in a greasy skin, although the condition is far more complicated. While the basic cause of acne is not known, there is a great deal of information on the pathogenesis. There are four major factors in the genesis of acne: (1) increased sebum production, (2) an abnormality of the microflora of the skin, (3) cornification of the pilosebaceous apparatus, and (4) an inflammatory process. Each of these will be discussed.

Causes of acne

While a great deal is known about acne, the primary cause still is not known. The four areas discussed are but pieces in a larger puzzle; while they help to define some of the acne picture, the whole still remains unclear. Keep this thought in mind as the etiology, or causes, of acne are discussed. The four etiologic factors are **sebaceous glands**; **androgens**; **keratin plugging**, or **ductal hypercornification**; and **bacteria**.

There can be no acne without an active **sebaceous gland**. The role of the sebaceous gland in human skin physiology remains a matter of much speculation. It's known that sebum production is increased in acne patients and that the amount of sebum produced correlates with the severity of the acne.[5, 6] (See **Figure 15-1**.)

Research on the role of male hormones, called **androgens**, in sebum production is extensive, but still not conclusive. That the androgenic balance is disturbed in 50–75% of females with acne is well known, but it does not establish androgens as a causative agent in acne. The relationship of other hormones such as growth hormone to sebaceous gland activity must be considered as well, for little is known in this area. The role of composition of skin lipids must be taken into account. Patients with acne have higher levels of squalene and wax esters with lower levels of free fatty acids. Linoleic acid, an essential unsaturated fatty acid, is much lower in epidermal lipids and comedonal lipids. There is some speculation that this may relate to **ductal hypercornification**.[7, 8, 9]

The comedo

Comedo has an interesting Latin derivation. It is a combined word *con* + *edo*, meaning "with" and "to eat." Used in a Latin context, it means glutton. Why the early dermatologists used the term is a mystery, except that many comedones contain demodex follicularum because they are reputed to feed on sebum. That could explain the use of the word glutton.

One key concept associated with acne is the change in the **pilosebaceous duct**. A review of the structure of the pilosebaceous apparatus is in order. (See **Figure 15-2**.) Note the hair shaft, or pilo; the sebaceous gland; and the duct leading to the surface.

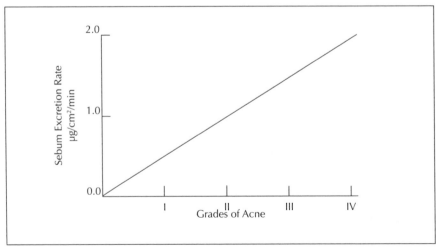

Figure 15-1. *The relationship between the excretion of sebum and the severity or grade of acne. Note the direct, or straight line relationship.*

Next notice that the epidermis lines the whole apparatus. This accounts for the growth of these cells.

Let's focus on the **infundibulum,** Latin for "funnel," which the top of the duct resembles. The infundibulum is divided into the epidermal part at the top and the dermal, or lower part. Notice that this dermal part goes to the level of the sebaceous duct. Here is where most of the action takes place in the formation of a comedo since cornification occurs at the lower level.

There are three types of pilosebaceous canals or follicles—the beard follicle, associated with a coarse long hair; the vellus follicle, which is not associated with acne; and the sebaceous follicle, which appears to be the main culprit in acne.[10] (See **Figure 15-3.**) The sebaceous follicle has a hair so short that it rarely is seen, even in microscopic sections, but it has a very wide infundibulum, frequently seen as a pore on the face.

The outer part of the infundibulum has a thin stratum corneum, very similar to the epidermis with the corneocytes shedding normally. This is the critical location in the follicle where the genesis of the formation of the comedo takes place. The cells of the lower infundibulum are more dense and more coherent. There is much cellular debris and amorphous compacted in the canal. In addition, the cell turnover rate is increased in this area. (See **Figure 15-4.**) In short, the cells appear to be immature and not fully differentiated.[10, 11, 12]

Three major organisms have been associated with acne. These are **P. acnes**, **P. epidermidis** and **Malassezia furfur**. The "P" stands for **propionibacterium**. Just what role the **bacteria** play remains a mystery because acne is not an infectious or bacterial

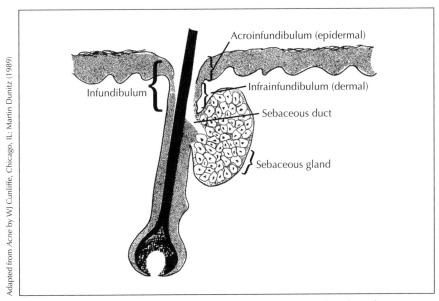

Adapted from *Acne* by WJ Cunliffe, Chicago, IL: Martin Dunitz (1989)

Figure 15-2. Structure of the pilosebaceous apparatus. Note that the sebaceous duct enters the infrainfundibulum, or dermal part of the infundibulum. This is where the abnormal keratin is formed.

disease. By-products of metabolism from the bacteria can produce inflammatory materials that incite the whole process of pustule formation. Injection of P. acnes into cysts causes severe inflammation and rupture of the cysts, while dermal injection of the organism produces only a mild inflammatory reaction. There is no real correlation between the number of skin bacteria and the severity of acne.[13, 14, 15]

Classification of clinical acne

Today there is a generally accepted classification of acne. Dermatologists like to divide acne into many variations, by "grades" and by "types," but for practical reasons a gradation based on the types and numbers of lesions present will be used. (See **Figure 15-1**.)

Grade I: Mostly open and closed comedones with few papules.
Grade II: Open and closed comedones with many papules.
Grade III: Open and closed comedones with papules and pustules.
Grade IV: Open and closed comedones, papules, pustules, nodules and cysts.
Always refer a Grade IV acne client to a physician for treatment.

Nodules are deep-seated palpable lesions that can last eight weeks or longer. They can be red, hard and often painful lesions that develop into softer fluid containing cysts.

Definitions

Cheilitis	Sores at the corners of the mouth
Cornification	Hardening of the cell
Etiology	The causes or origins of a specific disease
Hypercornification	Excessive amount of cornification associated with abnormal thickening of the area
Infundibulum	The top of the duct that is shaped like a funnel
Keratolytic agent	Tends to decrease the thickness of the stratum corneum or horny layer
Microflora	Bacteria or fungus
Pathogenesis	The production or development of a disease
Pilosebaceous	The whole apparatus including the hair, hair shaft and sebaceous gland
Propionibacterium	The specific species of bacteria associated with acne
Teratogen	A chemical or disease that causes malformation of a fetus
Transaminase enzymes	Special enzymes used in protein and amino acid metabolism, frequently associated with tissue destruction and/or inflammation

Cysts always are deep, serious lesions that require referral for treatment. Remember that while individual lesions are discussed, a series of progressive lesions are described. The comedo becomes a pustule or a nodule, which in turn becomes a large pustule or a deep cyst. (See **Figures 15-5** and **15-6.**)

The number of lesions relates to the severity of the acne. Obviously many pustules and papules represent an acute flare-up, while few lesions suggest the condition is quiet or in remission.

Systemic treatment of acne

Physicians speak of topical and systemic treatment methods for acne. Estheticians are limited to topical treatments, except for dietary recommendations. It is important, however, that you are familiar with the types of systemic treatments being used, since you may have a client that is being seen by both you and a physician.

Antibiotics. The major antibiotics prescribed are tetracyclines and erythromycin. The dosage is 1 gram daily given in divided doses 30–60 minutes before or after meals. There is no justification for giving less than a gram a day during active treatment, that can last three months to a year. Of the two drugs, erythromycin is less affected by food. Certain antibiotics combine with food, which interferes with the absorption of the drug. The question of tetracycline interfering with birth control pills seems to be a myth, but the last word has not been written.[2, 16, 17]

Minocycline is more expensive than its parent compound tetracycline. In some acne conditions it appears to be more effective than tetracycline, but it is not the drug of first choice. There are pigmentation side effects with minocycline therapy, brown or blue pigments, which usually disappear when therapy is stopped. Photosensitization always is a problem with the tetracycline-type drugs.

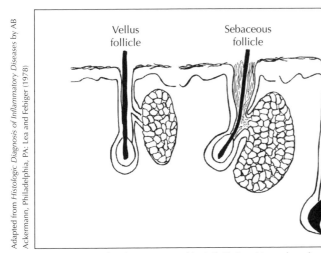

Adapted from *Histologic Diagnosis of Inflammatory Diseases* by AB Ackermann, Philadelphia, PA: Lea and Febiger (1978)

Figure 15-3. *The three types of hair follicles. Note that the sebaceous follicle has a large glandular portion and a smaller hair. This is the type of follicle associated with acne.*

Doxycycline is another tetracycline variant that can be taken on a once-a-day dosage. Two other antibiotics being used to treat acne are co-trimoxazole and trimethoprim. These drugs are used in resistant cases of acne and in special types of acne. Clindomycin, or cleocin, also is used as a system drug.

Just how antibiotics work in acne is not known. While the action is anti-microbial against P. acnes, it may be that the anti-inflammatory effects of the antibiotics play an important role. The reduction of bacteria reduces the inflammatory by-products. The antioxidant effect of the antibiotics must also be taken into account.[18, 19]

Hormones. Hormone therapy is used only in female acne patients who have not responded to conventional treatment. For reference only, they are: Estrogen plus prednisolone, a cortisone-type compound; estrogen plus cyproterone; and spironolac-tone. These agents are used for three to four months in combination with topical treatment. The results are slow to appear; being evident after six weeks or more of therapy.[2]

The use of cortisone-like agents with estrogen is to suppress the male-type hormones, called androgens, produced by the woman's adrenal glands. A side effect of acne hormone therapy is similar to those seen with birth control pills. Spironolactone is not a birth control pill and is associated with menstrual irregularities and pigmentation side effects. Anti-androgens also are used, one of which is cyproterone.

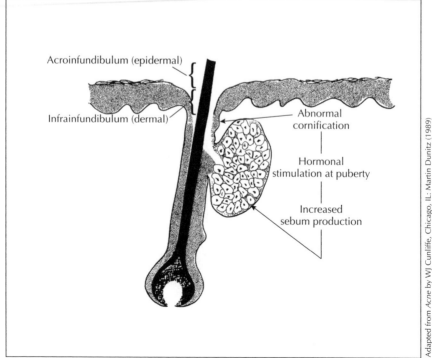

Figure 15-4. The pathogenesis of acne. Hormonal stimulation at puberty affects both the secretion of sebum and the cornification of the duct.

Isotretinoin. Isotretinoin (Accutane,[a] 13-cis-retinoic acid) has been one of the major breakthroughs in acne treatment in recent years. It has helped many acne patients who were considered as hopeless. It is important for the esthetician to be familiar with the use and side effects of this powerful drug. Isotretinoin is a variation on the vitamin A molecule, but it is not the same as retinoic acid or Retin-A.[b] Retinoic acid is a topical drug, while isotretinoin is a systemic drug.

There are three indications for isotretinoin treatment:

1. Physicians will vary in their selection of patients for isotretinoin treatment, but the most common indication is severe acne. This condition need not be described in detail since you will be aware of the term. Cysts, widespread inflammation and large pustules make up a sad clinical picture.

2. Failure to respond to conventional therapy or relapsing after successful treatment with conventional therapy.

3. A patient with Gram-negative folliculitis. This is a condition caused by Gram-negative bacteria usually associated with long-term treatment of acne. It is one of the most common reasons for clinically resistant acne.[2]

---

[a] Trademark of Hoffmann-LaRoche Pharmaceuticals, Nutley, NJ
[b] Registered trademark of Ortho-McNeil Pharmaceutical, Raritan, NJ

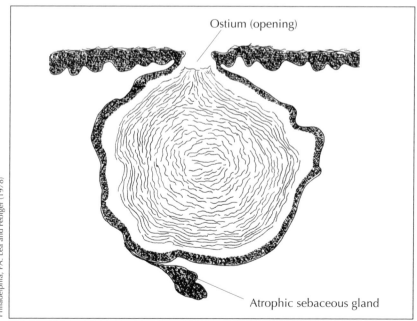

Adapted from *Histologic Diagnosis of Inflammatory Diseases* by AB Ackermann, Philadelphia, PA: Lea and Febiger (1978)

Figure 15-5. *The closed comedo. This nodule could develop into a cyst. The opening may not be visible without the aid of magnification. Note the squashed sebaceous gland. The hair follicle is obliterated completely by the size of the gland.*

Contraindications for use of isotretinoin. Isotretinoin is a known teratogen, causing multiple birth defects. Female patients of child-bearing age must use reliable birth control measures. A pregnancy test is mandatory before use of isotretinoin. After therapy is discontinued, there should be one or two normal menstrual cycles before pregnancy is planned.

Side effects of isotretinoin. Side effects of isotretinoin can be mild or severe. Everyone on this drug will expect to have some side effects. Major side effects are:

1. Cheilitis, sores at the corners of the mouth, 90% of patients;
2. Chapped, flaky skin, 90% of patients;
3. Dry nose and eyes, 80% of patients;
4. Loss of hair, 10% of patients;
5. Painful joints and painful muscles, 15% of patients;
6. Excessive peeling of the palms and soles, 10% of patients;
7. Elevation of triglycerides in the blood, 25% of patients; and
8. Abnormal liver function tests, especially the transaminase enzymes, 15% of patients.

Isotretinoin is taken for three to six months, but the side effects can last even one to two months after treatment is stopped. The good part is this: most patients respond well on this drug and there is a very low incidence of relapse after a course of treatment.[2, 16, 17]

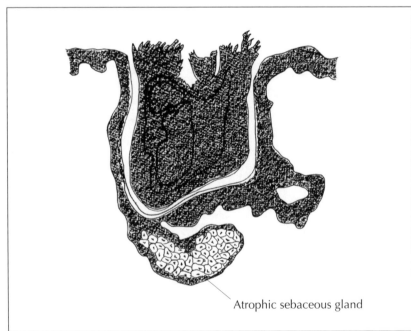

Atrophic sebaceous gland

Adapted from *Histologic Diagnosis of Inflammatory Diseases* by AB Ackermann, Philadelphia, PA: Lea and Febiger (1978)

Figure 15-6. *The open comedo. This is the type with a black surface that is then termed a blackhead. The hair follicle is completely obliterated by the size of the gland. Note the sebaceous gland is less squashed.*

Topical treatment of acne

There almost are as many topical treatments for acne as there are clients with acne. Generally, the therapeutic methods can be divided into three major categories: those that reduce sebum, those that reduce cornification and those that reduce inflammation.

To reduce surface sebum. Facial cleansing twice daily with gentle surfactants reduces surface sebum. Scrubbing with abrasives is not indicated and only can do harm. There is no evidence that these abrasive agents will remove comedones or in any way benefit the removal of sebum. In fact, it is my opinion that harsh stimulation of the skin surface will only increase the proliferative rate of the epidermis and thereby increase the degree of hypercornification in the comedo. The use of antiseptics in cleansers is not supported with convincing evidence. There is a list of unproven germicides in acne preparations on page 260 in Cunliffe's text on acne.[2, 24] I prefer liquid cleansers with an acid pH that consist of mild detergents rather than alkaline soaps.

Oddly enough, oil-based cleansers can help to suppress oil secretion in acne.

The only known topical agent that is proven to suppress sebum to my knowledge is the hormone cyproterone. This is a prescription item and not used in the United States.[20] Again, as with many new acne treatments, this method is controversial.

To reduce cornification. Much has been said in esthetics about exfoliation and the benefit of exfoliation in acne. The process of exfoliation is complex and has different meanings to various groups treating acne. Essentially exfoliation relates to the process of increasing the rate or degree of cells lost from the stratum corneum. Since the pilosebaceous duct is lined with stratum corneum, these cells are affected by any process that contributes to exfoliation. Agents that have been used are:

Benzoyl peroxide: Proven effective for more than 20 years of use, this chemical appears to work mainly as an anti-microbial agent.[21] The reduction in inflammation must account for some of the benefit. Many commercial forms are available. Side effects are mild, but the agent will bleach clothing.

Retinoic acid (Retin-A): Retinoic acid is a prescription-only item that has been used as an acne treatment for at least 20 years. The action seems to be diverse: keratolytic effects, reduction in comedogenesis and reduction in P. acnes, all contribute to the effectiveness of this product.

Salicylic acid: Salicylic acid is used widely in over-the-counter products and is an approved drug for acne treatment. The effect seems to be primarily keratolytic in mild cases of acne. Concentration ranges from 2–5% in creams and lotions. Commercial agents that use salicylic acid include Fostex[c] and Listerex Golden Lotion.[d] Some products combine salicylic acid with sulfur, but it is questionable if the combination is more effective than salicylic acid alone.

Azelaic acid: This product, a relative newcomer to the acne treatment field, still is in the experimental stage. This compound is termed a dicarboxylic acid and first was

[c] Trade name of Westwood Pharmaceuticals
[d] Trade name of Warner-Lambert

used as a depigmentation agent. Clinical trials with azelaic acid have shown it to be as effective as benzoyl peroxide or retinoic acid.[22] At present I know of no commercially available products in the United States. There are no known serious side effects.

To reduce inflammation. All of the above agents plus topical antibiotics shall have to be listed. The topical prescription-only antibiotics most commonly used in the United States are tetracycline, erythromycin and clindamycin. The action of these agents appears to be purely anti-microbial.

Ethyl lactate is a relatively new agent used in acne treatment to suppress the growth of P. acnes. The lactate is metabolized to lactic acid by the bacteria that lowers the surrounding pH to pH 3, a very hostile environment for P. acnes. Confirmation of this finding is needed.[23]

Finally, there are many products commercially available that have not been shown to be effective in the treatment of acne. The work by Mills and Kligman [24] is a landmark study in this area. This article is referenced whenever a choice of treatment product is made.

Treatment program for estheticians

The esthetician is in the best possible position to treat acne. What is lacking is an effective, clinically proven, product treatment program. There are so many products available to the esthetician, but so little data to back them up, that the esthetician often is left to trial-and-error selection. The outlined program is only a suggested one. Throughout the years, many estheticians have developed effective programs to treat the acne-afflicted client, but this is one that can help, or at least add to your program.[25]

1. Client education is first. Make sure that your clients know they are in for a long treatment period of two to ten years. Explain the condition in detail. Provide hand-outs. Explain the grades of acne. Immediately refer any clients with severe acne to a physician.

2. Plan your program to quiet down the inflammation first. This means reducing pustules and papules. Recommend twice daily cleansing with gentle surfactants and opening small pustules followed by a topical treatment with 5% benzoyl peroxide. See the client in one week. Do a facial cleansing, avoiding any heavy, greasy products. Check to see if the pustules are gone and the papules reduced. Weekly visits help before the condition begins to respond to treatment. Exfoliating masks can be helpful if they are not greasy. Use clay masks with herbal extracts, particularly those with chamomile, linden, meadowsweet and hibiscus.

Use essential oils only if you have both training and experience in this area. Essential oils only have anecdotal data to support their use in acne treatment. I know of no valid clinical study using essential oils in acne, though in theory they should work well in some cases.[25]

Do not massage the acne face; it is not helpful and may be harmful.

3. After you have quieted down the inflammatory reaction, you are ready for extractions. A mild sodium bicarbonate solution of 1–2% applied over the face before extraction is helpful. Sometimes a surfactant can be added to the

bicarbonate solution. These are available from some suppliers. Use a good comedo extractor. Do not use excessive force. Be very careful around the nose. It is best to wear gloves when you extract or open pustules.

4. Recommend benzoyl peroxide for home use; once or twice daily is enough. Supportive treatment is helpful. Watch diet and food intake. Caloric reduction rarely hurts anyone and it may help the acne client. Foods high in vitamin A and C are beneficial. Continue to provide emotional support and encouragement. These are positive forces that estheticians do so well.

5. The use of evening primrose oil can act as an anti-androgen, but it must be used topically as systemically it does not work to suppress sebum.

References

1. Burton JL and Cunliffe WJ, The prevalence of acne vulgaris in adolescence. *Br J Dermatol* 85: 119–126 (1971)

2. Cunliffe WJ, *Acne*. London, England: Martin Dunitz (1989)

3. Cunliffe WJ and Gould DL, Prevalence of acne in adolescence and in adults. *Br Med J* 1: 1109–1110 (1979)

4. Walton S, et al, Genetic control of sebum secretion and acne. A twin study. *Br J Dermatol* 118: 393–396 (1988)

5. Burton JL and Shuster S, The relationship between seborrhea and acne vulgaris. *Br J Dermatol* 84: 600–601 (1971)

6. Pochi PE and Strauss J, Sebum production, casual sebum levels, titratable acidity of sebum and urinary 17 ketosteroid excretion in males with acne. *J Invest Dermatol* 43:383–388 (1964)

7. Ebling FJG, et al, Interrelationships between body hair growth, sebum excretion and endocrine parameters. *The Prostate* 5:347–348 (1984)

8. Kanaar P, Lipolysis of skin surface lipids of acne vulgaris patients and healthy controls. *Dermatologica* 143:121–129 (1971)

9. Kellum RL and Strangefeld KE, Acne vulgaris: studies in pathogenesis. Fatty acids in human surface triglycerides from patients with and without acne. *J Invest Dermatol* 58: 315–318 (1972)

10. Shuster S, et al, Epidermal lipid biosynthesis in acne. *Br J Dermatol* 103: 127–130 (1980)

11. Strauss JS and Kligman AM, The pathologic dynamics of acne vulgaris. *Br J Dermatol* 5082: 779–790 (1960)

12. Woo-Sam PC, Cohesion of horny cells during comedo formation. *Br J Dermatol* 97: 609–615 (1977)

13. Marples RR, The microflora of the face and acne lesions. *J Invest Dermatol* 62: 326–331 (1974)

14. Leyden JL, et al, Propionibacterium levels in patients with and without acne vulgaris. *J Invest Dermatol* 65: 382–384 (1975)

15. Puvhel SM and Sakamoto M, An in vivo evaluation of the inflammatory effects of purified comedonal components in human skin. *J Invest Dermatol* 69: 401–406 (1977)

16. Reeves JRT and Maibach H, *Clinical Dermatology Illustrated, A Regional Approach*, Baltimore, Maryland: Williams and Wilkins (1986)

17. Hunter JAA, et al, *Clinical Dermatology*, London, England: Blackwell Scientific (1989)

18. Cunliffe WJ, Evolution of a strategy for the treatment of acne. *J Am Acad Dermatol* 16: 591–599 (1987)

19. Van Baar HML, et al, Tetracyclines as potent scavengers of superoxide radical. *Br J Dermatol* 117: 131–134 (1987)

20. Burton JL, Anti-androgen therapy in dermatology-a review. *Clin Exp Dermatol* 4: 501–507 (1979)

21. Cunliffe WJ, *Acne Update Postgraduate Series*, London, England: Update Publications (1981)

22. Nazzaro-Porro M, et al, Beneficial effects of 15% azelaic acid cream on acne vulgaris. *Br J Dermatol* 109: 45–48 (1983)

23. George D, et al, Ethyl lactate as a treatment for acne. *Br J Dermatol* 108: 228 (1983)

24. Mills OH and Kligman AM, Drugs that are ineffective in the treatment of acne vulgaris. *Br J Dermatol* 108: 371–374 (1983)

25. Pugliese PT, *Advanced Professional Skin Care*, Bernville, Pennsylvania: APSC (1991)

Chapter 16

Sun-related Skin Disorders

Sunlight has some positive effects on people. Sun exposure produces and maintains vitamin D in the body. A bright sunny day gives people a psychological boost after gloomy days. However, there are negative consequences as well.

There no longer is any question that prolonged exposure to the sun can produce skin disorders. Except for the production and maintenance of vitamin D, and perhaps a psychological lift after dark, rainy days, there is no known health benefit to sun exposure. The biological effects of the sun on the skin were discussed in Chapter 8. In this chapter the signs of the most common skin disorders associated with sun exposure will be discussed.

Prime candidates for sun-related skin disorders are those who work outdoors, the sunbather and the outdoor sports enthusiast, who are careless about or purposely do not use sunscreens.

In a book of this type an exhaustive treatment of the subject is not possible. As skin care specialists, recognize those skin conditions that must be referred to a physician for evaluation and treatment. Since you will not treat any of these conditions, it is sufficient if you recognize the lesion as abnormal and potentially serious. Do not be concerned about an exact diagnosis, for many physicians must await a histological examination of a biopsy from the lesion by a pathologist to establish a correct diagnosis. A biopsy is a surgical removal of tissue from the lesion. It may be either a small section of the lesion or the entire lesion. The skin disorders discussed in this chapter should be referred to a dermatologist.

Skin color and the sun

White-skinned individuals are more prone to the sun-related disorders than dark-pigmented individuals. With white skin the disorders mainly are found on the head, neck, arms and hands. With dark-pigmented skin, the covered areas are more frequently involved and the exposed areas seldom involved. Blond hair and blue eyes predispose to a greater response, or susceptibility to effects of sun exposure. Individuals with red hair and green eyes are even more prone to skin disorders than any other group. **Skin-type Classifications** lists the current classifications of skin types used to group sensitivity to sun exposure. This is only a guide. Most Type I and Type II individuals will have pale skin, blue eyes and may or may not have freckles. Some individuals with brown hair and blue eyes also burn as Types I and II.

Classification of sun-related disorders

The biological effects of the ultraviolet light (UV) coming from the sun produce both acute and chronic changes in the skin. The more serious changes are associated with chronic exposure. The most common acute change is sunburn, which can have long-term effects.

Acute sun damage or sunburn. Sunburn is easy to recognize. Erythema or redness occurs, sometimes with swelling and blistering. Pain is a frequent symptom. The pattern varies greatly. Most of the redness is seen on the forehead and cheeks as these areas require less ultraviolet energy than the legs, arms or hands to become red. It takes about four times the UV dose on the hands compared to the head to produce redness. No area can be free of sunburn, however, if the sun reaches it.

The clinical signs of sunburn represent an acute inflammatory reaction to the UV energy absorbed by the cells of the skin. The redness is due to vasodilation of the sub-papillary vessels rather than the dilation of the papillary capillaries in the papillary dermis.

The time course of sunburn also is variable. Fifteen to thirty minutes of sun exposure

Skin Type Classifications

Skin Type	Working Classification	Physical Characteristics
I	Always burns easily, never tans, extremely sun sensitive skin	Red-haired, freckles, Celtic, Irish-Scots
II	Always burns easily, tans minimally, very sun sensitive skin	Fair-skinned, fair-haired blue-eyed, Caucasian
III	Sometimes burns, tans gradually to light brown, sun sensitive skin	Average skin
IV	Burns minimally, always tans to moderate brown, minimally sun sensitive	Mediterranean-type Caucasian
V	Rarely burns, tans well, sun insensitive skin	Middle Eastern, some Hispanics, some Blacks
VI	Never burns, deeply pigmented, sun insensitive skin	Blacks

at noon is enough to produce a burn in many light-skinned individuals. Occasionally an immediate tan will appear, only to fade in a few minutes to an hour. Freckles are intensified in some individuals. The immediate tan is due to photo-oxidation of melanin. This is followed by a gradually deepening tan over the next three to four days and is due to the formation of melanin. Pigmentation is followed by peeling of the stratum corneum. Itching is a frequent symptom at this stage.

Sunburn can be distinguished from most other erythemas by history of recent sun exposure and the classical signs. Only rarely does sunburn require medical attention. Cold compresses relieve the pain and soothing lotions help the sting. Aspirin can benefit the client by slowing down the inflammatory reaction. Remember that sunburn has a heavy physiological cost, though the full price may not be paid for 20 years.

Polymorphous light eruption (sun allergy). Polymorphous Light Eruption (PLE) is an exceedingly interesting, but complex condition. It is called polymorphous, or having many forms, because of the many lesions associated with this disorder. The condition arises with sun exposure plus some related cause such as a drug or systemic disease. Other terms include photodermatitis and phototoxic.

The most common drugs associated with PLE are tetracyclines; psoralens; thiazides, or water pills; and sulfa drugs, but there are many others. A comprehensive list of drugs is included in *Dermatological Photobiology* by I. A. Magnus. The most common systemic diseases are lupus erythematosus, dermatomyositis and porphyria. These are complex and serious systemic conditions for which the patient most likely is under some form of medical treatment.

The rash of PLE is variable but it is seen on the forehead, nose, the malar eminences or zygomatic arch (cheek bones), upper lip, ears, sides and back of neck, the V area of the upper chest, and the backs of the arms and hands. The rash is not seen on shaded areas, such as the hair bearing scalp, eyelids, areas under the brow, lower lip and the shaded area of the chin. In all cases referral to a physician is indicated.

PLE further can be distinguished from sunburn by history and often by the age of the patient. Sunburn occurs mainly in younger individuals, while PLE occurs more often in people over 30.

Solar urticaria (sun hives). Solar urticaria is a sign of photosensitivity and is rather rare. About half of the cases are associated with some other systemic condition, but the other half have no known cause. The first sign after exposure to UV rays is an immediate erythema with itching and burning. This is followed in a few minutes by a welt or hive-like response. The pattern can be continuous, covering the erythematosus area, or there may be discrete small hives over the whole red area. The immediate onset of erythema and the appearance of hives distinguish this condition from all others.

Chronic sun-related skin disorders

The chronic skin disorders are those conditions, or lesions that result from long exposure to UV light, or that develop after many years of exposure to UV light. There are two basic groups: cancerous and noncancerous. The cancerous group is divided further into melanomas and non-melanomas. The cancerous group will be discussed first as this is the most important group to identify as early as possible. Any time a lesion is seen that even remotely resembles a malignant condition, refer the client to a physician.

Cancerous or malignant group

Squamous cell carcinoma. This is the second most common skin cancer. It occurs chiefly on the exposed areas of the face and hands and lower legs. Pre-malignant conditions such as solar keratosis, a non-cancerous disorder, can give rise to squamous cell tumors.

The appearance can be a warty-type plaque or a nodule, or a raised ulceration with rolled edges above the surrounding skin. Since these lesions arise from the keratinocytes, they will produce keratin and corneocytes. This hyperkeratosis can be crumbly or in the form of a cutaneous horn. The lesion generally is soft and friable, or easily crumbled, and can ooze or bleed. (See **Photo 16-1.**)

Basal cell carcinoma. The most common skin cancer. It most frequently is seen in the elderly and most often in exposed areas of the skin. Clinically, it has a more varied appearance than a squamous cell tumor. There are five types of basal cell carcinoma.

- Nodulocystic type is the most common form of basal cell cancer. It occurs most often on the face as pearly, translucent nodules of varying size, but up to 2 cm in diameter. The nodules can have flecked brownish black pigment associated with them, but the major characteristic is that they are tense and shiny. (See **Photo 16-2.**)

- Ulcerative type, or rodent ulcer, at one time thought to be a rat bite, has raised and rolled margins with a depressed ulcerative center which often oozes. This type frequently is seen near the nose, and the tumors usually are long-standing.

- Pigmented type is a nodular variation with a few, or many, pigmented areas, often so uniformly pigmented that they represent the appearance of a melanoma. (See **Photo 16-3.**)

- Superficial type most commonly is seen on the trunk or the limbs. The appearance is a slightly raised, red, scaly lesion that may resemble psoriasis. The margins are well defined. These tumors can be quite large, sometimes reaching 15–20 square centimeters.

- Morphoeic type is a thickened, pale, firm patch with tiny pearly papules at the border. It often resembles scleraderma, which medically is called morphoea in the United Kingdom. In the United States, it can be termed sclerosing or scarring basal cell cancer. (Page 185, R. Marks.)

Melanomas. These are pigmented lesions arising from melanocytes. They do not occur on sites of great sun exposure, except for lentigo maligna. There is evidence that they are, nevertheless, related to UV light exposure because they are most frequent in geographic areas with high sun intensity. The most frequent site of occurrence is the back in males and the thighs in females. In dark-skinned individuals, melanomas occur on the palms and the soles of the feet. They tend to occur in the prime of adult life. The ABCDs of melanomas are:

Asymmetry—not equally round or oval.
Border irregularity—notching, scalloping or poorly defined margins.
Color variegation—shades of brown, tan, red, white or blue/black.
Diameter—greater than 6 millimeters, about 1/4 of an inch, though earlier melanomas are smaller.

There has been an increased incidence of melanomas over the last 15 years.

- Lentigo maligna accounts for 30% of melanomas. The typical lesion is a dark macule, or discolored flat spot, usually of long duration, on the face of an elderly person. The edges are poorly defined, irregular and indistinct. This lesion ranges in color from tan to brown, black and even hypo-pigmented. It eventually can form into a nodule and become invasive. (See **Photo 16-4**.)

- Superficial spreading melanomas account for about 50% of melanomas. They appear as slight elevated plaques anywhere on the body. The edges are irregular with blurred pigment extending into the surrounding skin in various shades of brown, black or white. There can be a rim of pink inflammation, and the surface of the lesion can be fragile with bleeding and oozing. This lesion progresses from small plaques to an invasive nodule over a period of 6-24 months. (See **Photo 16-5**.)

- Nodular melanomas account for 20% of melanomas, but they also are the most malignant form. They arise as a papule or nodule that can bleed easily. The edges of the lesions are well-defined, but are irregular. The color may be blue-black or brown. They tend to grow upward and downward rather than to spread laterally. Nodular melanomas are highly invasive and rapidly spread throughout the body. Women are more often afflicted than men on a 2:1 ratio. (See **Photo 16-6**.)

- Acral lentignous melanomas are darkly pigmented flat to nodular lesions on the palms, soles and under the nails. This is an uncommon disorder.

Non-cancerous disorders

Actinic keratosis (solar keratosis). This is a pink, red or fleshy papule with an adherent white, gray or yellow layered scale. It occurs on areas of the skin frequently exposed to the sun such as the face and arms of fair-skinned individuals. While it rarely becomes malignant, actinic keratosis can develop into squamous cell carcinoma. At times the scale, or scab, will fall off but reforms, and it is painful to remove the scale prematurely.

Solar lentigo (liver spot). This is a flat, well-defined tan or brown spot with a distinct border. Occasionally slight scaling can occur. Solar lentigo varies in size from 2–30 mm. Usually it occurs on the forehead and temples, and the back of the hands and arms of middle-aged and elderly individuals. There is no malignancy associated with this condition.

Actinic damaged skin (solar elastosis). A result of long sun exposure, this is characterized by involvement of many layers and structures in the skin. The skin is discolored, from patchy gray to yellow brown, a color associated with solar elastosis. There is a parchment-like quality to some areas of the skin particularly the hands and the face. Many lesions are seen on the face and hands. Deep wrinkles and sagging skin further characterize this condition.

Overall appearance is a dry scaling skin with many pigmented lesions such as freckles, lentigo and hypo-pigmented spots, called guttae hypomelanosis. Telangiecgtasis, a profuse network of dilated capillaries, is present with an easily bruising skin. Many milia and large blackheads, or comedos, especially are seen around the eyes.

Keratoacanthoma. This is a fast-growing nodule seen on the sun-exposed areas of fair-skinned adults. It starts as a small slightly keratotic papule that rapidly develops a keratotic core with a fleshy rim. The core frequently falls out leaving a fleshy nodule. This condition usually resolves itself in about three months. These lesions usually are one centimeter in diameter, but can reach three or four centimeters.

Conclusion

The training to recognize skin lesions is lengthy and requires many repeat exposures to the various types of lesions to achieve modest skill. The general rule followed by physicians is this, "If you don't recognize it, refer it." You undoubtedly will see all of these common lesions resulting from sun exposure over a 20-year period. You will derive great satisfaction from recognizing a lesion, referring the client and participating in the after-care program. Remember that the specialty of the physician is the study and care of abnormal skin. As such, the physician is your ally, not a competitor. Both disciplines can be mutually beneficial in a cooperative vein.

References

Only general references are cited. For readers who wish to pursue this topic, the following references will serve as a good starting point:

Regan JD and Parrish JA, eds, *The Science of Photomedicine*, New York: Plenum Press (1982). Technical, but well worth reading.

Magnus IA, *Dermatological Photobiology*, London: Blackwell Scientific Publications (1975). An excellent first book on this topic.

Reeves JRT and Maibach HI, *Clinical Dermatology A Regional Approach*, Baltimore: Williams and Wilkins and Associates PTY Limited. This is an excellent pictorial reference with a workable classification of the many common skin disorders.

Fritzpatrick TB, Eisen AZ, Wolff K, Freedburg IM and Austen KF, *Dermatology in General Medicine* Third Edition, New York: McGraw-Hill (1987). This is a two-volume set with many articles in great detail. It is available in most hospital and university libraries.

Marks R, *Disease in Old Age*, Philadelphia: JB Lippincott (1987)

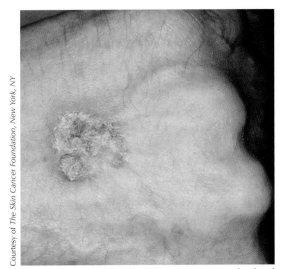

Courtesy of The Skin Cancer Foundation, New York, NY

Photo 16-1. *Squamous cell carcinoma on the back of the hand.*

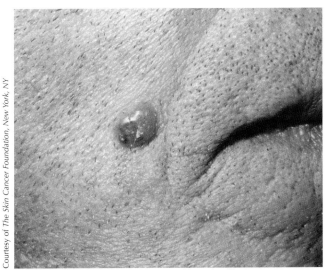

Courtesy of The Skin Cancer Foundation, New York, NY

Photo 16-2. *Nodulocystic type of basal cell carcinoma.*

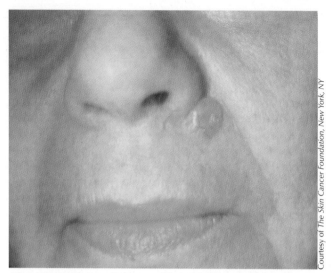

Photo 16-3. Pigmented type of basal cell carcinoma.

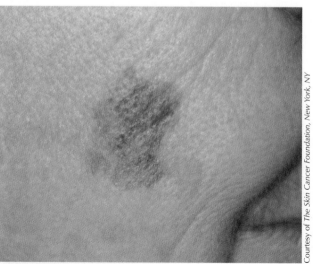

Photo 16-4. Lentigo maligna melanoma.

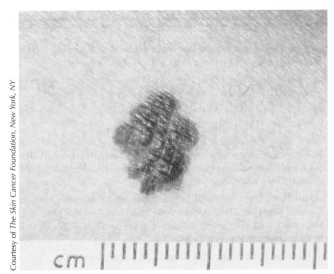

Photo16-5. *Superficial spreading melanoma.*

Courtesy of The Skin Cancer Foundation, New York, NY

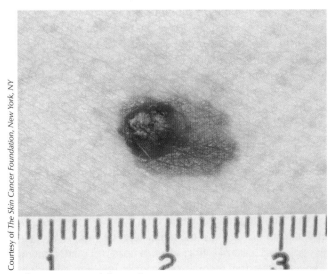

Photo16-6. *Nodular melanoma.*

Courtesy of The Skin Cancer Foundation, New York, NY

Chapter 17

Systemic Lupus Erythematosus

Why write about systemic lupus erythematosus for estheticians? Because it is part of human nature to minimize any physical condition, except in the case of individuals who are hypochondriacs. Most of us want to hear only good news. The bad news really is intended for the other person.

This can happen at skin care salons with clients who come in for treatments. You notice a "skin rash" that the client will want to be told "is nothing." In most cases it is nothing, but from time to time a serious condition is seen that requires expert medical treatment. As a skin care specialist you should be aware of the most serious conditions, such as cancerous lesions, but there are others—almost as serious—that also require your awareness.

One of these is a disease known as **systemic lupus erythematosus** (SLE), one of a complex group of immune disorders. The purpose of this chapter is to bring the disease to the attention of estheticians so that there is an awareness and understanding of it. As estheticians, you should be able to refer clients to a physician for diagnosis and treatment if there is reason to suspect the disease. By being informed about this disease, you also can participate in the continuing care of the client with the physician.

The origin of the disease's name is a combination of Greek and Latin terms. The word lupus is the Latin word for "wolf," and the word erythematosus is a combination of the Greek word *erythema*, meaning "a flush upon the skin," and the suffix *osus*, meaning "a process, condition or state."

SLE originally was named from the facial appearance of the first patients seen with this disease. Because of the rash that can appear on the face, the disease most likely was confused with another condition known as lupus vulgaris, which shares some, but not all, of the physical characteristics of SLE.

Incidence

SLE is not as common as other, better known, diseases such as pernicious anemia or leukemia. It generally is agreed that women are afflicted with SLE eight times more often than men, and that the disease is three times more common in blacks than in whites, particularly in young black females in America. For some reason, it is not as common in black females in Africa. Chinese and New Zealand Polynesians have a rate four to five times as high as whites throughout the world. The actual rate is unknown because of ethnic and geographic variations, but somewhere between 2.4–12 cases per 100,000 women can occur annually on a survey basis. For those readers who are interested in the epidemiology, or cause of SLE, there are many excellent references available.[1, 2, 3, 3A, 4, 5]

The condition

SLE is an autoimmune type of disease. This group of diseases includes rheumatoid arthritis and rheumatic fever, and shares some common features. The chief characteristics of this group are:

1. Each disease involves the immune system.
2. The body's immune system attacks native body tissue.

The cause of the condition remains unknown, but there are many theories and much research has been conducted over the years. Most authorities now believe the condition probably has a genetic component that predisposes the individual's immune system to the disease. It would be this underlying factor that allows both environmental insults, such as ultraviolet (UV) light, and endocrine, or hormone, abnormalities to initiate the disease. As a result, the manifestations of SLE involve many organs, as shown in the **Figure 17-1**.[6, 7]

Clinical signs of SLE

The presenting symptoms are the initial, or first, symptoms that cause the patient to seek help from a physician. With SLE, 58% of patients experience joint pain, or so-called articular pain, first. About 13% first visit a physician with a cutaneous complaint, or a rash, and 80–90% of patients with SLE eventually develop skin lesions. Fever is present in 90% of patients, but fatigue; kidney disease; inflammation of the tissue covering of the lungs, pleurisy, or the covering of the heart, pericarditis; abdominal pain; and Raynaud's phenomenon also can be present early in the disease. Raynaud's phenomenon is a blood vessel disorder that is characterized by intermittent bouts of blue to white discoloration of the fingers, toes, nose or ears, and is associated with cold weather or emotional stress. These symptoms are of less importance to the skin care specialist since they are so serious that the client would, most likely, have sought the advice of a physician beforehand.

Because of the variability of signs, symptoms and laboratory findings in the autoimmune diseases, physicians needed some standard by which they accurately could diagnose SLE. The American Rheumatism Association uses a number of findings to establish a diagnosis of SLE. A patient having four or more of the conditions listed in the **American Rheumatism Association Criteria for SLE** usually is diagnosed as having the disease. There are three conditions that affect the skin—a malar, or facial rash; discoid rash, a coin-shaped rash that appears on the head and neck; and photosensitivity, a sensitivity to the light or sun.

Other possible conditions that do not result in skin manifestations include oral ulcers, canker-like sores in the mouth; arthritis, painful inflammation of the joints; serositis, an inflammation of the serous membrane associated with a fluid-filled joint; renal disorders, problems associated with the vascular portion of the kidney; neurological disorders, associated weakness of the nervous system; hematologic disorders, blood-related disorders associated with a wide range of problems such as low iron, low hemoglobin and abnormal red cell count; immunologic disorders, over- or under-reacting to any type of stimulus that would create an immune response; and antinuclear antibody, a disorder found through the testing of the white blood cells and a characteristic found in many immune disorders.

I will focus on the skin manifestations of the disease, which make up the first three criteria. Many of the others are very complex medical conditions that require a deeper

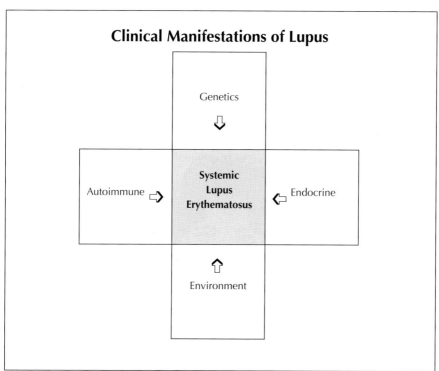

Figure 17-1. The multiple causes of **systemic lupus erythematosus**. *Most research scientists studying lupus now accept this multiple-cause theory. There is an underlying basis in the immune system that is generic in origin, and a precipitating cause in the environment and in the hormonal makeup of the individual.*

understanding of pathology and clinical medicine. As noted previously, skin manifestations occur in 80–90% of patients with lupus. These skin manifestations will be discussed in detail. Keep in mind that as an esthetician, frequently you will see the signs of SLE before anyone else. You also should be aware of the symptoms that the client can have along with the skin manifestations. If you see any suspicious-looking lesions, ask the client about the presence of fatigue, the most common symptom, and joint pain.

Clinical findings

Major dermatological findings related to SLE include:

Malar rash. The word malar comes from the Latin word *mala*, which means "cheek." It was the appearance of the malar rash on this area of the face that gave the name lupus to SLE, since it resembled the facial markings of a wolf. The classical finding that occurs frequently is the butterfly rash. If you look closely at the zygomatic arch—the area under the eyes, above the mouth and extending over both cheeks—you have described the wings and body of a butterfly. (See **Figure 17-2**.)

The butterfly rash is red and covered with fine scales. The redness can be a continuous blush, or appear as fine, discrete maculopapules, which are flat, red spots or bumps.

Edema can be present, particularly if there was recent trauma, such as an extraction of a tooth. Also, look on the neck for similar lesions. (See **Figure 17-3**.) The lesions can extend to the palms, the back of the hands, the back and the legs. Look for a bluish-red discoloration of the lesions on the hands, with small whitish areas of scarring. Changes in the nails occur in about 25% of patients with hyperkeratotic and ragged cuticles. Tiny splinter-like hemorrhages occur in the nails, along with pitting, ridging and white streaks.[8, 9, 10, 11]

Figure 17-2. A representation of the major characteristics of the butterfly rash. Most often it reaches to both sides of the face over the bridge of the nose, and extends into the neck. The shape and color of the rash will vary greatly from person to person.

Purpuric lesions are purple, flat lesions of varying shapes up to one centimeter in diameter that can be seen individually or clumped together. When lesions are grouped and touching, they are called confluent. Another sign is a bluish-red discoloration in the form of a network of veins that blanches on pressure but is not affected by temperature changes. It is called **livedo reticularis** and occurs most frequently on the outer aspects of the arms.[12]

You also can find that hair changes are common in conjunction with alopecia, the loss of hair that occurs in more than 50% of patients. The hair can be coarse and dry, and the frontal area quite fragile, which leads to short, broken-off unruly hairs. These symptoms represent the so-called "lupus hair" that occurs in about 30% of SLE patients with alopecia.[13, 14]

SLE can present different manifestations with the various races. For example, in Chinese individuals, thick heavy skin that looks very dry can be seen on the trunk, as well as on the arms and legs. These lesions also can be pigmented and frequently are grouped together. In addition, wide-spread coarse scaling, known as **ichthyosis**, and warty growths can appear on the knees and elbows.[15] With SLE, the esthetician must bear in mind that variable presentations of the disease, rather than the classic presentation, are the rule.

Discoid lupus erythematosus (DLE). This is another form of lupus and must be differentiated from SLE. While both require medical treatment, a diagnosis of SLE requires a lifetime of treatment. DLE is less serious and the process can undergo remission.

Characteristically, DLE lesions are found most often on the head and neck, and are circumscribed, coin-shaped or discoid, with hyperkeratosis and follicular plugging. The centers of these lesions are de-pigmented, while the periphery is hyperpigmented; central atrophic scarring occurs as these lesions progress. The scalp, ears and central

The Lupus Foundation of America, Inc.

Figure 17-3. Photograph of a person with acute systemic lupus erythematosus presenting with the butterfly rash. Note that the rash has irregular edges but the intensity of the erythema is fairly uniform over the entire rash, which is continuous rather than discrete as in discoid lupus.

face most frequently are involved, but other areas can be affected. Alopecia occurs on the scalp and is long-lasting or permanent. Hands and feet are involved at times, particularly the back of the hands and the sides of the toes, with the palms and the soles involved in only about 6% of cases.[16, 17] (See **Figure 17-4**.)

The differential diagnosis of lupus is difficult, even for experienced dermatologists, so don't be discouraged; these conditions are complicated. For the esthetician, the two most common conditions that must be distinguished from lupus are **seborrheic dermatitis** and **rosacea**. Here are a few pointers that can help to diagnose the right condition. I stress, though, that if you ever are in doubt, you must refer the client to a physician.

Seborrheic dermatitis involves the nasolabial folds and has a tendency to manifest itself on hairy regions of the body such as the scalp, eyebrows, eyelids, ears, chest, axilla, groin, buttocks and skin folds. The lesions are bilateral and usually symmetrical in distribution, have indistinct margins, and yellow greasy scales. Hair loss is uncommon in seborrheic dermatitis. Seborrheic dermatitis is caused by the yeast-like pityrosporum, the same organism that causes dandruff.

Rosacea is a chronic inflammatory disease of the blood vessels and the pilosebaceous glands of the face. The classical findings are **telangiectasia**, or cuperosis, and **erythema** with papules and pustules. Pustules are an important clue to this diagnosis. The disease seems to spare the lateral face, affecting only the central third. There usually are no comedones, which separates it from **acne vulgaris**.

One other possible diagnosis can enter the picture, and that is photo-dermatitis. This is actually a group of disorders related to sun exposure, and includes photo-allergy, photo-toxic reaction and polymorphus light eruption. Let's take a look at these conditions, because they frequently enter into a differential diagnosis of SLE.

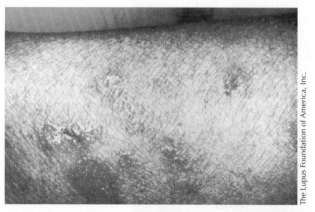

The Lupus Foundation of America, Inc.

Figure 17-4. A lesion of discoid lupus. Note the light color of the center of the lesion, which is devoid of pigment and scarred, while the edges are red and pigmented. In discoid lupus, the lesions usually are not confluent as they are in SLE.

Photosensitivity and other conditions. The photosensitivity disorders also are called light or sun sensitivities, and are divided into two major groups: those caused by known agents, and those with unknown causes, the so-called idiopathic group. The known group can be caused by external agents or internal agents. I won't go into great detail on these conditions because they are complex and present a topic that deserves a separate chapter. You should be aware of them, however. Here is the general classification:

Idiopathic types (causes unknown). **Polymorphus light eruption** is the most common of the idiopathic group, occurring in young adults after several hours of sun exposure, but rarely days later.[18] This appears as itchy papules, nodules, papulovesicles and plaques. Its course is usually chronic and progressive.

Solar urticaria (sun hives). This condition occurs mainly in women in their 40s and 50s, and appears within seconds to minutes after sun exposure. The condition is self-limiting and usually resolves spontaneously within a few hours.[19]

Exogenous photosensitizer (external causes). **Photo-toxicity** reactions can take place following the use of a particular drug and subsequent sun exposure. They can occur in anyone using such drugs as tetracycline, thiazide or water pills, quinidine, griseofulvin and many others.

Photo-allergy. This condition occurs only in individuals who previously were sensitized to a particular photo-allergen, such as sunscreens and perfumes. Both of these disorders are present as inflammatory reactions, but photo-toxic reactions usually are acute, with edema and erythema, as one often sees in sunburn. Photo-allergy usually shows some vesicular eruptions along with itching and redness. The clinical picture is quite variable for both of these conditions; however, and to a large extent you must rely on the history of drug intake or use of the allergen in question. These are acute rather than chronic disorders.

Endogenous photosensitizers (internal causes). **Porphyria** is a heritable or acquired disorder of heme synthesis. Heme is a compound used in the synthesis of hemoglobin, cytochromes and other critical compounds in the body. The basic defect in porphyria is an enzyme deficiency that causes an accumulation of metabolic intermediate compounds, which in turn are oxidized to **porphyrins**. It is the porphyrins that are the cause of the inflammatory response, since they absorb sunlight and undergo photo-toxic changes. There are two major types of porphyria: **porphyria cutanea tarda** and **erythropoietic protoporphyria**.

It is not necessary to memorize all of this information; just keep in mind that when you see a skin condition that looks like SLE, other possibilities can exist.[20, 21]

Precipitating factors

There are four major factors that can precipitate SLE. Remember that the underlying disease is present within the body but is either inactive or latent. One of these factors frequently will cause the disease to become manifest with one or more symptoms. The four factors are: UV radiation; infections, stress and hormone factors; viruses; and drugs. Let's look at these factors and see how they impact on SLE.

Ultraviolet light radiation (UVR). UVR is well-known to either precipitate or exacerbate SLE, though the mechanism is unknown. Surprisingly, there is no defect in deoxyribonucleic acid (DNA) repair, a major site of UVR damage; nor is there any correlation to denatured DNA antibodies and the clinical severity of the disease. The take home message is, keep out of the sun![22, 23, 24]

Bacterial infections. These types of infections are not handled well by patients with SLE, probably related to the reduced white blood cell function. The stress and hormonal factors can relate to the neuroendocrine factors that play a role in immunity, since normal humoral and immune responses are greater in females; this can tie into the sexual difference in incidence of SLE. Females with SLE have reduced levels of circulating androgens, while men with SLE have reduced levels of testosterone, the major male androgen.[25, 26, 27, 28, 29]

Viruses. For many years, these have been suspected as a cause of SLE. Myxovirus-like structures have been found in patients with SLE and in patients with kidney disease, but not in normal individuals. A virus, however, has not been isolated or found, though viral particles could be a definite cause of precipitation of SLE in predisposed subjects.[30, 31, 32]

Drugs. Drugs are known to precipitate SLE, particularly those, such as **hydrallazine**, used in the control of high blood pressure. An interesting aspect of drug-induced SLE

Drugs Inducing an SLE-like Syndrome

Allopurinol (used in gout)

Clofibrate (used in heart disease)

Gold salts (used in arthritis)

Griseofulvin (used to treat fungus infections)

Hydrallazine (used in high blood pressure)

Ibuprofen (Advil[a] and Motrin,[b] used to treat pain)

Methyldopa (used to treat high blood pressure)

Minoxidil (used to treat high blood pressure)

Oral contraceptives

Para aminosalicyclic acid (PAS)

Penicillin

Phenylbutazone (used to treat joint pain)

Reserpine (used to treat high blood pressure)

Tetracycline (an antibiotic)

[a] Trade name of Whitehall Laboratories, New York, NY
[b] Trade name of Upjohn Co., Kalamazoo, MI

is that it differs from the spontaneous disease in several ways: it is uncommon in blacks, more common in older people, DNA antibodies are absent, and kidney and central nervous system involvement is infrequent. I can't list all the drugs that have been known to precipitate lupus, but many common ones are listed in **Drugs Inducing an SLE-like Syndrome**.[33, 34, 35, 36] The importance of keeping up-to-date client history records can't be stressed enough. Accurate records will play an important role in determining your clients' treatments and at-home care.

Treatment

Now that you are aware of SLE's characteristics, consider treatment and what you can do as a skin care specialist to help the SLE patient.

The physician's responsibility is to keep the patient's disease under control and in remission, while your role is to keep clients attractive and happy. In the 20 years that I practiced clinical medicine, I saw only four women with SLE, all of whom were young and attractive and quite heroic. The treatment by physicians is complex, for it must take into account the multifaceted nature of the disease and all the organ systems that can be involved. Drugs that could be used include corticosteroids, cytotoxic agents and anti-malarial agents, all of which are potent chemical agents.

The client can go through a series of drastic changes, lose some or all hair, suffer depression and exhilaration from the cortisone, and have a cluster of skin manifestations. It would be wise and appropriate to inform the client's physician that you are helping with the care. In most instances the physician will welcome the help, because SLE treatment can extend 20 years or more. Vigorous and persistent treatment with strong, supportive care goes a long way to restoring the client to a relatively normal life.

Do's and don'ts

Caring for clients with SLE requires both knowledge of the disease and attention to details in the treatment. Hair care should be given special consideration since the hair can become dry and brittle during SLE and can fall out at various times. The positive approach is to treat these clients as you would other clients, except take extra care during treatments because of their underlying disease.

All types of skin stimulators should be avoided. This means no alpha hydroxy acids, no skin peels, no enzymes and no abrasives should be used during a treatment. The skin will be reactive to these agents. Use low detergent or soap-free cleansers, preferably oil-based. The use of oil-based cleansers will help moisturize the dry SLE skin. Gentle massage is fine, but be careful with heat. Use it sparingly. Moisturizers should be safe to apply; however, while many excellent products used by estheticians contain natural plant materials, some of these should not be used on clients with SLE. I have compiled a list, **Plant Materials—Sensitizers and Irritants**. Also, take note of **Cosmetic Ingredients—Irritants and Sensitizers**.

Remember that these are ingredients used by millions of people every day. The incidence of reaction is small, but for those who are allergic or sensitive to these agents, the reaction is serious.

Common Plant Materials—Sensitizers and Irritants[38]
(Listed in order of sensitivity)

Angelica—Scientific name *Angelica archangelica*. Angelica contains powerful phototoxic agents called psoralens. It contains both 5 methoxy and 8 methoxy psoralens. ***Do not use this plant material on clients with SLE.***

Celery oil and leaves—Scientific name *Apium graveolens* L. While safe for most of us, this seemingly innocuous plant contains psoralens and limonene. Included in this group are carrots, parsley and parsnips, all of which contain psoralens. ***Do not use this oil on clients with SLE.***

Ginkgo tree—Known as "ginkgo"; scientific name is *Ginkgo biloba* L. The plant contains two allergens, or sensitizers: bilobol and ginkgolic acid. It is interesting that ginkgolic acid is salicyclic acid with a long carbon side chain.

Mango tree—Scientific name *Mangifera indica* L. The mango tree contains powerful sensitizers known as urushiol and cardol in the leaves, stems, wood and pericarp of the fruit. Two other possible sensitizers, common to citrus fruit, are found in mangos; namely, beta-pinene and limonene.

Ylang Ylang—Scientific name *Unona odorata Dunal*. This oil contains geraniol and linalool which are known sensitizers. Cananga oil cross reacts with ylang ylang sensitive individuals. If you are not familiar with cananga oil, it is an inexpensive substitute for ylang ylang and comes from Java.

Anise—A fragrance that comes from the plant *Pimpinella anisum* L. Anise contains anethole as a sensitizer. Star anise also contains anethole and safrole.

THE COMPOSITAE FAMILY[38]

This is very large family of plants, all of which cannot be covered in this chapter. Fortunately this group prefers to sensitize men for some reason, rather than women or children. I shall use only the common names of these plants since most users are familiar with the common names rather than the Latin names. The major ones include:

Yarrow, ragweed, feverfew, pyrethrum (Chrysanthemum subgroup), tansy, cardoon, sunflower, ox-eye daisy, chamomile (both English and German), black-eyed Susan, dahlia, dandelion and marigold. The offending chemicals are too numerous to mention here, but the use of any of these agents in any form of oils or concentrates should be avoided in clients with SLE.

Common Plant Materials—Sensitizers and Irritants[38]
(Listed in order of sensitivity)

SOME OLD FAVORITES THAT MAY YIELD PROBLEMS:

Lavender oil—Scientific name *Lavandula latifolia* L. There have been reported cases of sensitization, but no known allergen has been identified. The oil contains linalool and geraniol, both of which have been known to sensitize some individuals.

Mint—Scientific name *Mentha piperita* L. Mint contains carvone and menthol, which have not been known as sensitizers, but are potential allergens.

Thyme—Scientific name *Thymus vulgaris* L. Thyme is a known sensitizer. The oil contains thymol and limonene as well as carvacrol.

Cinnamon—Scientific name *Cinnamomum cassia Blume*. Cinnamon contains cinnamic aldehyde and eugenol, both known sensitizers.

Eucalyptus—Scientific name *Eucalyptus globulus*. Eucalyptus contains cineole, pinene and citronella, which are known sensitizers.

Jasmine—Scientific name *Jasminum officinale* L. Jasmine contains jasmone, a possible sensitizer; the oil also contains cinnamic derivatives and benzylidenacetone.

Sesame oil—Scientific name *Sesamum indicum* L. Sesame oil contains known allergens such as sesamol, sesmolin and sesamin.

Primrose oil—Scientific name *Primula obconica* Hance. The offending ingredient is primin, a compex benzoquinone.

Citrus oils are known to be both sensitizers and phototoxic agents. This would include all oranges, lemons, grapefruits, limes and tangerines. Citrus oil is made up of 90% limonene (which is not a sensitizer although the hydroperoxide oxidation products probably are), and 10% citral and bergapten, both of which are powerful sensitizers. Bergapten is a phototoxic agent and possibly a photosensitizer.

Essential oils

Most estheticians use essential oils daily and find them very helpful in skin care. For the average client there are few concerns about sensitivity to essential oils, but they do occur. Excessive or improper use, poor source material, or contaminated oils are frequent reasons for some reaction. With clients who have SLE, great caution must be used with both perfumes and essential oils. Being natural does not make the oils harmless. Remember that a poison mushroom is very natural, but also can be very deadly.

Beware of some of the common ingredients found in essential oils. Those derived from hardwoods are of particular interest since they are both fragrant and plentiful.

Essential oils from trees.[38] An Indian variety of rosewood known as *Dalbergia melanoxylon* contains two known potent sensitizers: 4-methoxydalbergione and 4-hydroxy-4-methoxydalbergione. Rosewood from Brazil contains 4-methoxydalbergione.

Red cedar from Canada, known as *Thuya plicata*, contains more than two sensitizers, but reactions occur with betathujaplicin and thymoquinone. I would include all of the conifers, evergreens, in this group of "cedar" oils. Be particularly careful with pine tree extracts and compounds that contain rosin, which is a chemically abietic acid, a known sensitizer.

Cosmetic Ingredients—Irritants and Sensitizers[37]

1. Fragrance ingredients—listed in order of frequency of occurrence in 161 reported cases of dermatitis: *fragrance unspecified, the most common; cinnamic alcohol, also found in essential oils; hydroxycitronellal; musk ambrette which has been removed from all United States fragrances, but beware; isoeugenol, geraniol, cinnamic aldehyde (cinnamal), coumarin and eugenol.*

2. Preservatives—*listed in the ingredient section on the product, usually at the end of the list: quaternium; imidazolidinyl urea; parabens, all of them and usually listed as methyl, propyl and butyl parabens; formaldehyde; 2-bromo-2nitropropate-1,3 diol; and sorbic acid.*

3. p-Phenylene diamine (found in "coal-tar" type hair dyes)

4. Lanolin and lanolin derivatives

5. Glyceryl thioglycollate (found in acid perms)

6. Propylene glycol

7. Toluene sulfonamide/formaldehyde resins (found in nail polish)

8. Sunscreens and UV absorbers

9. Methacrylates (widely used now in cosmetics; forms the basis of sculptured nails formulae)

Sandalwood, known as *Santalum album L.*, often is considered to be anti-inflammatory and, in fact, no allergy or sensitization has been found to either sandalwood oil or to santalol, the active ingredient that makes up 90% of the oil. The problems that occur with oils reputed to be sandalwood usually are because those oils are adulterated or contaminated. Sandalwood, in general, probably is safe to use with SLE clients.

Balsam of Peru, known as *Toluifera perierae*, is a strong sensitizer. The resin contains many ingredients belonging to the cinnamic group of chemical compounds.

The list of materials in this chapter is not all-inclusive. The materials simply are some of the most common agents used in natural cosmetics and often used by estheticians. The main message is to use caution when employing natural agents, to know them well and to know how to use them. Understanding the chemistry is helpful in getting a handle on both how they work and what to avoid.

Summary

In this chapter I have outlined the major characteristics of SLE, what to look for during your clients' treatments, and how to separate SLE from seborrheic dermatitis, rosacea and discoid lupus. You need not understand the complex immunology behind SLE, though if you are interested, the references will take you deep into the subject.

SLE is a disease manifested by several signs and symptoms. If managed well it is not fatal, but requires a lifetime of treatment. Your role as an esthetician can be helpful to both the physician and the client in delivering the attention and concern essential to effective treatment. Remember that the SLE client has a very overburdened and sensitive immune system and can't detoxify chemicals very well, so use great care in your choice of topicals. The list of natural products is intended to guide you in their use, but in the final choice you are the judge. If you are not sure of the safety of an ingredient, do not use the product.

Though SLE is not a contagious disease, care should be taken with infected clients because of their reduced immunities. You don't want to transmit any infections to them. Wear gloves and be sure that equipment is sterilized and sanitized properly. Being concerned and conscientious in your care for the client with SLE will be rewarding and satisfying to all parties.

More information on SLE and SLE support groups is available from the Lupus Foundation of America, Inc., 4 Research Place, Suite 180, Rockville, Maryland 20850-3226, 800-558-0121.

New Web sites have appeared in recent years that are very helpful. Here are a few:

Patient information—www.mednets.com/lupus.htm

A treatnent from the National Institues of Health—www.nih.gov/niams/healthinfo/slehandout/treating.html

References

1. Rowell NR, The natural history of lupus erythematosus. *Clin Exp Dermatol* 9: 217–231 (1984)

2. Serdula MK and Rhoads GG, The frequency of systemic lupus erythematosus in different groups in Hawaii. *Arth Rheum* 22: 328–333 (1979)

3. Siegel M and Lees SL, The epidemiology of systemic lupus erythematosus. *Semin Arthritis Rheum* 3: 1–54 (1973)

3A. Siegel M and Selentreund M, Racial and social factors in systemic lupus erythematosus. *J Am Med Assoc* 191: 77 (1965)

4. Siegel M, Holley HL and Lee SL, Epidemiologic studies on systemic lupus erythematosus. *Arthritis Rheum* 13: 802–811 (1970)

5. Siegel M, Reilly EB and Lee SL, et al, Epidemiology of systemic lupus erythematosus: time trend and racial differences. *Am J Publ Health* 54: 33–43 (1964)

6. Taial N, The etiology of systemic lupus erythematosus, in *Dubois' Lupus Erythematosus*, third edition, Wallace DJ and Dubois EL, eds, Lea & Febiger: Philadelphia, p 39 (1987)

7. Lahita RG, ed, *Systemic Lupus Erythematosus*, Wiley: New York (1987)

8. Friedman SJ, Leukonychia striata associated with systemic lupus erythematosus. *J Am Acad Derm* 15: 536–538 (1986)

9. Mintz G and Fraga A, Arteritis in systemic lupus erythematosus. *Arch Intern Med* 116: 55–66 (1965)

10. Urowitz MB, Gladman DD and Chalmers A, et al, Nail lesions in systemic lupus erythematosus. *J Rheumatol* 5: 441–447 (1978)

11. Tuffanelli DL and Dubois EL, Cutaneous manifestations of systemic lupus erythematosus. *Arch Dermatol* 90: 377–386 (1964)

12. Yasue T, Livedoid vasculitis and central nervous system involvement in systemic lupus erythematosus. *Arch Dermatol* 122: 66–70 (1986)

13. Alarcon–Segouia D and Cetina JA, Lupus hair. *Am J Med Sci* 267: 241–242 (1974)

14. Armas–Cruz A, Harnecker J and Ducach G, et al, Clinical diagnosis of systemic lupus erythematosus. *Am J Med* 25: 409–419 (1958)

15. Rowell NR and Goodfield MJD, The connective tissue diseases in *Textbook of Dermatology*, Champion RH, Burton JL and Ebling FJG, eds, Blackwell Scientific Publications: London 55: 2163 (1992)

16. Parish LC, Kennedy RJ and Hurley HJ, Palmar lesions in lupus erythematosus. *Arch Dermatol* 1967 96: 273–276 (1975)

17. Prystowsky SD and Gilliam JN, Discoid lupus erythematosus as part of a larger disease spectrum. *Arch Dermatol* 111: 1448–1452 (1975)

18. Epstein JH, Polymorphous light eruption. *Dermatol Clin* 4: 243 (1986)

19. Horio T, et al, Production and inhibition of solar urticaria by visible light exposure. *J Am Acad Dermatol* 11: 1094 (1984)

20. Lim HW, Pathophysiology of cutaneous lesions in porphyries. *Semin Hematol* 26: 114 (1989)

21. Kochevar IE, Mechanisms of drug photosensitization. *Photochem Photobiol* 45: 891 (1987)

22. Epstein JH, Tuffanefli DL and Dubois EL, Light sensitivity and lupus erythematosus. *Arch Dermatol* 91: 483–485 (1965)

23. Le Feber WP, Norris DA and Ryan SS, et al, Ultraviolet light induces expression of selected nuclear antigens in cultured human keratinocytes. *Clin Invest* 74: 1545–1551 (1984)

24. Davis P, Antibodies to UV DNA and photosensitivity, *Br J Dermatol* 97: 197–200 (1977)

25. Clark RA, Kimball HR and Decker JL, Neutrophil chemotaxis in systemic lupus erythematosus. *Ann Rheum Dis* 33: 167–172 (1974)

26. Lahita RG, Bradlow HL and Ginzier E, et al, Low plasma androgens in women with systemic lupus erythematosus. *Arthritis Rheum* 241–248 (1987)

27. Lahita RG, Bucala R and Bradlow HL, et al, Determination of 16 alpha-hydroxyestrone by radioimmunoassay in systemic lupus erythematosus. *Arthritis Rheum* 28: 1122–1127 (1985)

28. Talal N, Sex hormones and modulation of immune response in SLE. *Clin Rheum* Dis 8: 23-28 (1982)

29. Rogers MP, Dubey D and Reich P, The influence of the psyche and the brain on immunity and disease susceptibility: a critical review. *Psychosom Med* 41: 147–164 (1979)

30. Haustein UF, Tubular structures in affected and normal skin in chronic discoid and systemic lupus erythematosus: electron microscopic studies. *Br J Dermatol* 89: 1–13 (1973)

31. Hurd ER, Eigenbrodt E and Ziff M, Cytoplasmic tubular structures in kidney biopsies in systemic lupus erythematosus. *Arthritis Rheum* 12: 541-542 (1969)

32. Rich SA, Owens TR and Anzola C, et al, Induction of lupus inclusions by sera from patients with systemic lupus erythematosus. *Arthritis Rheum* 29: 501–507 (1986)

33. Lewis Jones MS, Evans S and Thompson CM, Erythema multiforme occurring in association with lupus erythematosus drug therapy with doxycycline. *Clin Exp Dermatol* 13: 245–247 (1988)

34. Harmon CE and Portanova JP, Drug-induced lupus: clinic and serological studies. *Clin Rheum Dis* 8: 121 (1982)

35. Howard EJ and Brown SM, Clofibrate-induced antinuclear factor and lupus-like syndrome. *J Am Med Assoc* 226: 1358–1359 (1973)

36. Dodd HJ, Cox PM and Sarkany I, Bullous lesions in hydralazine induced lupus erythematosus-a review of three cases. *Br J Derm* 119: (suppl 33) 27 (1988)

37. Maibach HI and Engasser PG, Dermatitis due to cosmetics, in *Contact Dermatitis*, Fisher A, ed, Lea and Febiger: Philadelphia (1986)

38. Benezra C, Ducombs G, Sell Y and Foussereau J, *Plant Contact Dermatitis*, B.C. Dekker, Inc.: Philadelphia (1985)

Chapter 18

Males and Females: Physiological Differences

The appearance of a prepubescent child's skin essentially is the same whether male or female. While male hormones are present in the prepubescent male, they are not at a level high enough to express "maleness." This changes at puberty and the sexes take diverse pathways. In this chapter, the physiological and anatomical differences between male and female skin through the various stages of life will be explored. In addition, some special conditions that affect the skin of females will be discussed.

Beyond the obvious physical appearance, there are unseen differences between male and female physiology that relate primarily to the sex hormones. The terms androgenic and estrogenic hormones are used in order to include other compounds besides testosterone and estrogen. To understand the effects of the sex hormones on the skin, some of the biochemistry and physiology of these compounds must be understood. First, let's take a brief look at how sexual differences happen.

Genes and chromosomes

Genetic sex is determined at the moment of conception. Males have one X and one Y chromosome, while females have two X chromosomes. The genes that determine sex type are located on a pair of X chromosomes in the female and on the Y chromosome in the male. All of the information needed by the embryo to produce a male, or female, infant is located on these chromosomes.

At birth, the visible differences mainly are in the genital organs and possibly the facial features. This remains the case until puberty. The onset of puberty is believed to initiate in the brain, but the exact initiating mechanism is unknown. The following sequence of events produces the physical changes seen at puberty.

Physiological changes at puberty

Puberty begins with a rise in the level of special-releasing gonadatropic hormones (GnRH), which are hormones secreted by the hypothalamus. These releasing hormones stimulate the pituitary gland to release the gonadatropins, the primary stimulators of the gonads, or sex organs. Gonad is another word that means either ovary or testicle. These hormones are designed to affect only the targeted sex organs, such as the ovaries in the female or the testicles in the male.

Puberty in the female. The pituitary gland, located deep in the brain, secretes two major gonadatropins that are effective both in the female and in the male. The first of these is the follicle stimulating hormone known as FSH, or follitropin, a newer term. The second is luteinizing hormone known as LH, or lutropin in the new terminology. The major target organ for both of these gonadatropins in the female is the ovary. Under the influence of the FSH, the ovary responds with the production of several hormones.

The egg, or ovum, is produced as a consequence of FSH stimulation. This is the mechanism that regulates the menstrual cycle. The LH stimulates the ovary after ovulation to prepare the uterus for conception. The ovary produces progesterone to achieve this action. If pregnancy occurs, the cycle stops; if there is no pregnancy, the cycle repeats.

As the ovary is stimulated and the egg develops, the ovary secretes estrogenic hormones and two other hormones—progesterone and androgen. The ovary is the major source of female hormones; without ovaries a woman is neuter, or essentially "castrated."

These hormones don't need to be looked at in great depth, but you need to know a little about each to understand the action on the skin. Note that androgens are male-like hormones, while progesterone is a precursor hormone of both androgens and estrogens. When estrogen in mentioned in this chapter, I will be referring to estradiol, but there are two more estrogens, estrone and estriol, which are of lesser importance in the skin.

As the estrogen is produced by the ovary, it will have certain effects on the developing female. The secondary sexual signs will appear with budding breasts, pubic and axillary hair, thickening of the vaginal lining and finally, the placement of female fat. Pubic hair in the female is believed to be induced by androgens rather than estrogens. Once menses begins, the hormone levels will fluctuate with each cycle.

Prolactin also is a gonadatropin that has effects on the ovaries and on the breasts. Prolactin is essential for milk production, but also is important in providing additional functions for both male and female tissues. For the purpose of this chapter, prolactin will not be discussed further.

Puberty in the male. The same gonadatropins operate in the male as in the female, only the target organs are different. The LH in the male stimulates a special tissue in the testicle known as the Leydig cell. The androgenic hormones are made within this cell. These hormones include testosterone, androstenedione and dihydrotestosterone (DHT).

The FSH stimulates the Sertoli cell which is inside the sperm tubes, the seminiferous tubules in the testicle. Here the FSH causes the Sertoli cell to make an androgen-binding protein that combines with the testosterone from the Leydig cell. The net result is that sperm is produced.

General Physiological Effects of Estrogen

- On the brain, estrogen maintains sexual behavior and libido.
- On the vagina, estrogen causes thickening of the mucous membranes.
- On the uterus, estrogen causes mucous secretion and increased blood flow.
- On the breasts, estrogen causes growth of the small ducts and supporting connecting tissue and accumulation of fat.
- On the skin, estrogen causes sebaceous gland secretion to be thin (less fatty), and increases the amount of ground substance in the skin.
- On the mucosa of the mouth, estrogen promotes thickening of the mucous membranes and helps blood vessels to become more permeable.
- On the sebaceous gland, estrogen decreases the size and the production of sebum.

General Physiological Effects of Androgens

- On muscle tissue, androgens cause hypertrophy (overgrowth such as with bodybuilding) and normal growth.
- On bone, androgens cause epiphysial close (bone fusing when a child stops growing). Men genetically are programmed to have more androgens, consequently, men generally are taller than women.
- On the vocal cords, androgens cause thickening with voice change.
- On the skin, androgens cause coarse hair growth of beard, axillary and pubic region.
- On the penis and scrotum, androgens cause growth and maturation.
- On the brain, androgens promote sexual activity.
- On the sebaceous gland, androgens cause an increase in the size of both the gland and the hair.
- On the bone marrow, androgens cause an increase in the production of red blood cells.[3, 4]

Estrogens are produced in the male from breakdown products of androgens. This occurs mainly in peripheral tissues. Gynecomastia, breast enlargement in adolescents, can be due to increased estrogen production by the peripheral tissues, or perhaps increased estrogen receptor sensitivity in the male breast tissue. Another reason is failure of the enzyme aromatase to breakdown the estrogen to androgenic hormones.

With the onset of testosterone, the male undergoes changes that produce the secondary sexual signs. First, there is enlargement of the penis and then the appearance of pubic hair. Sebaceous gland enlargement also occurs, often followed by acne. Facial hair and axillary hair appear later along with skeletal muscle development. Unlike the female, the stimulation to the male androgen production is constant rather than intermittent.

The hormone receptors

Most hormones work their magic by binding to specific receptors either on the cell surface or inside the cell on specific proteins. There are receptors for estrogenic hormones and androgenic hormones in the cells at various sites in the body where the action of the sex hormones is targeted. This is an important concept, for there can be no hormone activity without the receptors first binding with the hormone. There are certain sexual conditions in which the receptors are lacking and even though the hormone level is high, there are no sexual characteristics present.

Cells that contain androgen-binding proteins are more numerous in the genital skin and less numerous in the neck, abdomen and wrist. The number of receptors binding androgens in the genital region is the same for both males and females. Estrogen receptors in the skin are not as numerous as androgen receptors. The highest levels are found in the skin of the face and the lowest in the breasts and the thighs. Progesterone adds a mystery to this picture in that the highest levels of progesterone receptors are in the breast skin and the lowest levels are in the genital skin.

Keep in mind as the effect of sex hormones on the skin is discussed, that the number of each of these receptors plays a part in how the skin responds to the sex hormone. The more receptors in a certain area in the skin, the more sensitive that area will be to a particular hormone.[2, 3, 5]

Action of the hormones on the skin

With this background, let's look at the action of the sex hormones on the skin. The action of the hormones on the skin needs to be divided into four areas or structures: the hair, the epidermis, the glands and the dermis.

The hair. The first hair to appear in the hair follicle is lanugo hair—fine, soft and unpigmented. It usually is shed at the seventh month of gestation. These hairs are replaced at birth with vellus hairs, also soft and unpigmented, and some terminal hairs that are coarse and pigmented.

Vellus hairs are replaced at puberty, first in the pubic region of males and females, and then in the axillary about two years later. In males, facial hair appears at about the same time. Vellus hairs continue to be replaced over different areas of the body and at different times. The sequence is the calves, thighs, abdomen, buttocks, chest, back, arms and shoulders. The amount of hair varies tremendously with individuals, depending on race and amount of hormone present.

Women are less affected than men, but at times, one sees gradations of the male pattern in women. Hair on the upper lip and cheeks in women is not uncommon, nor is hair around the nipples. This is related most likely to the high number of sebaceous glands in the nipple area. Hairs are never seen in the nipple or the areola, rather they are seen on the periphery. Even in men one does not see hairy nipples.

Women with high levels of androgen will exhibit greater hair growth in these areas. Vellus hairs on the face and arms of young females eventually will be dark terminal hairs as the women age. Again, great variation exists and prediction is difficult. In Asians, there is less body hair both in males and females. Women with excessive body hair and no serious disease can have what is known as idiopathic hirsutism. In this condition, there is a moderate rise in testosterone, but a greater rise in androstenedione. There is no counterpart of this condition in the male.

In the male, excessive androgens can be associated with male pattern baldness. This is a hereditary condition and so far there is no adequate treatment.

Male pattern baldness is known as andro-genetic alopecia and is a reverse of what happens in female hirsutism. The dark coarse terminal hair reverts to a soft, colorless vellus hair. Andro-genetic alopecia also affects females, mostly as older adults. In young women, it can be a sign of excessive androgen production and should be evaluated by a physician. This is a great mystery in biology. How does a hormone that produces hair in men also cause them to lose hair?

Baldness in males is carried on the X chromosome and thus is inherited from the mother, not from the father. Although baldness is a recessive gene, that is, a trait that will not be expressed in the presence of a normal gene, in males who have one X and one Y, any trait on the X chromosome will be expressed as there is no counter gene on the Y. In women, the baldness gene on the X chromosome from the father will be suppressed if the other X chromosome is normal. (See **Figure 18-1**.)[1, 5, 6, 7]

The epidermis. Both androgens and estrogens will affect the growth and size of the epidermis. Testosterone and estrogen are known to have a proliferative effect on the basal layer, causing the epidermis to be thicker and more cellular. Estrogen causes sebaceous gland secretion to be thin and increases the amount of ground substance in

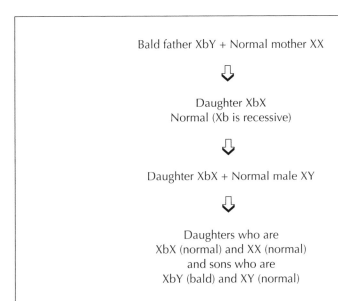

Bald father XbY + Normal mother XX

⇩

Daughter XbX
Normal (Xb is recessive)

⇩

Daughter XbX + Normal male XY

⇩

Daughters who are
XbX (normal) and XX (normal)
and sons who are
XbY (bald) and XY (normal)

Figure 18-1. *Baldness in males passes from grandparents to daughters to grandchildren. Women who are XbX carry the gene for baldness, but women who are XbXb will be bald. Males who have only the Xb and a Y chromosome will be bald. This is an illustration of a recessive-type gene, that is, a gene that cannot be expressed in the presence of a normal gene.*

the skin. On the sebaceous gland, estrogen decreases the size and the production of sebum. The effect does not appear to be local and is not an antagonist to testosterone. Administered androgen will, however, reverse the activity of estrogens.[3]

On the skin, androgens cause coarse hair growth of the beard, axillary and pubic region. On the sebaceous gland, androgens cause an increase in the size of both the gland and the hair. The amount of sebum secreted is related to the level of androgens produced at various ages. Too much androgen will cause the epidermis to become thick and coarse. Sebaceous glands enlarge and the pores appear larger. Acne can develop and the hairline recedes in males and females.

Excessive estrogen will produce many of the signs seen in pregnancy, which is discussed later in this chapter. In males, feminization is apparent, while in the non-pregnant female, spider veins will appear along with pigmentation changes.

Too little androgen will produce a dull, finely wrinkled, thin epidermis. Facial pores are small, and there is little or no acne. There is no facial, pubic or axillary hair. The skin has a very characteristic pallor due to decreased pigment and fewer blood vessels.

Lack of estrogen in women will produce similar, but less extreme results. If estrogen is lacking before the age of 12, there will be no puberty and secondary sexual signs. Estrogen deficit in mature women is characterized by a dull, thin skin with fine wrinkles and some slackness.

The glands. The action of the androgens on the sebaceous glands and also of the action of estrogen on these glands has been discussed. Now let's look at another set of glands, the apocrine glands which are dominated by the sex hormones. These glands are located in the ear canal where they produce wax; in the axillae; around the nipples; the peri-umbilical area, the navel; and in the anogenital region. The glands secrete a white milky fluid that appears at times of stress, fear, anger or sexual excitement. Apocrine glands are dormant until puberty. The breast is a large apocrine gland that has responded to estrogenic stimulation.

There is little information on the effects of various hormones on the apocrine glands in terms of material secreted. It is possible to induce the gland to secrete by injecting epinephrine, adrenaline, into the skin around the gland. Epinephrine is a hormone that occurs whenever there is stress. The odor produced by the apocrine gland is a by-product of bacterial action on the secreted material. Sterile armpits or well-washed armpits have little or no odor.

The dermis. The greatest biochemical and biophysical differences between the sexes are seen in the dermis. It only is necessary to feel both male and female skin to perceive the great difference. There virtually is no difference, as it's been noted, between male skin and female skin before puberty. Much research has been done on the dermis of rats in an attempt to explain the effect of hormones on the physical properties of the skin. Here is a summary of this data.

In the dermis, the fibroblast is the target cell for both testosterone and estrogen type hormones. Fibroblasts produce both collagen and elastin fibers which are responsible for the skin's strength and resilience. Little work has been done on the effect of the sex hormones on elastin fibers, so the discussion will be confined to the effects of sex hormones on collagen.

Testosterone increases collagen production by stimulating the fibroblast to produce specific proteins that are involved in collagen synthesis. Estrogen, on the other hand, decreases collagen synthesis. The net effect of this is not surprising—female skin is more soft and less strong than male skin. When males are given large doses of estrogen, they develop the skin characteristics of females.[8, 9, 10]

Another effect of estrogen is increased action of an enzyme that produces hyaluronic acid. This is the enzyme hyaluronidase. Hyaluronic acid is responsible for the turgor, the resistance to stretching, in the dermis. It is a chief component of the so-called ground substance in the skin. The ground substance is made up of complex molecules called glycosaminoglycans. Estrogen therefore makes skin more firm and moist, giving it a smooth, soft feel.

Skin changes in pregnancy

The major changes seen in the skin of pregnant women are pigmentation changes; spider angiomas; hair loss, known as telogen effluvium; and stretch marks, or striae.

Hyperpigmentation is a common disorder of pregnancy, occurring in 90% of women. The most frequent body sites are the areolae; axilla; genitals; umbilicus; linea alba, the center line between pubic hair and chest; perineum; and thighs. Most of these hyperpigmented areas will regress after pregnancy. At times, pigmented lesions such as moles, birthmarks and freckles can get darker.

On the face, a condition called melasma, a blotchy generalized pigmentation of the skin, occurs in 70% of pregnant women, affecting all races equally. The most frequent areas involved include the forehead, cheeks, temple and upper lip. This most likely is a hormonal change that is aggravated by sun exposure. While most melasmic changes resolve with delivery, a few cases will require treatment. The standard medical treatment is 2–4% hydroquinone cream used topically if melasma persists postpartum.

It now is believed that androgen components are responsible for the pigmentation increase. Androgens, particularly testosterone, will stimulate the enzyme tyrosinase in the melanocyte. This enzyme will convert tyrosine to dihydroxyphenylalanine (DOPA), a precursor of melanin.

The changes in blood vessels seen in the skin during pregnancy are believed to be the result of increased blood volume and impairment of blood return. The internal physical pressure of the fetus and swollen uterus places a burden on the vascular system to return the venous blood to the heart. As a result, the peripheral vessels swell and this swelling is seen as dilated veins and congestion. Dilated veins that are quite large are called varicosities and are seen in the legs, rectum and vagina. At least 40% of pregnant women have these conditions.

Red palms are frequent in pregnancy. Known as palmar erythema, it is seen mainly on the palm and the base of the thumb.

Spider angiomas occur in 60% or more of pregnancies. These lesions are dilated arteries with connecting branches. They occur over the upper chest, arms, hands, face and neck. In addition, these women will exhibit signs of capillary fragility. Petechiae, or tiny blue spots, indicate capillar bleeding into the skin. Facial flushing and hives, reticular patterns on the legs and sensations of heat and cold are all common vascular phenomena seen in pregnancy.

Many myths exist about pregnant women and hair loss. The individual variations seen in hair loss are quite large. Postpartum hair loss occurs during the first five months after delivery. At times, instead of losing hair, some women will experience an increase of body hair or darkening of the head hair. In most cases of postpartum hair loss, it will resolve without incident if the situation is left alone.

It is believed that about 90% of women will have some form of stretch marks during pregnancy. Extremely overweight men and women also suffer from stretch marks. While the cause is unknown, it has been found that women with a high blood sugar during pregnancy tend to have large stretch marks. This does not mean that they are diabetic or that there is a casual relationship between blood sugar level and stretch marks, but there is some evidence pointing this way. Recent studies have not confirmed this finding. However women who are overweight have more estrogen since it is produce by the fatty tissue. It is now known that estrogen stimulate fibroblasts to release collagenase, an enzyme that dissolves collagen. This is most likely the basic reason for stretch marks and cellulite in women,

At present, there is little understanding about the nature of stretch marks. They appear to be of dermal origin, but the manifestation is distinctly epidermal. How the pattern persists in the epidermis with constant renewal of the stratum corneum is a mystery. No official or recognized treatment has been devised. The use of retinoic acid has been proposed and low frequency alternating current has also been tried with varying degrees of success, but seems to hold promise. Much more work needs to be done in this area.[11] Most likely this is a natural process generated in the fibroblast by hormones secreted during pregnancy. We know that estrogen will stimulate fibrblast to produce collagenase which dissolves collagen, thus there can be a related factor.

No preventive regimen has been developed. While the size of the abdominal increase has been proposed as a cause of stretch marks, this does not appear to be the case. Weight gain and poor nutrition with poor prenatal care can be factors. Heredity factors also can come into play.

Summary

The differences in male and female skin is due to the action of the sex hormones testosterone and estrogen. Both of these hormones have profound effects on the skin itself and the skin appendages. The body and the sex organs change dramatically at puberty—sex glands develop and the pituitary axis swings into action. In the skin, the androgens will make the dermis stronger and the estrogens will make it more soft and resilient.

References

1.   Hadley ME, *Endocrinology*, Prentice Hall, Inc.: Englewood, NJ (1988)

2.   Baxter JD and Funder JW, Hormone receptors, *New Eng J Med*, 301: 1149–1161 (1979)

3.   Fitzpatrick TB, et al, *Dermatology in General Medicine*, Vol 1, McGraw Hill: Monterey, CA p 367 (1987)

4.   Fitzpatrick TB, et al, *Dermatology in General Medicine*, Vol 1, McGraw Hill: Monterey, CA p 185 (1987)

5. Stumpf WE, et al, Estrogen target cells in the skin, *Experientia*, 30: 196–198 (1976)

6. Ebling J, The effects of cyproterone acetate and estradiol upon testosterone stimulated sebaceous activity in the rat, *Acta Endocrinologica*, 72: 361–365 (1973)

7. Hasselquist MB, et al, Isolation and characterization of the estrogen receptor in human skin, *J Clin Endocrinol and Metabol*, 50: 76–82 (1980)

8. Uzuka M, et al, Induction of hyaluronic acid synthetase by estrogen in the mouse skin, *Biochim Biophys Acta*, 673: 387–393 (1981)

9. Hershman JM, *Endocrine Pathophysiology*, Lea & Febiger: Philadelphia (1988)

10. Yang SL, et al, The effect of estrogen on collagen synthesis at the site of a skin autograft, *Amer J Obstet Gynecol*, 116: 694–697 (1972)

11. Elgart ML and Callan JP, eds, *Dermatologic Clinics*, April, WB Saunders Co.: Philadelphia (1990)

General References

Bardin CW and Catterall JF, Testosterone: A major determinant of extragenital sexual dimorphism, *Science* 211: 1285–1294 (1981)

Wilson MJ and Spazani E, The melanogenic response to testosterone in scrotal epidermis: effect on tyrosine activity and protein synthesis, *Acta Endocrinologica*, 81: 435–448 (1976)

Chapter 19

Estrogens and Phytoestrogens

Estheticians need a basic knowledge of biochemistry if they are to keep abreast of new developments in the health care industry. The biochemistry of estrogens and phytoestrogens follows, and while there is an enormous literature base on both estrogen and phytoestrogens, this information includes hormone receptors, estrogen and phtyoestrogen chemistry, how phytoestrogens work and their benefits to estheticians. With this information in hand, you can decide what path to follow. You will need this information; though not easy, it is a part of your life and your business.

What are estrogens?

Estrogens are hormones, but what are hormones? The word hormone comes from the Greek word *hormaein* meaning "to set in motion, or "to spur on." It is a very apt word for the action of hormones since ***all hormones are chemical messengers that are sent to specific target cells to evoke a response***. In this chapter, the action of estrogen hormones and estrogen-like hormones will be explored.

There are two classes of hormones: **peptide** or **glycoprotein hormones**, and **steroid-type hormones**. Estrogens are steroid hormones, the basic hormones of females. Estrogen is the basic hormone of reproduction and without it there would be no life as it is known today. **Endocrinology** is the medical specialty that studies the cause and treatment of hormonal disorders. In discussing estrogens, the endocrinology of female reproduction is a good starting point.

Phytoestrogen is the related plant-derived hormone. ***There are no natural estrogens or progesterones in plants***. There are precursors of these hormones, and biochemicals that have a similar action to the animal hormones, but no exact matches. To understand the actions of hormones requires a general knowledge of endocrinology, a topic that would easily fill a very large book. The physiology of the menstrual cycle will be covered because it is critical to any discussion of estrogens and forms the basis for most of female endocrinology.

Female endocrinology

All mammals essentially have the same hormonal sequence in reproductive physiology. The human female is no exception. The rise and fall of reproductive hormones is the result of a cyclic action by three glands secreting hormones, which results in ovulation and prepares the female body for pregnancy. These three glands are the **hypothalamus**, the **pituitary** and the **ovaries**.

It is easier to understand the relationship between the glands and hormones if the whole system is viewed as a domino effect. As children, everyone has stacked dominos on end and watched them fall one by one. Endocrine glands have a very similar mechanism. Gland A secretes a substance, which causes Gland B to secrete a substance, which causes Gland C to secrete a substance, which causes tissue X to respond. It happens in this manner:

Gland A (hypothalamus) ==> Gland B (pituitary) ==>
Gland C (ovary) ==> Tissue X (uterine tissue)

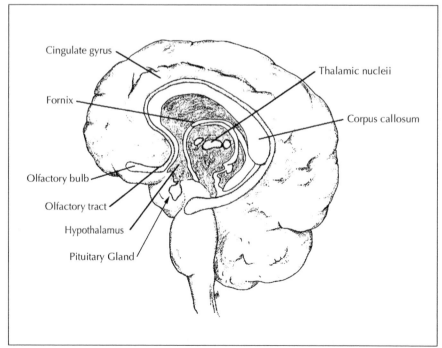

Figure 19-1A. *Location of the hypothalamus in the brain. Note that the hypothalamus is under the thalamus.*

Hypothalamic hormone secretion

Hypothalamus, pronounced hypo-**thal**'-ah-mus, accent on the *thal*, means "under the thalamus." Thalamus is from the Greek word *thalamus*, meaning "inner chamber." We need not go into the neuroanatomy, except to state that this gland is located in the brain. A diagram is included for anyone who likes anatomy. (See **Figure 19-1A**.) In the hypothalamus, special cells[1] secrete **gonadotropin-releasing hormone**, or **GnRH**, a polypeptide. The **gonads** are the ovaries in females and the testicles in males, from the Greek *gone* meaning "a seed." The Greek word *trophikos* means "to nourish." These gonadotrophic hormones indirectly have some effect on the ovaries or testicles. First, however, they must stimulate the pituitary gland to secrete the actual substance that has an effect on the gonad.

Pituitary hormone secretion

The pituitary has a posterior lobe and an anterior lobe, which is the one to be concerned with for this chapter. When the hypothalamus secretes GnRH, the pituitary

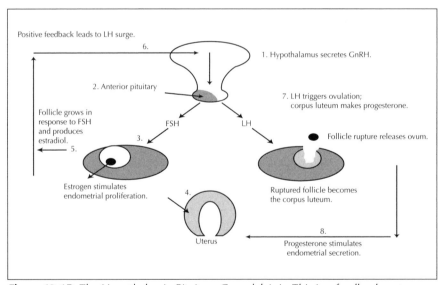

Figure 19-1B. The Hypothalamic-Pituitary-Gonadal Axis. This is a feedback system. As one hormone is released, it stimulates a second hormone that stimulates a third hormone and so on. The menstrual cycle is illustrative of this process. The hypothalamus secretes (1) gonadatrophic-releasing hormone, or GnRH, which causes the pituitary gland (2) to release follicle-stimulating hormone, or FSH (3). FSH induces the ovarian follicle, which contains immature ova, to ripen and to release and the ovum. Estrogen (4) is secreted which causes the endometrium to ripen and prepare for pregnancy. At the same time it causes the GnRH to stimulate the pituitary (5) to release luteinizing hormone, or LH (6). LH causes the ruptured follicle to release progesterone (7), which stimulates endometrial secretions (8). In the absence of a pregnancy the whole cycle repeats each month.

is triggered to release two of the many pituitary hormones—**follicle-stimulating hormone** or **FSH**, and **luteinizing hormone** or **LH**—into the bloodstream in a pulsating fashion and stimulate the ovaries to produce estrogen. In males, the same FSH and LH hormones target the testicles.

Ovarian hormone secretion

The ovaries produce estrogen and progesterone in response to FSH and LH. The effects of these compounds are essential to understand their importance in pregnancy and in biology. The whole process is diagrammed in **Figure 19-1B**. There are many actions of estrogen and progesterone that are known, and perhaps many that remain to be discovered.[2] (See **Major Actions of Estrogens and Progesterone.**)

Major Actions of Estrogen and Progesterone

Estrogen

- Pubertal growth spurt
- Closing of epiphyses, the plates in the growing ends of the bone, at puberty
- Pubertal maturation of uterus and vagina
- Proliferation of endometrial lining
- Breast development
- Pigmentation of breasts and pubic area
- Female distribution of body fat
- Maintains normal skin
- Maintains normal vasculature
- Decreases bone resorption
- Reduces bowel motility
- Increases blood clotting factors
- Increases HDL cholesterol
- Increases triglyceride turnover
- Increases hepatic-binding protein synthesis
- Increases renin substrate
- Influences libido
- Increases blood coagulation

Progesterone

- Breast development
- Endometrial gland development
- Maintains uterus during pregnancy
- Inhibits lactation during pregnancy
- Contributes to insulin resistance
- Increases body temperature

Estrogens and hormone receptors

Estrogens occur in three major forms—**estrone, estradiol** and **estriol**. Two of these chemical forms are shown in **Figure 19-2**. The most active form is estradiol, also known as **E2**. All hormones must react with a specific receptor to produce a biological effect. Estrogen receptors are in the nucleus, while other hormone receptors are on the cell membrane. Hormones that are lipid-soluble enter the cell easily so they usually have receptors within the cell. Hormones that are water-soluble require a receptor on the outside of the cell membrane. The hormone receptor is the key to understanding how the phytoestrogens work.

Figure 19-3 and **Figure 19-4**, are diagrams of membrane receptors and nuclear receptors respectively. Remember, hormone receptors can be either on the cell membrane or in the nucleus. Only lipid-soluble hormones, such as the sex hormones, can cross the membrane without requiring a membrane receptor. In **Figure 19-3**, note

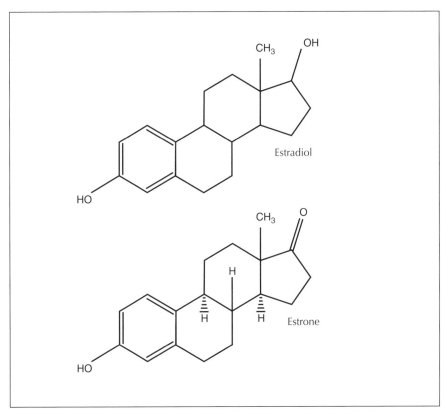

Figure 19-2. Estradiol and estrone. These are the two major estrogenic hormones. They are produced by the ovary and also by the adipose, or fatty tissues, of the body. A third estrogen—estriol—is not shown since it is a very weak estrogen. Note that the estrone molecule has a double oxygen, = O, on carbon 17, whereas estradiol has an hydroxyl group, OH, on carbon 17.

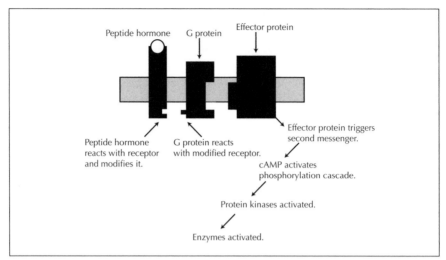

Figure 19-3. *Action of peptide hormones. While the diagram appears complex, the action is rather simple, since it is a series of related reactions. Essentially the peptide hormone stimulates the receptor in, or on, the cell membrane. The stimulated receptor activates a protein called the G protein, which activates the effector protein. Once the effector protein is activated, it triggers second messengers, such as cAMP, to activate a process, such as burning fat or making a new a new compound by enzyme reactions.*

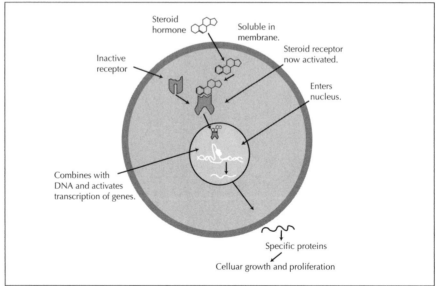

Figure 19-4. *The nuclear hormone. This is the realm of the steroid, or estrogen hormones. Estrogen passes easily through the cell membrane, combines with a transfer, or receptor, protein and enters the nucleus. The receptor protein combines with the DNA and starts the transcription process to produce a specific protein, which may trigger several actions on the cell or other cells.*

the peptide hormone on the membrane receptor, the action of the hormone on the receptor changes the configuration of the receptor allowing it to bind with the G Protein. The G Protein now is changed, allowing it to bind with the effector protein, which triggers a second messenger, such as **cyclic adenosine monophosphate**, or cAMP. Follow these details in **Figure 19-3**.

Membrane hormone receptors

Almost all membrane receptors are water-soluble peptide hormone receptors. When the peptide hormone, also called the first messenger, reaches the cell membrane, it reacts with the hormone receptor in the membrane by binding to the receptor. The binding of the hormone changes the conformation of the receptor, resulting in a reaction that forms the second messenger or cAMP. The cAMP initiates a chain of events that results in phosphate being added to enzymes, which in turn starts many types of enzyme activity. Fat burning, or lipolysis, begins as lipase is activated. There are many more peptide hormones then there are steroid-type hormones.

Nuclear hormone receptors

Since estrogens are lipid-soluble, they penetrate the cell membrane easily. Once inside the cell, they combine with an intracellular receptor that transports them through the cytoplasm and into the nucleus where the receptor-hormone complex reacts directly with the deoxyribonucleic acid (DNA) at the site known as the hormone response element (HRE). After binding to the HRE, the transcription factors are activated and gene transcription, protein synthesis and altered cell function occur. This may sound complex, but the steps are easy to learn since it remains the same for all nuclear hormones.

Transcription is the name given to the process of reading the code on the DNA molecule and converting it to a messenger ribonucleic acid (RNA) molecule. It is then translated or made into protein in the ribosomes of the cell. These mechanisms are covered in Chapter 7, "Biochemistry." Estrogen, being a steroid-like compound, falls into the nuclear receptor class. See **Figure 19-4**.

Two estrogen receptors

Originally estrogen was believed to be only a reproductive hormone, but hormone replacement studies soon established other actions of the estrogens. Estrogens were found to help maintain muscle strength, improve cardiovascular function, protect against tooth decay and colon cancer, and to help improve mental function and prevent macular degeneration in the eyes. This could not be explained until it was discovered that there were two types of estrogen receptors and that hormone selectivity was the answer. It became apparent that all estrogens do not act in the same manner and that different estrogens are not interchangeable.

The two estrogen receptors are known as **ER-alpha** and **ER-beta**. The alpha and beta receptors are found at different concentrations in the tissues. For example, ER-alpha is found in moderate amounts in the ovaries, uterus, testicles, kidney and pituitary, while

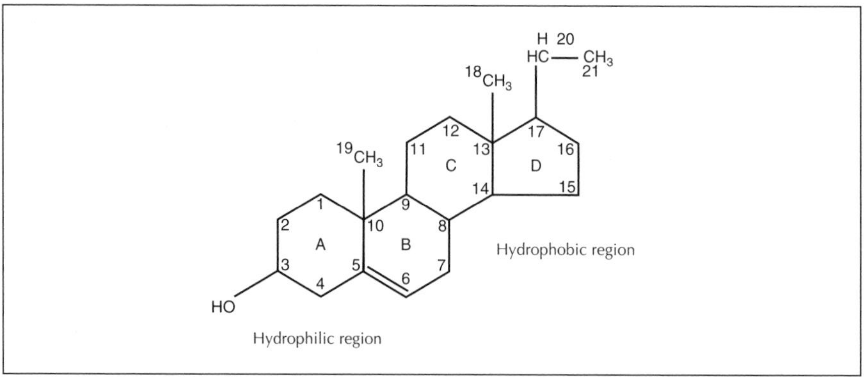

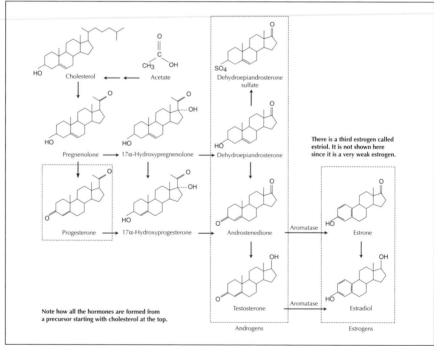

Figure 19-5. *The numbering system for steroid hormones. A basic understanding of steroids requires knowledge of their nomenclature. Three benzene rings are joined to a fourth five-carbon ring. These rings are designated A, B, C and D. The carbon numbering starts on ring A at the top, progressing counterclockwise around ring B. The numbering then changes directions and proceeds clockwise around ring C and counterclockwise around ring D. Difficult to remember, but somehow it all makes sense to chemists. Just remember carbon 3 and carbon 17—this is where the action is with estrogens.*

Figure 19-6. *Estrogen synthesis. All steroids start from cholesterol that is made from a simple molecule called acetate. Both male and female hormones follow this pathway. This synthesis is the complex sequence and shows how phytoestrogens may be related structurally to some of these compounds.*

the ER-beta is found in high levels in the prostate, the ovaries, lungs, bladder, brain and testicles. ER-beta seems to be much higher in bone tissue than ER-alpha. Much more needs to be learned in this area before the last word is written.[3]

A second surprise is that not all estrogen activity is based on nuclear DNA binding. A second type of estrogenic hormone reaction follows the same route of the membrane hormones. These estrogenic reactions often act to produce second messengers, just as the membrane hormones.

Chemistry of estrogens

Estrogens are steroids—lipid compounds made of ring structures. **Figure 19-5** shows the formation of estrogens from the precursor pregnenolone. Notice there are three rings of six carbons each, called benzene rings, and one ring structure of five carbons. All of the carbon atoms on these rings are numbered and the rings are designated by letters. Chemists start counting with the carbons in the A ring, first in a counterclockwise manner, then B ring, C ring and D ring. Then the outer carbons on ring carbons 10 and 13 are counted. These are carbons 18 and 19 respectively. The rest of the carbons are on ring carbon 17. So when you hear the term 17 beta estradiol, you will know what that means—it has a hydroxyl group on carbon 17. The male hormone testosterone is called a C19 hormone because it has a methyl group on carbon 19. Estradiol has no C19 carbon.

The carbons are numbered in **Figure 19-5**. All of the steroid hormones are formed from cholesterol as seen in the synthesis pathway in **Figure 19-6**. Estradiol is formed from testosterone by an enzyme called aromatase. It is because of the similarity between the chemical structure of the isoflavones and estrogens that physiological actions occur with the phytoestrogens.

Phytoestrogens

Why are phytoestrogens so important to our health? Because they are part of our regular diet and they have a chemical characteristic that is very similar to our own native estrogens. Since estrogens have so many biological actions and are so important to our biological functioning, the effects of phytoestrogens cannot be ignored. Phytoestrogens belong to two groups of compounds known generally as **flavonoids**. There are perhaps 4,000 or more compounds in this group. More specifically, the phytoestrogens are members of a class of **bioflavonoids** known as **isoflavones**, and a second group known as **lignans**, which are found in flax seeds and grains. **Figure 19-7** illustrates the basic flavonoid structure. Note that only the two benzene rings are given designations of A and B. The center ring contains oxygen, so it is not a benzene ring as in the estrogen molecule. Note also that the B ring is not numbered. The carbons in the rings are designation 1', 2', 3' and so forth to distinguish them from the A ring.

Flavones, also diagrammed in **Figure 19-7**, are compounds with a double-bond oxygen on the number 4 carbon of the center ring. The configuration of the isoflavones is different from the flavones seen in **Figure 19-7**. When an *iso* prefix is used in chemistry, it denotes the molecule is the same, but the position of one or more components has changed.

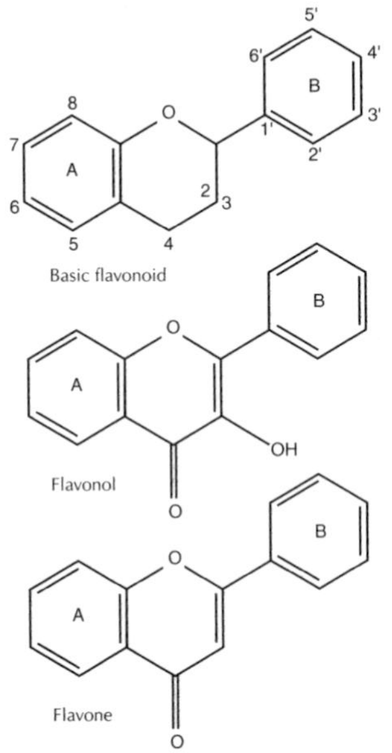

Figure 19-7. *Basic structure in bioflavonoids. As in steroid hormones, bioflavonoids are ring structures. There are two main rings—A and B—connected by an oxygen-containing ring. The naming of flavonoids is complicated by the ring structure, but dealing mainly with flavones makes it easier.*

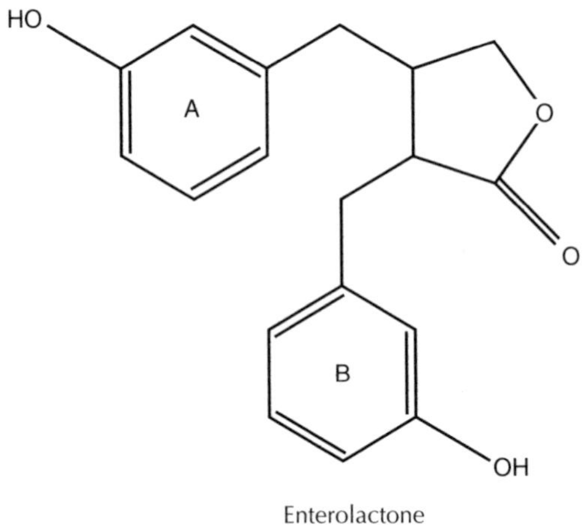

Figure 19-8. *Structure of a lignan. Lignans are derived from plant seeds. They are not flavonoids and are more complex structures. They have an A and B ring separated by a third ring, and an open ring structure. Lignans can have some phytoestrogen activity.*

The lignans are somewhat more complex, having a partial ring structure separating the A and B rings. You can see this in structure in **Figure 19-8**.

Estrogenic activity

In a study of 23 flavonoids for estrogenic activity, the following compounds were found to be the most active:[4]

Flavanones—naringenin

Flavones—apigenin

Flavonols—kaempherol

Isoflavones—genistein, daidzein, B chanin A

Dihydrochalcones—phloretin. It does not have an OH on 4′, but has an OH at 4 in the A ring.

Soybean isoflavones

The two major isoflavones in soybeans are **genistein** and **daidzein**. These compounds are diagrammed in **Figure 19-9**. Note that the difference is in the positions of the B ring. It is on carbon 2 in most flavonoids, but in isoflavones the B ring is attached to carbon 3 of the center ring. Note that the multiple ring structure and the presence of

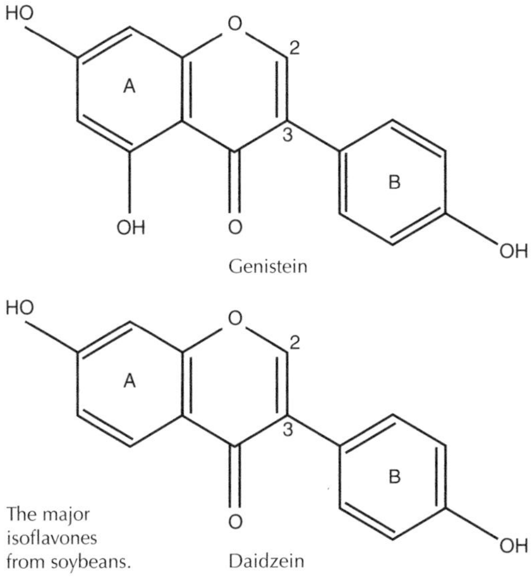

The major isoflavones from soybeans.

Figure 19-9. *The main isoflavones with estrogenic activity. Genistein has many biological activities. It currently is being studied for cancer prevention and treatment. Daidzein is very similar to genistein especially if the molecule was rotated 180 degrees on its central axis. Biologically, they differ in both specificity and potency as to estrogenic activity.*

the hydroxyl group (OH) are common to both estrogens and isoflavones. The major characteristic of flavanoids that have estrogenic activity is the presence of a hydroxyl group at the 4' carbon in the B ring. How these compounds react in the body to produce estrogenic effects can be illustrated by the action of genistein.

Action of genistein

Most of the research work on genistein has been done with tumor cells, mainly breast tumors of the type known as MCF-7. A study by Fiorvanti et al[5] explored a number of cellular mechanisms to try to explain why individuals who consumed a high soy diet had a low incidence of breast, prostatic and colon cancers.[6, 7]

Previous research had shown the binding of genistein to estrogen receptors in the uterus and the breasts.[8, 9] A second early finding was the ability of genistein to inhibit an enzyme, known as **tyrosine kinase**, responsible for new cellular growth, or cell proliferation, a characteristic of cancer cells.[10] Tumor cell growth requires a constant supply of new blood vessels, a process known as **angiogenesis**. Genistein is known to inhibit angiogenesis.[11]

These studies suggested a preventive role for phytoestrogens in hormone-related cancers. The finding of Fiorvanti and her associates confirmed the role of genistein in inhibiting breast cancer cells in vitro. They also found that estrogen stimulated cell growth in cancer cells could be blocked with genistein. One of the mechanisms revealed by this research was the common finding of a partial block in the cell division mechanism, which occurred in late DNA synthesis.

Effect of phytoestrogens

Asian populations consume the most phytoestrogens, therefore they became the focus of many studies to determine the impact of phytoestrogens on health. Asians consuming 100 grams of soybeans were getting between 50–300 milligrams of isoflavones in the form of daidzein and genistein. Compared to Westerners, the scientists found that Asians had a much lower incidence of hormone-related diseases; had a lower rate of breast, uterine and endometrial cancer; a lower rate of prostatic and colon cancer; and a lower rate of cardiovascular disease.

When Asians switched to Western-style diets—high in fat and protein and low in fiber and soy—their risk for certain hormonally related diseases increased.[12]

The studies with animals and tissue-cultured cells has proved mechanisms for these actions, but in addition to inhibiting cancer cells, genistein has been shown to convert cancer-type cells into mature non-cancer type cells, a process called **differentiation**. Some new information on the action of phytoestrogens suggests quite a different role for isoflavones. A disorder known as the Osler-Weber-Rendu syndrome (OWR) is characterized by multiple episodes of nose bleeds lasting as long as three to six days.[13] An initial study at Yale University with OWR patients on a soy diet containing isoflavones experienced an almost complete cessation of bleeding.[14] The fascinating part of this finding is that OWR is caused by genetic mutations that produce defects in proteins involved in signaling pathways initiated by **transforming growth factor beta**, or **TGFb**. The investigators do not know why this occurs, but it suggests that TGFb may be involved in other signaling disorders such as cancer, heart disease and osteoporosis since all these diseases have some response to soy treatment.[15]

Estheticians and phytoestrogens

What does all this data mean to estheticians? For one thing, many products will contain higher levels of phytoestrogens as more knowledge is gained and they become more available commercially. Presently, there are no known products on the market that contain adequate levels of phytoestrogens because of its high cost. Research continues, however, and within the year new phytoestrogen skin care products may be found in the professional market. **Phytoestrogens and Future Skin Care Products** lists some of these. Much more needs to be done before there is a final answer on phytoestrogens, but the evidence so far is encouraging for a wider acceptance and application.

Any product that contains genistein will be good for skin disorders such as psoriasis. Soy-based products contain genistein and daidzein, which inhibit rapid cellular growth, and also are effective hydration ingredients found in a number of plant materials. Acne treatment programs can benefit from phytoestrogens, as can dry skin and mature skin programs. Cellulite should respond to isoflavones since they will block the effect of estrogens on the connective tissue surrounding the fatty tissue. Estrogens support collagenase secretion, which attacks connective tissue making it weak. By blocking this action, isoflavones will reduce, or prevent the tendency of the fatty tissue to herniated into the dermis.

Phytoestrogens and Future Skin Care Products

Based on the current understanding of the mechanisms of phytoestrogens, here are some things to look for in new skin care products.

1. Acne products containing phytoestrogens and other bioflavonoids.

2. Oral and topical anti-aging products containing phytoestrogens and lignans.

3. New treatments for cellulite and other connective tissue problems.

4. Safe inhibitors of proliferation to treat psoriasis and eczema.

5. Products that accelerate wound healing.

6. Safe, non-irritating de-pigmenting agents, or skin lightening agents.

7. A range of oral products that will work synergistically with topical products.

8. Ultraviolet protection. One patent has been issued for this product.

HRT and phytoestrogens

A great deal of information exists on the subject of hormone replacement therapy (HRT)—many pros and some cons. It appears from the literature that estrogen replacement has three major benefits in women who have reached menopause.

1. The prevention of osteoporosis, a debilitating disease that deforms and incapacitates the individual.

2. The positive effect on the cardiovascular system. Although greatly debated, the evidence strongly favors HRT for protection of the cardiovascular system.

3. The positive effect on the nervous system, particularly the brain, in delaying and perhaps helping to prevent Alzheimer's disease.

There are many others, therefore I have listed references for the interested reader. Here are a few examples. Autoimmune disease afflicted women 4:1 compared to men, and while we know that gender and sex hormones have a clear effect in these diseases, we do not know why. The phytoestrogens open an avenue to using hormone-active compounds without the side effects of our native hormones.[16]

Much has been written about postmenopausal use of phytoestrogens, yet little had been written about pre-menopausal use. Interesting research showed that soy consumption had no significant effect on the menstrual cycle, serum sex hormones or urinary estrogen metabolite ratio, either in women who used oral contraceptives or those who did not use them.[17]

An excellent reference for the vascular effects of estrogen centers on the direct effect of estrogen on the blood vessel.[18]

Finally, there is a reference on the effect of estrogen during menopause to prevent Alzheimer's disease. One clearly written article shows that estrogen in menopause decreases the risk of Alzheimer's, or delays the onset of the disease.[19]

While I strongly urge hormone replacement for menopausal women, it remains an individual decision. A physician is the best professional to advise on the risks versus benefits. As an esthetician, you should know if your client is taking estrogen, since those who do will have a slower progression of changes associated with aging skin. It also is important to know as new products are introduced that are not prescribed drugs. Use of these products may not be compatible to estrogens that are prescribed by physicians.

A happier client

We stand on the threshold of a very exciting period in esthetics. A better understanding of human physiology, of the skin, and the action of the products used in treatments and for home care, will make for better treatment modalities, a happier client and a more successful esthetician.

References

1. Actually in the arcuate nucleus of the medial-basal hypothalamus and in the preoptic area of the ventral hypothalamus. Check Sheppard G, *Neurobiology*, second edition, New York: Oxford Press (1988)

2. Niewoehner CB, *Endocrine Pathophysiology*, Madison, CN: Fence Creek Books

3. Estrogen Receptors U.S. Pharmacist Continuing Education Web site, *www.uspharmacist.com*

4. Breinholt V and Larsen JC, Detection of weak estrogenic flavonoids using a recombinant yeast strain and a modified MCF-7 cell proliferation essay. *Chem Res Toxicol* 11:622–629 (1997)

5. Fiorvanti, L et al, Genistein in the control of breast cancer cell growth: insights into the mechansims of action in vitro. *Cancer Letters*, 130:143–152 (1998)

6. Adlercruetz H, Setchell KDR, Mammalian lignans and phytoestrogens. Recent studies on their formation, metabolism and biological role in health and disease, in Rowland LR (Ed.), *Role of the Gut Flora in Toxicity and Cancer* London: Academic Press, 315–345 (1988)

7. Adlercreutz H, Western diet and western diseases: some hormonal and biochemical mechanisms and association. *Scand J Clin Lab Invest* 50:3–23 (1990)

8. Cox RI, Shutt, DA, Steroid and phytoestrogen binding to sheep uterine receptors in vitro. *J Endocrinol* 52:299–310 (l972)

9. Horwitz KB, Martin PM, McGuire WL and Ryan DS, Phytoestrogen interaction with estrogen receptors in human breast cancer cells. *Endocrinology* 103:1860–1867 (1978)

10. Akiyama T, Fukamo Y, Ishida J, Itoh N, Nakagawa H, Shihuy AM and Watanabe S, Genistein: a specific inhibitor of tyrosine-specific protein kinases. *J Biol Chem* 202 (1987)

11. Adlercreutz H, Fleischmann T, Fotsis M, Hase R, Montesano L, Pepper H and Schweigerer L, Genistein, a dietary-derived inhibitor of in vitro angiogenesis. *Proc Natl Acad Sd USA* 90:2690–2694 (1993)

12. EHP 104 (5) Focus, available from *ehpnet1.niehs.nih.gov/docs/1996/104-5/focus.html* and from *www.mayohealth.org/mayo/common/htm/womenpg.html*

13. Guttmacher AE, Marchuk DA, White RI, Jr, Heredity hemorrhagic telangiesctasia. *New Engl J Mdc* 333:918–24 (1995)

14. Korzenik JR, Barnes S, White RI, Jr, A pilot study of soy protein isolated in the treatment of hereditary hemorrhagic telangiectasia (HHT): possible efficacy in HHT associated epistaxis, gastrointestinal hemorrhage and migraine. *Am J Clin Nutr* accepted for publication.

15. Baldwin MA, Gaffione C, Grogg KM, Helmbold EA, Jackson CE, Johnson DW, Markel DS, McAllister KA, McKinnon WC, Murrell J and et al, Endoglin, a TGF-beta binding protein of endothelial cells, is the gene for hereditary hemorrhagic telangiectasia type 1. *Nature Genetics* 8:345–51 (1994)

16. Schuurs AHWM and Verheul HAM, Effects of gender and sex steroids on the immune response. *J Steroid Biochem* 35:157–172 (1990)

17. Martini MC et al, Effects of soy intake on sex hormone metabolism in pre-menopausal women. *Nutr Cancer* 43:133–139 (1999)

18. Farharm MY et al, The vascular protective effects of estrogen. *FASEB* 10:615–624 (1996)

19. Ming-Xin Tang et al, Effect of estrogen during menopause on risk and age of onset of Alzheimer's disease. *Lancet* 384:429–432 (1996)

Chapter 20

Menopausal Skin

A knowledge of reproductive physiology is needed to appreciate the relationship of menopause to the structure and function of the skin. Human reproduction, in the simplest of terms, is the sum total of all of the events that occur in the act of uniting an egg cell and a sperm cell to produce a newborn child.

A review of female reproductive physiology forms the basis of the discussion on skin and menopause. The main physiological event in the female involves producing an egg, or ovum, in a periodic fashion throughout her reproductive life. Beginning with the hormonal system that produces the rhythmic menstrual cycle, how these hormones relate to skin care is then studied. Finally, what happens when these hormones are withdrawn and menopause begins is discussed. Keep in mind that hormones are nothing more than messengers—chemical signals that communicate instructions to other cells. Here is a brief overview of the endocrine system.

The endocrine system

Many functions of the body are regulated by a series of glands called endocrine glands. A gland is a special type of organ that secretes a specific chemical substance. There are many types of glands such as digestive glands that act on food; sebaceous glands that secrete oils onto the skin and affect acne; glands that make tears; and glands that secrete chemical messengers, which work directly on other cells, each carrying with it a specific message. These messengers are called hormones. All the glands that secrete hormones are combined into a system called the endocrine system. When a message is sent, there must be a receiver; in the case of the hormone message, the receiver is called the target cell. These are the three essentials of the endocrine system: the **endocrine gland**, the **hormone** and the **target cell**.

One more very important concept needed to understand hormone action on the target cell is the concept of the **hormone receptor**. It is far beyond the scope of this chapter to discuss hormone receptors in detail, but an understanding of the role of hormone receptors in receiving and reacting to chemical signals is essential. Without a specific cellular receptor to interact with the hormone, no action can take place regardless of the amount of hormone present. Some hormones act on the cell surface while other hormones, such as the sex hormone, penetrate the cell membrane and act within the cell.

Since this topic is limited to reproductive physiology let's look at the hormones involved in reproduction, for they are the same hormones that are related to skin and menopause.

Reproductive endocrinology or the sex hormones

The ovary is the key organ in reproduction. The eggs, or ova, are produced in the ovary, usually one each month. While the ovary contains hundreds of thousands of unripe ova, oocytes, at birth, only 360–400 ova reach maturity in a woman's reproductive lifetime.

There are four organs and three levels of hormones involved in ovulation. The organs are the inner brain, the hypothalamus; the anterior pituitary gland; the ovaries; and the uterus. The three levels of hormones are the follicle stimulating hormone (FSH), the luteinizing hormone (LH), and estrogen and progesterone which, although different hormones, are produced at the same level of the system.

Ova production is under hormonal control, starting with the inner brain. The inner brain secretes a **gonadatropic-releasing hormone*** (GnRH), that works on the anterior pituitary gland, the most important gland in the endocrine system. The anterior pituitary gland can be looked at as the master gland for the rest of the menstrual cycle. This master gland secretes FSH and LH, two very important hormones that work primarily on the ovary. These two hormones operating on the ovary produce estrogen and progesterone, the major female hormones that in turn have effects on the sex organs and other tissues. As these hormones and events are related to the menstrual cycle, their functions will be clarified.

Hormones and phases of the menstrual cycle

The ovary contains immature eggs, or oocytes, each with 46 chromosomes and each contained in a primary follicle. Look at **Figure 20-1** and follow the 28-day menstrual cycle.

The menstrual cycle is divided into two phases, the follicular phase and the luteal phase. The follicular phase starts on day one with menstrual bleeding. Estrogen and progesterone levels are low while FSH and LH are mildly elevated. For the next five days not much occurs except that the primary follicles begin to develop. On day seven, the FSH and LH hormones begin to rise under stimulation of the initiating hormone from the inner brain. Also, the dominant follicle is selected from among many primary follicles. How and why a particular follicle is selected is unknown. The other developing follicles vanish and degenerate.

Over the next six days the estrogen will rise sharply with a slow rise in progesterone. Just before ovulation this ovum undergoes a mitotic reduction division known as meiosis during which two daughter cells are produced with 23 chromosomes each.

---

* Gonad-o-trophic means toward, or directed to the gonads. The gonads are the ovaries and the testicles.

Only one of these will become a mature ovum. Eighteen hours before ovulation there is a large rise in LH and a small rise in FSH.

On day 14, the follicle ripens and ruptures releasing the ovum, which ends the follicular phase and starts the luteal phase. The ovary secretes estrogen under stimulation of FSH. The ruptured follicle will become the *corpus luteum*, which in Latin means "yellow body," a transient part of the ovary that continues to secrete both estrogen and progesterone.

If no pregnancy takes place, the estrogen level will fall while the progesterone level will begin to rise. Progesterone is under control of LH and is secreted in the follicle. There also is a very rapid fall in LH and FSH. Between days 20 and 25 progesterone reaches a peak while estrogen rises again and then falls. Both estrogen and progesterone fall rapidly between day 25 and day 28. Around day 27, FSH and LH begin to rise again to start the cycle anew. This pattern is diagrammed in **Figure 20-2**.

This is the basic menstrual cycle and the essential hormones involved in the cycle. The effect these hormones have on the reproductive tissues is the next topic.

Hormone effects on the uterus

Estrogen and progesterone act on the uterus to prepare the inner surface, the endometrium, for pregnancy. After the menstrual bleeding stops the endometrium goes through a proliferative phase, first under the action of estrogen, and later under the combined action of estrogen and progesterone. This proliferative phase lasts ten days and is characterized by a buildup of the tissues in the endometrium. Estrogen primes the endometrium for the action of progesterone, which induces the tissue to produce an environment that is hospitable for an embryo.

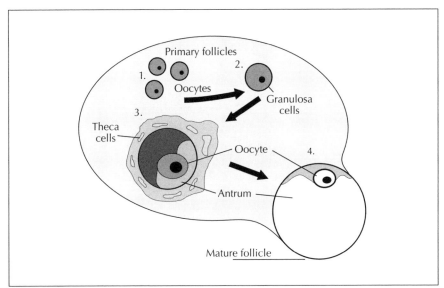

Figure 20-1. *Stages of follicular development in the ovary: 1–3) primary follicles to mature follicle is part of follicular phase, and 4) follicle ruptures, starting luteal phase.*

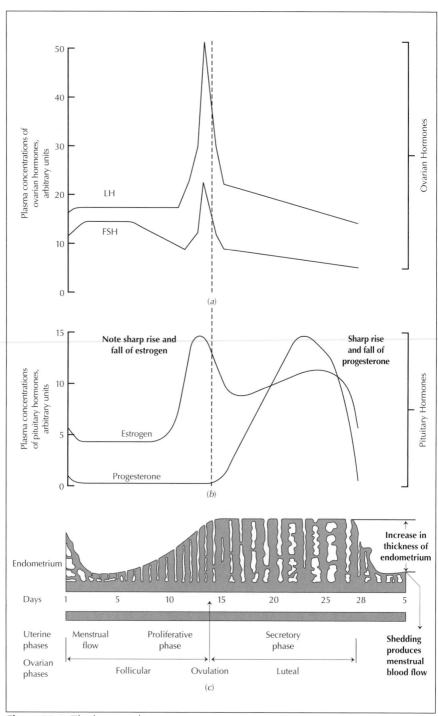

Figure 20-2. The hormonal pattern.

Glycogen-containing glands and increased blood vessels are produced under the action of progesterone. Glycogen is a complex sugar used as an energy storage molecule. It is the shedding of this tissue that forms most of the bleeding stage of menses. An additional function of estrogen is to produce a clear, thin cervical mucous that will allow easy flow of the sperm cells, should they be present. Progesterone, on the other hand, creates a thick mucous to prevent the passage of sperm or bacteria into the uterus after ovulation.

Estrogen also is responsible for increasing the contraction and ciliary action of the uterine tubes. The cilia are hair-like projections that move the ovum along the tubes. The tissue of the vagina undergoes increased thickening, a cornification, of the surface cells in the presence of estrogen. Progesterone has the opposite effect on the uterine tubes and on the vaginal tissue. This process repeats itself each month as long as everything is functioning well.

As a review, the major female reproductive hormones are FSH, LH, estrogen and progesterone, and the organs involved are the inner brain, the anterior pituitary gland, the ovaries and the uterus. Next, the effects of these hormones on other body tissues are examined.

Physiological effects of estrogen and progesterone

Estrogen is a decidedly female hormone, so the effect of estrogen to augment female attributes would be expected. Typical female body contours, such as narrow shoulders and broad hips, as well as female fat deposition in the breasts, buttocks and abdomen, are estrogen-induced. Development of external genitalia and pubic hair distribution patterns are estrogen-regulated, although pubic hair growth is androgen-controlled. Breast development, mainly ductal and fat deposition, is stimulated by estrogen, while progesterone stimulates the milk glands of the breast to develop.

There are profound effects of estrogen on the growth of bone since estrogen regulates calcium metabolism in the bones; more of this will be brought out when menopause is discussed. Estrogen also affects the vascular system, helps keep blood vessels supple and controls vasomotor reactions, such as hot flashes. Pregnancy produces several pigment changes in the skin particularly about the nipples, the genitalia and the linea alba, which is the line running up the middle of the abdomen. The appearance of a mask-like hyperpigmentation on the face is the most common pigment change seen in pregnancy, occurring in about 50% of women. The cause of these pigment changes is not understood completely, but there is some evidence that the melanocytes become activated by higher levels of estrogen and progesterone.

The concept of the hormone rececptor

In later chapters hormone receptors will be covered in more detail, but it is critical that the newer developments in molecular biology that have thrown light onto the various actions of estrogen be understood. Previously it was thought that only one estrogen receptor was responsible for all the effects of estrogen on the cell. It's now known there actually are two estrogen receptors, or ER, **ER alpha** and **ER beta**.

Both estrogen receptors share 97% of the amino acids in their deoxyribonucleic (DNA)-binding domain, that is the part of the receptor that binds to the DNA, but the ligand-binding domains share only about 60% of the amino acids. This finding has helped in understanding the various effects of estrogens on different tissues and organs. For example, it's been known for a long time that estrogens have a very positive effect on brain cells, but the amount of estrogen receptors found in the brain was quite low. Now it's known that ER alpha, the first estrogen receptor identified and studied, was not prevalent in the brain, **but ER beta is plentiful.**

While this concept is complex, consider first that some estrogens will bind to only one type of receptors and that not all tissues have the same receptor types, so a different response with various tissues and various estrogens can be expected. ER alpha is found in the uterus, pituitary, ovary, kidney and adrenal gland, while ER beta is found in the prostate, ovary, lung bladder, brain, uterus and testes. Thus *it is known that estrogens are selective hormones and have selective effects.*

Physiological effects of sex hormones on the skin

The skin contains receptors for several types of hormones, but this discussion shall limit the interest mainly to estrogen and progesterone activity in the skin.[1] Receptors for hormones can be either on the cell membrane surface or within the inner liquid portion of the cell, the cytoplasm.

The purpose of the receptor is to recognize the presence of the hormone and then convey the message to the nucleus where the definitive action takes place. The response to hormones can be increased cellular proliferation, secretion of some substance or an inhibition of some activity. These are the actions of estrogen on the skin:

1. increase mitotic rate in the epidermis,[2]
2. reduce the size and activity of the sebaceous gland,[3]
3. slow the rate of hair growth,[4]
4. stimulate the synthesis and turnover of collagen,[5] and
5. increase the production of hyaluronic acid.[6, 7]

The action of progesterone on the skin is unknown. Receptors for progesterone are present in the skin, being more prevalent in the skin of the breast and less in the skin of the pubic area.[8] It has been suggested that progesterone blocks the action of estrogen receptors in the skin. The time course of the estrogen block was most effective after ovulation.[9, 10] In lower primates, a turgid pink to red sexual skin is a sign of receptivity. It is evident that a prime function of estrogen in the skin is to keep it metabolically active, producing a soft, supple and well-hydrated skin.

Study continues on the effects of estrogen on skin fibroblasts. Fibroblasts are known to contain estrogen and to produce hyaluronic acid. Sequential treatment of primates with estrogen and progesterone results in increased hyaluronate and collagen biosynthesis and an increase in fibroblast estrogen receptors.[11] This activity indicates a very important role for sex hormones in the skin, much of which is reduced in menopause. In order to appreciate the impact of menopause on the skin, it is helpful to see the global effects of menopause on the body.

Menopause—winding down reproduction

The end of a woman's reproductive years is signaled by a gradual shutting down of the reproductive organs. This process, starting between 45 and 55, and continuing for about seven years, is brought about by a cessation of sex hormone production. It is easy to see why the manifest symptoms of menopause are present.

The first step appears to be in the ovaries, starting with a slow narrowing of the size of the arteries that leads to a reduction in ovarian size with eventual replacement of the functional structure of the ovary, parenchyma, with connective tissue. This of course reduces estrogen production, causing increased production of FSH, and unopposed progesterone activity. The net result is irregular periods, heavy bleeding and heat flashes until the whole system finally shuts down. Withdrawing estrogen stimulation results also in atrophy of the breasts, vagina and vulva. The effects on bone metabolism are even more marked.

Bone metabolism and menopause—osteoporosis

Calcium and vitamin D are needed for bone growth and maintenance. The action of vitamin D is to increase the rate of transfer of calcium from the stomach to the bloodstream. About 600 mg of calcium is needed daily at a minimum just to meet the normal demand. In menopause this is too little; the required amount can exceed 1000 mg or more a day, since the loss of bone mass varies from 0.5–3% a year during menopause.[12] The greatest decline occurs between the ages of 45 and 70.

In osteoporosis, the major effect of estrogen is to block activation of bone metabolism. Estrogen has two effects on bone metabolism; the first is to facilitate the uptake of calcium from the blood into bone, and the second is to inhibit loss of calcium from bone by blocking bone resorption. The osteoblast cells in the bone are responsible for both building up and tearing down bone structure. When bone mass is lost, the condition known as osteoporosis results due to a decrease in bone density. Bones of the spine and hips are fractured easily from even moderate stress. Loss of height occurs first in osteoporosis followed by a postural change known as the Dowager's Hump. If estrogen therapy is started at the time of menopause, the loss of bone will be minimal and bone density will remain the same.

It is beyond the purpose of this chapter to go into this topic in great detail, although the dangers of osteoporosis cannot be overstated. An excellent treatment of this topic with rich references on osteoporisis and bone physiology along with the effects of estrogen can be found on the Web site **http://uwcme.org/courses/bonephys/opestrogen.html**.

Estrogen replacement for menopausal women

This is a much-discussed and debated topic, too involved for a book of this type, but it is important to mention some aspect of it. An excellent reference can be found on the Web at **http://www.hcrc.org/contrib/taylor/menop.html**, which describes alternatives to conventional medical management of menopause.

Changes in the skin

The lack of estrogen within the skin produces a decrease in dermal glycosoaminoglycans, which in turn causes a decrease in both the thickness and suppleness of it. The feel of the skin, while less smooth, can remain quite soft. Light reflectivity decreases, leaving the surface looking dull and dry. Dryness though, from a physiological viewpoint, that is less total water in the skin, has not been shown to be a characteristic of aging skin. Accumulation of by-products due to free radical-induced peroxidation of lipids, fatty material, adds to the discoloration of the skin; however, this is not directly related to estrogen deficit.

Perhaps the most important aspect of decreased estrogen in the skin is the unopposed action of testosterone. Estrogen helps to control acne and to keep the size of the sebaceous gland small while reducing sebaceous secretion. Unopposed by normal levels of estrogen, testosterone is free to work its havoc. Remember that testosterone is an androgenic, male, hormone and in the female is produced mainly by the adrenal glands. Testosterone is converted to estrogen in the ovaries during the reproductive years, but as the ovaries cease to function the level of testosterone increases.

Testosterone effects on the skin are not pleasant for women. An increase in terminal hairs on the face makes its unwelcome appearance around the middle of menopause. Sebaceous glands grow larger and the pore size increases. Sebum becomes more abundant, and the return of acne or appearance of seborrheic dermatitis occurs.

Keratoderma climactericum can occur at the time of menopause. This is thickening of the stratum corneum that is most frequently seen on the soles of the feet and palms of the hands and frequently is associated with obesity. The heel often is involved and can show marked hypertrophy of the stratum corneum.

Recent studies have shown that estrogen replamcement will increase collagen fibers in the skin and that the extracellular matrix is improved as well as the hair and other skin appendages.[13]

Treatment of menopausal skin

Hormone replacement therapy is number one. Without the loss of the ovaries there would be no lack of sex hormones and thus no menopause. The use of estrogen and progesterone replacement therapy has had a pronounced beneficial effect for women in menopause. Hormones have been studied extensively since the 1940s. After a great deal of research, most physicians believe that hormone replacement therapy is both safe and effective.[14, 15] This therapy must be controlled by a physician skilled in the art of hormone replacement. Many physicians use a combination of estrogen and progesterone, while some use only estrogen for three weeks out of the month. In any event, it is best to recommend your client to a physician to determine if she is a candidate for hormone replacement. Most hormones are synthetic, although some are obtained from the urine of pregnant mares.

It is well established that replacement hormones have a positive effect on the skin.[16, 17] The collagen will thicken and the tone and hue of the skin will improve.[18] While the effect is most noticeable in women with marked collagen atrophy, even mild cases can benefit.

Calcium replacement therapy

As was mentioned previously, calcium is essential for strong bones—something that's been heard since grade school. As individuals age and the diet changes, there is a slip away from high calcium food to low calcium food just when calcium is needed the most. At least 1,000 mg of calcium a day are needed by menopausal women and about 600 mg a day for those women who are still in their reproductive years. Along with the calcium, vitamin D and an exercise program that will provide a moderate amount of bone stress is needed. Bone will not develop strength unless it is stressed. Most fitness programs offer a range of exercises that are designed to stress the bones.

Calcium tablets can be taken, though some of these are not easily dissolved in the stomach. Taking vitamin C with the calcium helps to overcome this problem. Calcium citrate is one form that does dissolve easily. The intake of high calcium foods such as dairy products, particularly yogurt, also sardines and canned mackerel, can be increased. Vegetables are not loaded with calcium, but they are a calcium source with collard greens and mustard green having a high content.

What the esthetician can do

The challenge for the esthetician with a client in menopause is to restore a potentially dull and sagging skin to a skin that is firm, resilient and radiant—a tough problem, but quite doable. Here are some suggestions.

A monthly facial for cleansing and massage is recommended. Use gentle cleansers. You do not need a rough abrasive cleanser; they do not "deep clean." This is a myth; besides they raise havoc with sensitive skin.

The benefit of a massage with heat is the increase in the epidermal growth factor that it produces. Use moist heat and massage gently for at least five minutes.

Develop a positive mental attitude

Assuming you have a client who is under hormone replacement therapy, this is a great opportunity to help that client improve her skin. Foremost is the psychological benefit you can provide. Stress produces a great deal of adrenaline—and cortisone-type hormones. The adrenaline increases blood pressure, decreases circulation to the skin and increases heart rate. These actions speed up metabolism, producing more metabolic by-products such as lipid peroxides that destroy or impede normal body functions. An increase in cortisone-type hormones has profound effects on many body functions, such as fat and sugar metabolism, and the content of elastin and collagen in the skin. These are stress hormones designed to be available for brief moments in times of emergency. Imagine living in a constant state of emergency! A healthy mind with a positive outlook will go a long way to maintaining the sex hormones in optimum balance.

Women who are well-nourished, happy and considerate of their bodies tend to enter menopause at a later age than depressed women who are poorly nourished. Not too many years ago women who became pregnant at 50+ years were quite rare, but today it has ceased to be a rarity. A positive lifestyle does a great deal to keep the mind functioning well. The interaction of mind and body can harmonize to produce a healthy, young body far beyond traditional expectations. Here are some suggestions to share with your clients.

Exercise. Approaching menopause from the inside and the outside gives us a therapeutic advantage. The body does not recognize aging or aging changes as something that needs to be fixed or repaired. No one knows why this is the case, but it is. The reparative process always is present in the body, but it needs to be activated. Simple exercise can produce firmer, stronger muscles even in individuals who are 85 and older. Walking three times a week, or exercising moderately even 15 minutes a day goes a long way to keeping the body in shape. This activity forces the repair system into action to restore body tissues to a more youthful and functional state.

Sun protection. Sunscreens and sunscreens and more sunscreens are needed as women enter menopause. The number of melanocytes decreases with age so there is less natural protection. Using sunscreen of SPF 8–15 is adequate in most cases, but women with red hair or type I skin may need an SPF 20+ sunscreen. You do not outgrow the need for sunscreens. In fact, using a sunscreen even when going shopping can help maintain healthy skin.

Good dental hygiene and chewing muscles. Here is another area that cannot be overstated. You must chew food to have a good-looking face. The mandible is the key bone in the face that determines the shape of the rest of the face. All the muscles of mastication relate to moving the mandible. If you lose your teeth and stop chewing the following catastrophic events happen:

1. the mandible will atrophy causing the chin to protrude and the mouth to recede;

2. the upper jaw, or maxilla, will atrophy and the mouth will assume a turtle-like shape;

3. the cheekbone, or zygoma, will no longer need to support the masseter muscle, the major chewing muscle, so it will atrophy and give the face the sunken-in appearance of a very old face; and

4. the temporalis muscle anchored to the head, will no longer need a strong anchoring point so the skull will thin out and become smaller.

The net result is a small head, shrunken face and turtle-mouth. Save your teeth, and keep chewing. You just can't have good-looking skin over a shrunken, toothless head.

Stop smoking. Old-looking skin is guaranteed by cigarette smoking. In fact, this is one of the few absolutes in this universe; smoking absolutely can promise you terrible-looking skin. There also is convincing evidence that smoking will hasten the onset of menopause and the more cigarettes smoked, the earlier the menopause.[19]

Lymphatic drainage massage. Venous stasis, the accumulation of blood in the veins, is not uncommon in menopause. It can lead to varicose veins. Women in the 50+ group often experience swollen legs and ankles. This condition can be helped with support hose and walking, but lymphatic drainage massage at regular intervals will help the appearance of the legs and the well-being of the client. Facial lymphatic drainage massage also is of great benefit if done by a skilled and knowledgeable practitioner.

The art of applying makeup. Women who know how to apply makeup effectively are less depressed than those who don't. It is not the quantity of products used, but how well they are applied. Part of the task of the esthetician is to instruct the client in the proper application of makeup. Not only will this service give you a great deal of satisfaction, but also will make your client happier and more productive. Remember that good-looking clients are your best business-builders.

Menopause is a milestone in life, produced by some physiological responses, causing the ovaries to shut down the production of sex hormones. With hormone replacement therapy there is no need to fear menopause.

A lifestyle that is characterized by a positive mental outlook, continuing activity and a healthy diet is the backbone of delaying the onset of menopause. Calcium intake must be increased to at least 1000 mg daily during menopause along with vitamin D and continuing moderate exercise. The use of multiple vitamin supplements and antioxidants, protection from the sun, and regular treatment by a competent and caring esthetician will go a long way in keeping the menopausal skin looking supple and radiant.

References

1. Hasselquist MB et al, Isolation and characterization of the estrogen receptor in human skin, *J Clin Endocrinol Metab* 50: 76 (1980)

2. Stumpf WE et al, Estrogen target cells in the skin, *Experientia* 30: 196 (1976)

3. Bullough WS, Hormones and mitotic activity, *Vitam Horm* 13: 261 (1955)

4. Ebling FJ, The effect of cyproterone acetate and oestradiol upon testosterone stimulated sebaceous activity in the rat, *Act Endocrinol* 72: 361 (1973)

5. Johnson E, Quantitative studies of hair growth in the albino rat–the effects of sex hormones, *J Endocrinol* 16: 351 (1958)

6. Koa KY, Effects of estradiol benzoate upon collagen synthesis by sponge biopsy of connective tissue, *Proc Soc Exp Biol Med* 119: 364 (1965)

7. Sobel H et al, Effects of estrogen on acid glycosoaminoglycans in skin of mice, *Biochem Biophys Acta* 101: 225 (1965)

8. Uzaka M, Induction of hyaluronic acid synthetase by estrogen in mouse skin, *Biochem Biophys Acta* 673: 387 (1981)

9. Mowszowicz I et al, Multiple steroid binding sites in human skin cytosol, *Br J Dermatol* 107: (suppl 23) 35 (1982)

10. West NB et al, Progesterone treatment suppresses estrogen receptors in the skin of the Macaca nemestrina, *J Steroid Biochem* 35: 481 (1990)

11. Bentley JP et al, Increased hyaluronate and collagen biosynthesis and fibroblast estrogen receptors in macaque skin sex, *J Invest Dermat* 87: 668 (1986)

12. Gambrell RD, The menopause: benefits and risk of estrogen/progesterone replacement therapy, *Fertil Steril* 37: 457 (1982)

13. Brincat MP, Hormone replacement therapy and skin. *Maturitas* 36:107–117, 2000

14. Campbell S and Whitehead M, Oestrogen therapy and the menopausal syndrome, *Clinics in Obstet and Gynecol* 4: 31 (1977)

15. Byrd B et al, The impact of long-term estrogen support after hysterectomy: a report of 1016 cases, *Ann Surg* 185: 574 (1977)

16. Punonen R, Effects of castration and peroral estrogen on the skin, *Acta Obstet et Gynecol Scand*, suppl 21: 1 (1972)

17. Punonen R and Rauramo I, The effects of long-term oral estriol succinate therapy on the skin of castrated women, *Ann Chir Gynecol* 66: 214 (1977)

18. Brincat M, Skin collagen changes in post–menopausal women receiving estradiol gel, *Maturitas* 9: 1 (1987)

19. Jick H et al, Relationship between smoking and age of natural menopause: report from the Boston Collaborative Surveillance Program, Boston University Medical Center, *Lancet* 1: 1354 (1977)

General References

Alberts B et al, *Molecular Biology of the Cell*, Garland Publishing, Inc.: New York (1989). An excellent review of hormone receptor physiology and general cell physiology.

Cutler WB and Garcia CR, *Menopause–A Guide for Women and the Men Who Love Them*, WW Norton Company: New York (1992). An excellent comprehensive treatment of the subject.

Hershman JM, *Endocrine Pathophysiology*, Lea and Febiger: Philadelphia (1988). A very good text that covers what happens when things go wrong with the endocrine system.

Vander AJ, MD, Sherman JH, PhD, and Luciano DS, PhD, *Human Physiology*, McGraw Hill: New York (1990). An easy-to-read explanation of the reproductive physiology.

Chapter 21

New Concepts on Aging

What is aging? No one knows. Why do we age? Everyone has some answer or theory. Never have so many known so much about so little. Detailed studies of the literature on aging will confound readers at first and disappoint them later. In the last few years, a great deal of data has been generated on aging mechanisms trying to determine if the aging process is a single event, a one-gene process, or a multifaceted process produced by many events and perhaps many genes. No one knows as yet.

This chapter introduces concepts in aging mechanisms, some definitions of aging, some very current developments and some possible means to delay the onset of the aging process. It also presents an introduction to **telomeres**, the marvelous structures that make very long life possible.

Why is knowledge of aging mechanisms important to an esthetician? By the end of this chapter I hope you will know the answer to this question.

Anti-aging miracle products

At every industry trade show, skin care specialists are flooded with the wonder products of anti-aging, but often are offered little scientific background for how these products work. Estheticians need to look in-depth at everything and anything presented about a product. Education is the key to the effective practice of esthetics. Here are a few basic concepts about aging mechanisms that will help in your evaluation.

What is aging?

Most of us define aging in terms of the appearance of people in our life experience. One scientist said that aging is the process that allows us to tell teenagers from their grandparents, which is a good definition. Other scientists studying aging mechanisms define aging as a decrease in functional capacity. This essentially means that at 60 you can't do the things you could do at 20—your body just is not the same. If you are still in your 20s, you will not fully understand this until you reach 60.

Not all bodily functions slow down or stop. In fact, very few actually shut down completely. The thymus gland, for example, atrophies at a very young age. This being the case, many scientists began looking at the aging process from a cellular viewpoint rather than looking at the whole body. At this stage of knowledge, it may be the best way to study aging.

Cellular basis of aging

In **Figure 21-1**, a simple cell with the major components is shown. Consider the cell as a small transparent ball, much the same as a bubble filled with water would be viewed. Outside is the **cell membrane**, a lipid-filled layer that contains many receptors to catch signals from other cells and then transfer these signals into the cell. The receptors can be compared to the process of answering the doorbell. You hear the ring, go to the door, check to see who rang the bell, and then decide if you will open the door. The cell must have the means to recognize and interpret these signals and then transmit them through the cytoplasm to the nucleus. The **cytoplasm** is a fluid that fills the cells.

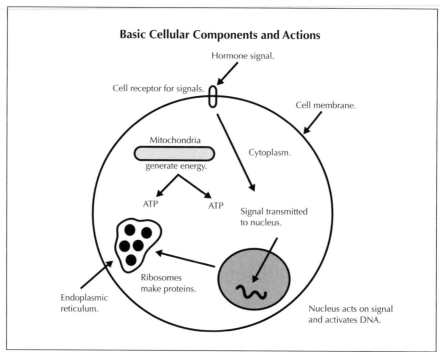

Figure 21-1. Note that the cell membrane receives signals that are transmitted to the interior of the cell. This process causes the cell to start activity in the nucleus, all of which involves deoxyribonucleic acid (DNA).

It is an extraordinarily complex material that surrounds the three basic structures that will command our interest in this chapter. The first is the **nucleus**, the second is the **mitochondria** and the third is the **endoplasmic reticulum**.

The cell is designed to survive, not to age. There are no known inherent, or normal, aging mechanisms in cells that would make it dysfunctional over time. We are not programmed to self-destruct and only adverse conditions cause us to age.

Multi-cellular organisms do have a gene that will destroy a cell that is abnormal and detrimental to the rest of the cells, or one that can no longer contribute to the good of the entire body. This gene is the p53 gene and it is a separate topic, but deserves mentioning here.

Three basic cellular structures

The **nucleus** contains deoxyribonucleic acid (DNA). This material holds the genetic code of all life processes. It is a topic all by itself and entire books have been written on DNA. You need to know that the DNA code consists of a sequence of just four compounds known as adenine, thymine, cytosine and guanine, or ATCG. The sequence is exact for each type of protein made in the body. Any variation from the sequence leads to either a misfunction of the protein or no protein at all. DNA can be viewed as a template on which the proteins are made. The template is tightly wound in a double coil called a helix. When a code is needed to make a protein, the coil unwinds and exposes the code to be duplicated. In certain diseases, the sequence of the DNA can be changed, or one of the ATCG units can be made abnormal by damage or mutation.

The mitochondria

The **mitochondria** are fascinating organelles that are small structures in the cell and are not part of the cell's original structure. Sometime in evolution they entered the cell and became a working, contributing, permanent guest. Without mitochondria, life as we know it would not be possible since only single-cell organisms are able to live without oxygen. Many cells maintain the ability to survive without oxygen, but they do not function normally. In fact, some scientists believe that the lack of oxygen, that is the inability of oxygen to reach the cell in adequate amounts to be processed by the mitochondria, cause a shift in cell respiration to the anaerobic state and this can lead to cancer. Other scientists feel there is more than enough oxygen in the tissue but the mitochondria are too damaged to process the oxygen which forces the cell to go to anaerobic respiration. As yet there is no answer.

The role of mitochondria is to utilize oxygen in the production of energy. This process, called oxidative phosphorylation, extracts energy from electrons generated during the metabolism of food. Oxidative phosphorylation sounds ominous, but it simply means the addition of a phosphate molecule to adenosine diphosphate (ADP), to make adenosine triphosphate (ATP) through a process of transferring electrons to oxygen. When energy is used, the ATP is converted to ADP by giving up energy. The mitochondria couple the low energy electrons and hydrogen ions with oxygen to make water. In this process, many molecules of ATP are produced. ATP is the energy source of all reactions in the body. You can consider ATP as the electrical energy in a storage battery that supplies energy when needed. The role of mitochondria in energy production is diagrammed in **Figure 21-2**.

You will notice the letters ROS in this diagram. They stand for Reactive Oxygen Species. As a by-product of oxidative phosphorylation, many free radicals are generated which impart damage to the mitochondria and to the cells in general. One of the basic causes of aging may lie in the mitochondria-oxidative damage to mitochondrial DNA. This process will be discussed later in the chapter.

Endoplasmic reticulum

When a cell needs a biochemical such as protein, the coiled DNA opens to reveal the code used to construct the protein. The code, a sequence of ATCG molecules, is transcribed and made into a copy called messenger ribonucleic acid (RNA) by an enzyme called RNA polymerase. This process is called **transcription** and is critical to the function of DNA. The copy leaves the nucleus and goes into the cytoplasm where it is made into the protein within the ribosome of the **endoplasmic reticulum** of the cell. The process of making the protein is called **translation**. This is diagrammed in the third step of **Figure 21-3**.

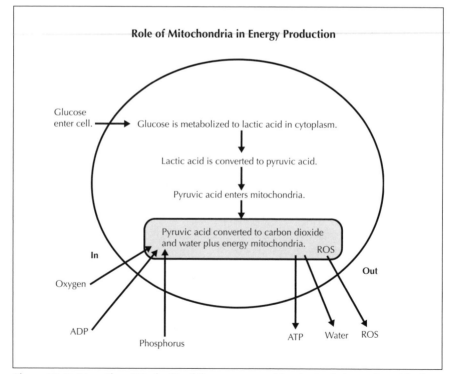

Figure 21-2. *More than 90-plus% of the energy used by the body is produced in the mitochondria as adenosine triphosphate (ATP). An enormous number of free radicals are generated in this process that damage the mitochondrial DNA.*

RNA has three roles, but it would take much more space to go into the necessary details to make it clear. The take-home lesson is this: DNA contains the codes for cellular proteins, and RNA uses the codes to make the proteins that operate most cell functions, including the very enzymes that reproduce the DNA. A round robin process exists that perpetuates itself—DNA makes RNA that makes protein, which makes more DNA. The subject just discussed is called **molecular genetics** and is about understanding the DNA code, learning how to duplicate the code, how to manipulate it and how to study it. Keep this three-step process in mind to help understand what follows.

Cell growth and maintenance, and cancer

A characteristic of all living things is the ability to both reproduce and to maintain themselves. We eat to maintain our bodies by providing the necessary building materials and energy to achieve this activity. Next, we can reproduce our own kind by sexual reproduction. The very nature of sexual reproduction assures us of a varied offspring through certain selective processes. Now here comes the problem—all this activity is biochemical and must be extremely well-regulated to function normally. Think about this for a moment. The body must regulate every action of every cell for the good of the whole body. With 60–100 trillion cells in the body, this is an enormous task. Just imagine a political system that would tell every person on earth when to eat, what to eat, when to reproduce and how often to reproduce, where to live and so on ... and you'll have an idea of the complexity of this system.

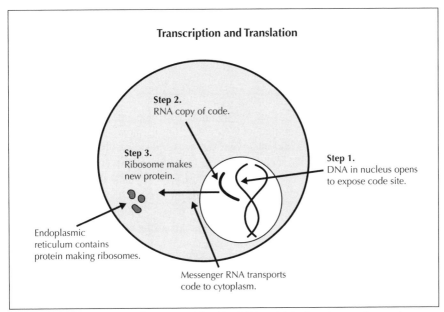

Transcription and Translation

Step 1. DNA in nucleus opens to expose code site.

Step 2. RNA copy of code.

Step 3. Ribosome makes new protein.

Endoplasmic reticulum contains protein making ribosomes.

Messenger RNA transports code to cytoplasm.

Figure 21-3. The DNA code is transcribed by RNA, which then leaves the nucleus. In the cytoplasm, the RNA's message is translated into a protein by the ribosomes in the endoplasmic reticulum.

The body has two types of cells—those that divide periodically and those that never divide. The brain, heart and most muscle cells do not divide. They are permanent cells. Cells in the skin, eyes, bones, blood and intestines are proliferative cells and divide constantly. The means by which these proliferative cells get their signals to divide is the subject of intense research, for it holds the key to two of life's major problems—aging and cancer.

Cancer is a condition in which abnormal proliferative cells somehow get beyond the controls of the body. These cells grow and move about without regard for the rest of the body, and they have become both autonomous and immortal cells. Aging is just the opposite condition—some cells die too early in the life span of the individual. The two conditions are linked in the minds of many researchers, for most cancers occur in older individuals. Let's take a look at the aging process and see how the molecular biology just discussed fits into the new concepts of aging.

Free radicals and oxidative stress

More and more you'll hear of the role of free radicals and oxidative stress in the aging process. If you continue to increase your knowledge about skin and life processes, you will need to be more familiar with the free radical concept. The term oxidative stress is being used more often than the term free radical theory, although essentially the two terms are the same. The ROS has been mentioned as a by-product of mitochondrial oxidative phosphorylation. There are four identified ROS—**singlet oxygen**, **superoxide**, **hydrogen peroxide** and **hydroxyl radical**. Only superoxide and hydroxyl radical are free radicals since they have an unpaired electron in their molecular structure. Discussion in this chapter will be confined to the effects of the ROS on DNA and how that affects the function of the cell, and how the net effect relates to the aging process.

Oxidative stress

Oxidative stress is defined as the reaction of oxygen-derived species including free radicals, or ROS, on cellular components, which results in damaged or abnormal cells. These ROS are produced by normal aerobic cell metabolism—cells that use oxygen in their energy cycle. Many other cell functions produce free radials such as the response to infection, or inflammation; the metabolism of arginine; and the action of many enzymes known as oxidases.[1] Outside of the body there are many sources of oxidative stress such as ultraviolet (UV) radiation, X-rays, air pollution, drugs and social stress. In the case of DNA, the single most important target of oxidative stress, the effect of the ROS, can result in either a poorly functioning cell, a cancerous cell or in cell death. Antioxidants are the body's defenses against oxidative stress.

First line of defense: antioxidants

As a brief review, the body has many antioxidant defenses, many of which you know. They are classified in many ways, but I prefer to separate them into two major groups—the protein and enzyme group, and the vitamins and metabolite group.

Protein and enzyme group.

1. *Proteins.* These include transferrin, ferritin and ceruloplasmin. These are proteins that bind metals in the blood stream.

2. *Enzymes.* These include superoxide dismutase, catalase, glutathione peroxidase, glutathione transferase, thio-specific peroxidases and others.

Vitamins and metabolite group.

1. *Vitamins.* These are ascorbic acid, tocopherol and retinal—vitamins C, E and A respectively.

2. *Metabolites.* This group includes bilirubin, uric acid, glutathione, nicotinamide dinucleotide phosphate complex (NAD(P)/NAD(P), magnesium, manganese, zinc and lipoic acid.

The amount and the type of antioxidants plus the amount of oxidative stress presented to the body determine if cellular damage results. The antioxidants combine with the oxidants and in effect neutralize them. The earlier this can happen, the better for the cell, since many oxidative reactions start devastating chain reactions that result in considerable cellular and tissue damage.

Second-line defense: DNA repair

Since most of the harmful oxidation affects the DNA, this is where the interest will be concentrated.

When DNA is damaged by oxidative stress, the genetic code is messed up and must be repaired. Fortunately the body can repair most of the DNA damage by excising the abnormal part and replacing it with a new part. These excised DNA segments are called **adducts** and are excreted in urine. By measuring the amount of adducts present in urine, a good index of the rate of aging for any individual can be obtained. Fortunately for us, the body can repair most of the DNA damage suffered each day. This amounts to about 1000–10,000 oxidative hits per cell per day.

Third-line defense: cell death

When a cell's DNA is so badly damaged that it possibly could degenerate into a malignant cell, the cell's watchdog gene–the p53 gene–destroys the cell first by fragmenting the DNA. This process is known as **programmed cell death**, or **apoptosis**[2] (pronounced *a-pop-tosis* or *apo-ptosis*). This is a very interesting concept to understand. Why? Well, every keratinocyte that becomes a stratum corneum cell must go through apoptosis. Remember how the granular layer of the epidermis is filled with black material? That is the DNA of the cells after it has been fragmented. The keratinocyte daughter cells are programmed to die in order to become stratum corneum cells.

Cell death then is just a normal process of physiology in many tissues, but the very same mechanism is used to protect us from the production of cancer cells. Unfortunately, when the p53 gene is damaged such as occurs in repeated sunburns, it no longer can function to protect the sun-damaged cell. This is one reason skin cancer is the most common cancer in the world.

Mitochondria and aging

I find mitochondria to be a fascinating enigma—no one knows their origin; they appear to be bacterial, yet they are not bacteria. Somehow they entered our ancestral cells and became synergistic with the host cell, and they are the only cellular component wholly transmitted by the mother.

There are, however, a few things known about mitochondria. First, they divide independently of the cell nucleus, even though they are dependent on the nucleus for most of their genetic material. Second, they have a circular DNA, called **mtDNA** for mitochondria DNA, there are no telomeres on the mtDNA and only a limited repair system exists. Mutations occur more frequently in mtDNA than in nuclear DNA, which results in abnormal mtDNA. More than 20 known diseases are associated with abnormal DNA, including adult onset diabetes mellitus.[3]

A major concept in aging suggests that the production of ATP is reduced in cells over time. This reduction is believed to be the result of constant oxidative stress in the mitochondria as a result of the oxidative phosphorylation process. More than 98% of the oxygen we breathe must pass through the mitochondria as part of cell respiration. Diseases such as Alzheimer's, Parkinson's, heart and muscle disease, and diabetes are believed to be related to defects in mitochondria. A general decline in muscle strength is noted with aging, along with a decrease in higher mental functions in some individuals, but not all. Muscle cells and the neurons do not divide, so they could accumulate large numbers of abnormal mitochondria that do divide in these cells. This process of mitochondrial defects is called **bioenergetic diseases** since they involve a decrease in ATP, or energy production. The problem is that cells having defective respiration can affect other cells and induce oxidative damage in these cells. A rotten apple in the barrel! Still there is much to learn in this area.

Now here is an interesting concept that suggests how the body gets rid of these rotten apples. If the cell's respiratory system declines low enough, it can trigger apoptosis and the cell will die. Thus is can be removed from the system, allowing only good healthy cells to survive.[4] The exact role of mitochondria in the total scheme of aging remains to be determined, but much research is being done. Treatment of mitochondrial disease with antioxidants has shown some promise, but this also is a separate topic.

Nuclear DNA and aging

The bulk of aging research is focused on nuclear DNA and especially the detection of damage and the methods of repair. This is a complex topic for it involves a great deal of genetics and biochemistry to explain only a few concepts. Unless you are interested in being a molecular biologist, the following information will provide information you need and hopefully spark your interest go further into the subject. First, let's take a closer look at the DNA molecule and point out the various components in order to have the proper guidelines and the right terms.

Mystery of the DNA molecule

Go back into the cell, across the cell membrane, through the sticky cytoplasm and to the nucleus. Cross another membrane that separates the nucleus from the cytoplasm, and you'll find the cellular DNA. In **Figure 21-4**, various forms of DNA starting with the chromosomes, are diagrammed. The DNA of all cells with a nucleus, called **eukaryocytes**, is organized into distinct units called **chromosomes**. Each chromosome contains a single enormous DNA molecule. The DNA molecule is very long so it must be highly compacted to fit into the space of a chromosome. Two features characterize a chromosome—one is the **centromere**, and the other is the **telomere**. The centromere can be seen as at the center of a chromosome where it functions in the process of cellular division. There is one telomere at each end of a chromosome. The telomere's special function is to stabilize the chromosome.

Normally the chromosomes are not visible in the cell nucleus until the cell is ready to divide. The DNA is spread out, uncoiled in the non-dividing cell and only becomes compacted when the cell divides. A DNA strand is an extremely thin but very long molecule that consists of two winding chains containing billions of molecules. In fact, the human chromosomes contain three billion base pairs. A base pair is one of the AT or GC previously discussed. The base pairs are organized into **genes**. Genes are segments of DNA that when expressed will yield a functional product. The genes are

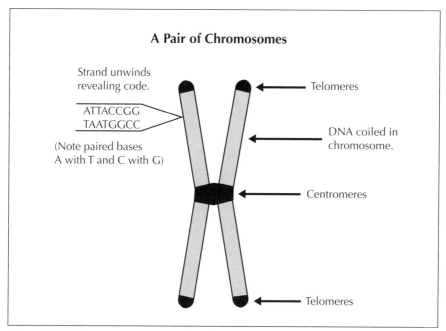

A Pair of Chromosomes

Strand unwinds revealing code.

ATTACCGG
TAATGGCC

(Note paired bases A with T and C with G)

Telomeres

DNA coiled in chromosome.

Centromeres

Telomeres

Figure 21-4. *There are two copies of each DNA code in every cell. When the code is ready to be transcribed, the DNA must uncoil to expose the various bases such as A for adenine, T for thymine, G for guanine and C for cytosine. The sequence of the bases forms the genetic code for all body proteins.*

spaced along the DNA and separated by non-coded bases. A particular gene sequence, called an **exon**, is recognized by a start and stop sequence called **introns**. As the RNA transcribes the code, it can tell where to start and stop the transcription.

To understand the current proposed mechanisms of aging, the steps in **cellular division** must be discussed. Before a cell enters the dividing stage, it is in a resting stage called the **G0 Phase**. Some stimulation-type mechanism causes it to go into a growth, or division stage, and it then enters the **G1 Phase**. At this stage the cell is committed to divide but must undergo several other steps with critical checkpoints before it can divide. In G_1 Phase the cell has two copies of each chromosome, the normal amount. Then the cell enters **S Phase** in which the chromosomes are duplicated. Now four pairs of chromosomes are present. This is a checkpoint. If everything is OK, the cell will go on to prepare for division by entering the **G2 Phase**. This is the last stage before the cell actually divides in **M Phase**, or the mitotic phase. The cell then splits into two cells; each of the new cells now has two sets of chromosome.

There are three checkpoints in the process. Checkpoint one is in G_1 Phase. If the DNA is damaged, the cell will not allow the process to proceed until the DNA is repaired. If it is not repaired the cell can be destroyed by the p53 gene.

The second checkpoint is at the G_2 Phase. Here the cell checks to make sure the DNA is replicated. If there are any errors the division is arrested. Any DNA repairs that have to be made are made at this time. If all is well, the cell proceeds to M Phase, the last checkpoint before division. The cell checks to make sure that all the chromosomes are aligned correctly on the spindles at the centromeres and that a complete set will be delivered to each new cell. If this point fails, the cell is arrested and may be destroyed if the fault cannot be repaired. We are ready to take up the theories of aging and try to understand why we go through a process marked by physical and mental deterioration that ends in our death. (See **Figure 21-5**.)

Molecular mechanisms of aging

From the very first time a cell divides it faces many hazards—correct replication of the DNA, correct division and pairing of the chromosomes, and foremost, the repair of any damaged DNA pairs. All of this activity is without the addition of oxidative stress. Here is a partial list of all the things that can happen to the DNA to produce damage, both from the outside of the body, **exogenous**, and from the inside of the body, **endogenous**:

- p53 activation ending in cell arrest at G_1 or apoptosis
- Replication arrest
- Transcription arrest
- Single- and double-stranded breaks in the DNA
- Signal transduction abnormalities
- Failure of DNA repair mechanisms
- Gene induction

These are examples of the various types of damage that can result in a cell failing to grow, or failing to function normally. This is another way of saying that the genes cannot be expressed normally. The end result is a cell that is not able to carry out its function, so that the burden must be born by other cells. Several top scientists have proposed that the basic concept of aging is a process whereby cells become **senescent**, or express aging changes in order to suppress tumor formation. This concept is supported by the following findings: a) aging cells arrest growth in G_1; b) aging cells become resistant to apototic death; and c) aging cells express changes in differentiated functions. They don't do what they are designed to do. These changes in aging cells all result in decreased function, the hallmark of an aging organism.[5]

How aging mechanisms relate to cancer

Recently, more and more scientists are finding a biological link between cancer and aging mechanisms. It's not necessary to cover all of the details, but there is an excellent review given below for those who are interested in following the details.[6] The importance of telomeres in aging and cancer is the particular point to be discussed. Cancer cells somehow have escaped two major biological control systems: the first is loss of control of cell division, and the second is loss of the limitation of cell division. Without the control of these two mechanisms, the cancer cell is free to divide endlessly and go anywhere in the body. The aging cell also has lost some control mechanism so that it can continue to exist without being destroyed by the body. Aging cells, however, do not divide as cancer cells do, but the very fact that they have lost some control

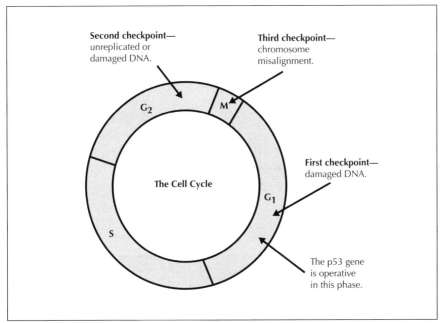

Figure 21-5. The process of cell division is controlled tightly by a series of checkpoints that prevent the reproduction of faulty DNA. Somehow cancer cells escape this process and go on to produce an abnormal cell that repeatedly avoids this checkpoint.

systems makes them very vulnerable to cancer induction. One aspect of the DNA in the cancer cell is the presence of functional telomeres due to an active **telomerase**, the enzyme that produces the telomeres.

Telomeres and aging

Telomeres have been mentioned many times and now will be discussed in detail. Telomeres are structures on each end of a chromosome as seen in **Figure 21-6**. They are composed of sequences of base pairs known as the TTAGG (thymine, thymine, adenine, guanine, guanine) sequence. There are from one hundred to thousands of these base pairs on each chromosome end. In **Figure 21-6**, the process by which telomeres are made shorter with each replication of the chromosomes is shown. The **primer** is the substance that tells the DNA polymerase to reproduce the DNA. Since the primer sits on one end of the DNA molecule, the part that is covered by the primer cannot be reproduced. With each cellular division, the telomeres become shorter until the whole telomere is gone and then the primer must sit on the actual coded part of the DNA. At this stage the DNA is damaged and the cell can no longer reproduce.

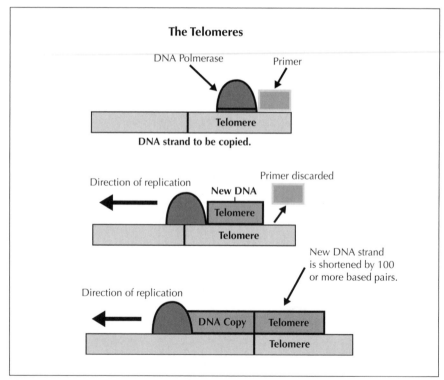

Figure 21-6. *At the end of each chromosome is a telomere that has many functions. As cells divide, the telomere is destroyed so that after a number of divisions the telomere is worn away. This exposes the DNA carrying the code. Destruction of code segments leads to cell death.*

Relatively little is known about the total function of the telomeres. They appear to protect the chromosomes from "sticking" to each other. They also appear to temporarily protect the DNA from primer-related damage, but there must be more to telomere function than what presently is known.[7] For example, the cancer cell has long telomeres and in some manner they must relate to the immortality of the cancer cell. Cells that age rapidly, such as the fibroblast in patients with progeria—also called Hutchinson-Gilford syndrome—have very short telomeres, similar to those from much older people. The average life span of these patients is 12.7 years. Only after the telomeres were discovered did we realize they played an important role in regulating the aging of the cell.

Breaking through the Hayflick Limit

This finding, discovered in 1973, made it possible to understand why cells had a limited number of divisions and thus were mortal cells. Leonard Hayflick discovered that cells in tissue culture died after 50 cell divisions. No one knew why cells died after this number of division until his paper was published in 1961.[8] One cell type that did not fit the Hayflick Limit was the cancer cell. When answering the question, "Why is the cancer cell immortal," it was stated that the cancer cell was abnormal and therefore did not fit the Hayflick Limit. It was discovered later that most cancer cells had long telomeres that did not diminish with each cell division. This finding offered one reason why cancer cells were immortal—they always had very youthful telomeres. The telomeres were replicated by telomerase, which is coded as a gene in every cell. Somehow in cancer cells this enzyme is activated and rebuilds the telomeres each time the cell divides. In normal cells, the telomerase is not activated.

Open door for immortality

With the finding of telomeres and the enzyme telomerase, the next step was to see if telomerase could be activated and made to repair telomeres in normal cells. A great deal of work has been done in the last few years and now scientists have been able to clone the gene that produces telomerase, and have used the telomerase to make normal human cells immortal. This is an incredible discovery. The next step will be animal models and then on to humans, if all goes well. It may take 15 years or more before this will happen or maybe even less time. In any event, the knowledge to prevent aging exists from several aspects. Surely the advent of the discovery of telomerase and the telomeres will be a major step forward in longevity science. Here is an overview of what has happened in the past and what may occur in the future in aging research, including the prevention and treatment of aging.

Where we've been

Aging has been considered the natural end of life, as we know it. A clock that has run down, an old car, a weathered house and a dying tree all have one thing in common—their usefulness is coming to an end. It is the way of life, and so it has been for thousands of years. Now we know none of this needs to be true. Aging is not the natural end of humankind, for aging is not natural. Aging is a process that reflects cellular damage at the molecular level. This damage results in decreased function of the cells and therefore of the body. Creating energy in the body by the oxidative process induces much of the damage. This process produces oxidative stress that creates free radical damage to the molecules in the cells. It's not a question of whether this process is very real, it's a question of how the onset and timing of this damage be controlled.

It's known that cancer cells share some characteristics of aging cells, and that the immortal characteristic of cancer cells is due to telomerase activity and escape from growth control. It's also known that normal cells can be made immortal without making them malignant by activating the telomerase in the cell. We are on the threshold of extending life far beyond anything we even dreamed of five years ago.

Here is a bit of a paradox. The germinal cells—sperm and ova—do not show signs of aging until they are joined in fertilization. This means that some aspects of the germinal cells must be more than three billion years old since all life forms share some common characteristics. At each cellular division of the germinal cells they are set back to day zero. It can be concluded from this that age alone does not determine aging, but only some change in genetic expression. The best scientific evidence suggests that aging changes are not due to DNA damage per se, or to faulty transcription, but rather is due to lower rates and altered patterns of transcription. There may be a role for telomeres in this transcription mechanism, or gene expression.[9, 10, 11]

Where we are going

The findings in cancer cells that cell cycle errors exists and that telomere expression is different can provide clues to the eventual treatment of cancer and a greater understanding of aging.[12] Evidence that dietary restriction alone will increase the life of rats by 40% has been found. If the same could be done for humans, this simple change would raise the life span to 150 years. Just the change of a single gene can add years of productive living. In lower life forms, change in two genes has increased the life span by sixfold. Antioxidant therapy and food supplements coupled with a regular exercise program to control weight and maintain muscle mass will help while we are waiting for the major breakthroughs in telomere and other gene therapy. This is where the esthetician comes into the picture. With the conquest of cancer and the advent of gene therapy with telomerase, we can expect to live out a healthy, productive life well beyond 200 years.

The esthetician and age control

First, estheticians must understand the mechanisms of aging to provide the best care for their clients. If the basic underlying mechanisms in aging are not understood, estheticians might be tempted to turn to every fad of treatment that comes down the road. It is important to get clients looking as good as possible before new therapy is developed because it will not necessarily turn back the clock in all cells. Surely it will rewind the clock for most cells, and set the hands back for others. Look at the total care of the client, not just the skin, because the skin is only part of the person. Science today tells us that using current methods alone—without telomeres—many individuals can be expected to live 100 years or more and to have the physical and mental capacity of a 60-year-old.

You cannot keep abreast of the aging topic without constant study and awareness of the ongoing research. You must make the decisions as to what treatment course to follow, so only you can evaluate the new methods and new products. Ask for answers, but keep in mind the ability to evaluate them is only as good as your knowledge of the subject.

I have listed some references that are current on the topic and some journals that you can consult for regular updating. A good resource is the *Journal of Anti-Aging Medicine*. I have included a few books that can help. Much of the research on aging is focused on molecular genetics, so I have added a few texts for those who are interested. It is not an easy subject, but one that will fascinate you and bring great intellectual rewards if you pursue it.

References

1. Berett BS and Stadtman ER, Protein oxidation in aging. Disease and oxidative stress. *The J of Biological Chem* 272:20313–20316 (1997)

2. Sen S, Programmed cell death: concept, mechanism and control. *Bio Rev* 67:287–319 (1992)

3. Wallace DC et al group report: The role of bioenergetics and mitochondria DNA mutations in aging and age-related diseases. *Molecular Aspects of Aging*, eds Esser K and Martin GM, New York: John Wiley and Sons Ltd. (1995)

4. Dipassquale B, Marini AM and Youle RJ, Apoptosis and DNA degradation induced by 1-methy-4-phynlypyridinium in neurons. *Biochem BioPhys Res Comm* 181:1442–1448 (1991)

5. Campisis J, Replication senescence. An old lives tale? *Cell* 84:497–500 (1969)

6. Chiarugi V and Magnelli L, Senescence, immortilization and cancer. *Pharmacol. Research* 35: 95–98 (1997)

7. Marcand S, Gasser SM and Gilson E, Chromatin: a sticky silence. *Curr BioL* 6: 1222–1225 (1996)

8. Hayflick L and Moorhead PS, The serial cultivation of human diploid cell stains. *Exp Cell Res* 25: 585–621 (1961)

9. Harley CB, Pollard JW, Chamberlain JW, Stanner CP and Goldstein S, Protein synthetic errors do not increase during aging of cultured human fibroblasts. *Proc Natl Acad Sci USA* 77: 1885–1889 (1980)

10. Harley CB, Futcher AR and Greider CW, Telomeres shorten during aging of human fibroblasts. *Nature* 345: 458–460 (1990)

11. Guarante L, Do changes in chromosomes cause aging? *Cell* 86:9–12 (1996)

12. Kim NW, Piatysaek MA, Prowse KR, Harley CR, West MD and Ho PLC, Specific association of human telomerase activity with immortal cells and cancer. *Science* 266: 2011–2015 (1994)

General References

Aging Mechanisms:

Austad S, *Why We Age*, New York: John Wiley and Sons, Inc. (1997)

Fossel M, *Reversing Human Aging*, New York: William Morrow and Company (1996)

Regelson W and Colman C, *The Super-Hormone Promise*, New York: Simon & Schuster (1996)

Genetics and Molecular Biology:

Cooper GM, *The Cell, a Molecular Approach*, Washington, DC: ASM Press (1997)

Darnell J, Lodish H and Baltimore D, *Molecular Cell Biology*, New York: Scientific American Books (1990)

Old RW and Primrose SB, *Principles of Gene Manipulation*, 5th edition, Cambridge, MA: Blackwell Science (1994)

Journals:

There are too many journals on cell biology and genetics to list. All are very advanced types. If you are interested in pursuing this topic, visit a medical school library and look over the selection on the current racks.

Literature Citations:

Anhein N and Cortopassi G, Delterious mitochondrial DNA mutations accumulate in aging human tissues. *Mutation Research* 275: 157–167 (1992)

Banks DA and Fossel M, Telomeres, cancer and aging. *JAMA* 278: 1345–1348 (1997)

Bodnar AR, et al Extension of life-span by introduction of telomerase into normal human cells, *Science*, 279: 349–352 (1997)

Bryan TM and Reddel RR, Telomere dynamics and telomerase activity in in vitro immortalized human cells. *European J. of Cancer* 35: 767–773 (1997)

de Grey A, A proposed refinement of the mitochondrial free radical theory of aging. *BoEssays*, 19: 161–166 (1987)

Miller RA, When will the biology of aging become useful? Future landmarks in biomedical gerontology. *J Amer Geriat Soc* 45: 1258–1267 (1997)

Wallace DC, Mitochondrial DNA in aging and disease, *Scientific American*, 40–47 August 1997

Wallace DC, Mitochondrial DNA variation in human evolution, degenerative disease and aging. *Am J Human Genet* 57: 201–223 (1995)

Chapter 22

Supplements and Beyond: The Keys to a Long and Healthy Life

I n recent years, estheticians have become aware of the internal-external concept of skin care, both by education and through advertising. Anyone new to dietary supplements is presented with a vast array of products and claims that promise everything from increased sexual energy to eternal life. The goal of this chapter is to provide the necessary background information to understand the need for micronutrients and to evaluate supplements. A list of supplements that I believe are beneficial is included in this chapter as a guideline and does not represent the endorsement of any product.

Micronutrients—metabolic miracle workers

What are micronutrients and why are they so important? Micronutrients are vitamins, minerals and other compounds required for normal metabolism. At least 40 of these materials are required in the human diet to maintain a healthy body. The presence of essential micronutrients allows the body to function in an optimal manner, while the absence or deficiency of some micronutrients disrupts metabolism and produces overt, or sub-clinical disease.[1] A sizable number of the population is believed to be deficient in micronutrients to the point that their health suffers.[2]

Many of the micronutrients play an important role in metabolism. Generally, the micronutrients are responsible for prevention of deoxyribonucleic acid (DNA) damage, cancer prevention and slowing of the aging process. Any one of these benefits would be enough to warrant an interest in micronutrients. While some controversy exists, there is very strong evidence from 200 epidemiological studies showing that a low consumption of fruits and vegetables is associated with a higher risk of cancer.[3, 4] Greater consumption of fruits and vegetables is associated with a lower risk of degenerative diseases, cataracts, cancer, brain dysfunction and cardiovascular disease.[5] It is interesting that Seventh-Day Adventists, who mostly are vegetarian, have about half the cancer rate and a longer life than the average American.[6]

It is sad to say that most Americans do not consume a healthy diet.

Notes on specific vitamins

Vitamins, by definition, are essential for life. Low intake of vitamins usually means poor health. Here are some of these important vitamins and the reasons for taking adequate amounts.

Folic acid. This is a little known vitamin, obscured by the common ones such as A, C and E. Lack of folic acid produces chromosomal breaks, and it is now known how this occurs. Folate is essential for methylation of uracil to thymine, an essential base for DNA production. The uracil cannot be incorporated into DNA in place of thymine, so it is excised from the DNA, causing a single strand break. Colon cancer, neurological problems, heart disease and vascular disease are associated with low intake of folic acid. Adding folic acid can reverse many of the early DNA breaks.

Vitamin B_{12}. This interesting vitamin is essential for normal red blood cell production and its absence produces a serious medical condition known as **pernicious anemia**. Until B_{12} was discovered, this disease was fatal. It mimics many other diseases and frequently was not diagnosed. Lack of B_{12} also causes strand breaks in DNA. Neuropathies, or nervous system disorders associated with symptoms of numbness, pain and tingling in the extremities, are caused by both folic acid and B_{12} deficiencies in some cases.[7] Today, it is treated easily due to better diagnostic methods, medical awareness, good treatment and better nutrition. The major source of B_{12} is meat, so vegetarians must get it from supplements since it is not found in plants.

Vitamin B_6. An essential part of the B-complex group of vitamins, the chemical action of this vitamin is to supplement the methylene groups ($CH_2=CH_2$) to the folic acid reaction. The same process of chromosomal breakage results from this deficiency, which can affect 10% of the U.S. population. Heart disease, stroke, atherosclerosis and prostate cancer are associated with low levels of vitamin B_6 intake. Green beans, cereal, whole grain bread and bananas are good sources of vitamin B_6.

Vitamin E. This is the major fat-soluble vitamin in the body. About 20% of Americans consume less than half the recommended daily allowance (RDA) of vitamin E. You may have heard of α (alpha) tocopherol, but actually γ (gamma) tocopherol, the main form in our diet, is equally important. The action of both α and γ tocopherol works together to trap free radicals in the cell membrane. Interestingly, it is γ tocopherol that combines with nitrogen oxidation products to neutralize their free radical damage. Vitamin E is important in reducing heart disease, prostate cancer, colon cancers, brain dysfunctions and neuropathologies.[8, 9, 10] High levels of vitamin E—above 1,000 mg—can increase lipid peroxidation.[11]

The immune system begins to fail with age, so anything that boosts the immune system potentially is beneficial. Vitamin E and selenium have been shown to enhance the immune system in animals, while vitamin E alone at 200–400 mg a day has been shown to enhance human immunity.[12, 13]

Vitamin C. In recent years, vitamin C, or ascorbic acid, has become the darling of health product suppliers and skin care product manufacturers, with everyone becoming aware of vitamin C for every possible use. Old forms are given new names and new dressings, and rather spectacular claims are added to this hype. Yet, little is known about the real biological role of ascorbic acid itself. Sadly, 15% of the population still consumes less than half of the RDA, 60 mg/day, of vitamin C in the form of fruits and vegetables. Since it is so important in the diet and well-being, more time will be spent on some of the more recent findings reported on vitamin C.

While vitamin C has many physiological actions, it is an antioxidant. It is well established that oxidative damage to the DNA molecule results in both single and double strand breaks and that ascorbic acid can provide some protection against this process.[14, 15] One very interesting and significant aspect of research with vitamin C has been the conflicting evidence from various studies in cancer research. Strong evidence suggests that ascorbic acid protects against cancer, but some studies say this is false. Analysis of this data and the subject studies provide clues to this apparent conflict.

Low serum ascorbate levels and smoking were two of the variables found in some studies. For example, vitamin C provided significant protection against renal cancer in nonsmokers, but not in smokers.[16] Smoking is a severe oxidative stress and men who smoke oxidize the DNA of their sperm as well as somatic cells, the body's germinal cells other than sperm cells. In fact, smokers with low levels of ascorbic acid have twice as much oxidative DNA damage to their sperm.[17] Smoking depletes both ascorbic acid and vitamin E levels in the blood; this means that smokers must ingest two to three times as much vitamin C as nonsmokers, which they rarely do.[18] It is becoming more apparent that children of smoking fathers have an increased rate of childhood cancers.[19, 20] An epidemiological study from China makes the case even stronger. The incidence of acute lymphocytic leukemia lymphoma and brain tumors is three to four times higher in children with fathers who smoke.[21]

The significance of these findings is that diets poor in fruits and vegetables also are low in folate, antioxidants and many other micronutrients. The lack of these vitally important nutrients leads to increased risk of cancer due to DNA damage.[22, 23]

Niacin or vitamin B₃. While only 2.3 % of the U.S. population is reported to be low in niacin, that still is a lot of people—almost 6 million. Niacin comes from meats and beans as major sources, but only 15 mg a day are needed as the RDA. Lack of niacin causes DNA damage by compromising the repair process of DNA breaks.

Notes on essential minerals

Minerals have many functions in the body from maintaining cellular integrity, cell membrane transport, nerve conduction, muscle contraction and enzyme structure, to name a few. Any good nutrition text can provide a rundown on the minerals, and here are two—iron and zinc.

Iron. Just about everyone asked about iron believes it is good and that you can't have too much iron. Iron is an essential mineral, but it also is a toxic mineral. The major source of iron in the human diet is meat; this is why an estimated two billion people in the world are at risk for iron deficiency, according to the United Nations Food and Agricultural Organization. In the United States, 19% of women from 12–50 have less than 50% of the RDA.[24] Low iron intake results in anemia, immune dysfunction and complications in pregnancy. In children, iron deficiency is associated with cognitive dysfunction.[25]

The metabolism of iron is a complex subject, well beyond the scope of this chapter, but you should be familiar with the process of iron absorption and utilization. The mechanism of iron toxicity appears to be oxidative damage leading to increased incidence of cancer and heart disease.[25, 26] How much iron is enough? Women lose about 1.5 mg of iron per day, while men lose 1 mg daily. The obvious difference is the menstrual blood loss. Iron intake of 15 mg daily for women and 10 mg daily for men is the current RDA.

Zinc. This is one mineral that is biologically fascinating for many reasons. Zinc is found as an active component of at least 300 proteins in the body—more than 100 DNA binding fingers have zinc; the enzyme superoxide dismutase contains both zinc and copper; estrogen receptors contain zinc; and nerve transmission requires zinc for synaptic transmission, the junction of nerves. Zinc deficiency slows growth and development in neonates.[27] Zinc deficiency also is associated with esophageal tumors.[28] The mechanism appears to be oxidative damage with chromosomal breaks and surely the lack of an active superoxide dismutase would support this concept.[29] While one of the main sources of zinc is meat, plants also provide a good source. Food supplements can provide many of the micronutrients needed in the diet.

What is a dietary supplement?

A **dietary supplement** is any product taken **by mouth** that contains a dietary ingredient and is **labeled** as a dietary supplement. These ingredients can include vitamins, minerals, herbs, enzymes, amino acids, organ tissues, metabolites and extracts, or concentrates of plants, or organs. They can be in the form of pills, tablets, liquids, powders or capsules.

Dietary supplements and the FDA

A division of the U.S. Food and Drug Administration (FDA) known as The Center of Food Safety and Applied Nutrition (CFSAN) is the agency that oversees the dietary supplement products. Under these regulations, any dietary supplement must be labeled with enough information about the composition of the product to allow the consumer to make an informed choice. The manufacturer also must make sure the information is truthful and not misleading, and that the product is safe. All this information must be presented in an FDA-approved format. This is the most important aspect of the FDA regulations: **Manufacturers and distributors do not need to register the product with FDA or get FDA approval before producing or marketing the product**. So there are no FDA-approved dietary supplements, just as there are no FDA-approved skin care products that are not over-the-counter (OTC)[30] or prescription products.

Claims

There are specific claims about individual ingredients that the FDA allows manufacturers to place on labels, including health claims. This is long list and requires a great deal of space. The FDA stresses that it does not maintain information on all the dietary supplements; contact the manufacturer for this information.

Safety issues

In June 1993, the FDA asked for comments on supplements from the public to try to ascertain the safety of many of these products. Since that time, consumers have spent $3.3 billion for supplements, 70% for vitamins. Because of this, there was some consideration for public safety. The major concern was for products such as amino acids, herbs, glandular extracts and other substances of dubious value as dietary supplements. The FDA concluded that there was insufficient data to evaluate the safety of these products. The main findings are as follows:

Amino acids. The FDA requested a recall of the amino acid L-tryptophan after published reports associated its ingestion with a connective tissue disease. Reported diagnosed cases of illness totaled more than 1,500, including 38 deaths. The FDA contracted for a review of scientific literature on all amino acids. The findings indicated that the data to evaluate safety are inadequate.

Chaparral. Five cases of chaparral-related acute toxic hepatitis had been reported when studied. Chaparral is claimed to slow aging, "cleanse" the blood and treat skin problems—all unproved claims.

Guar gum. This is a complex carbohydrate that swells when wet and is used in weight-loss products. It can cause diarrhea, vomiting, bloating and intestinal blockages.

Germanium. Germanium used for extended periods can cause serious, irreversible kidney damage and has resulted in death. It is promoted as an "electro-nutrient" for uses such as neutralizing heavy metal toxicity. No evidence of effectiveness has been reported.

Glandular extracts. These extracts are taken from adrenal, pancreas, thyroid and other animal glands. The concern is that glandular extracts might be derived from cattle with a fatal encephalopathy, or brain degeneration, called "mad cow disease."

Dietary supplements

With this information in mind, some of the dietary supplements currently available can be discussed. Trade names and specific company names have been avoided as much as possible.

Antioxidants. The last word on antioxidants remains to be written. The two camps concerned about antioxidants are equally vocal, though neither knows the complete story. What is well-known and agreed to by all is that antioxidants are essential to life. Fruits and vegetables contain large amounts of antioxidants, otherwise complex life forms that use oxygen would not have survived.

Everyone agrees also that radiation—X-ray or gamma—can cause death, yet the very same chemical species produced by radiation are products of the normal energy metabolism, that is, superoxide, hydrogen peroxide and hydroxyl radical. Even the defense system against bacteria produces these same reactive oxygen species. As long as you live you cannot escape the relentless damage to your DNA caused by oxygen.

You've learned about some of the benefits of vitamins C and E as antioxidants, but in addition, there are carotenoids, such as beta-carotene and lycopene, glutathione, lipoic acid, and the metals selenium and zinc. These are not all the antioxidants in the body but they are some of the most important ones. Other antioxidants derived from plants include phenolic compounds such as quercetin; thymol; gallic acid; tannins; catechins, as found in green tea; rutein; ellagic acid; eugenol; and rosemarinic acid from rosemary. Most of these compounds work by either inhibiting the generation of free radicals or by directly scavenging free radicals.

Guide to using supplements

I'm often asked about what supplement to take, where to get them and what brands to use. How do you avoid being taken by unscrupulous manufacturers or super salespeople? Many so-called public protectors, some nutritionists, physicians, the media and certain public officials seeking higher visibility, would have you believe every manufacturer of supplements is a crook and out to get you, one way or the other. In reality, most supplement manufacturers are reliable and honest, as they depend on good results from their products to have repeat customers.

What to check before you buy

Manufacturers. Good products are manufactured by companies that follow **Good Manufacturing Practices** (GMPs), guidelines developed by the federal government to help manufacturers assure their products are made well. GMPs assure that products do what they are to do before being purchased. The purpose of GMPs is to assure that what is on the label is in the product, that the product disintegrates, and is bio-available and unadulterated. Retailers should have this information from the manufacturers or suppliers. Ask for it.

Name brands. While there are many manufacturers of supplements, there are few manufacturers of the raw materials that go into the supplements. Large manufacturers with a long history of good business practices—which means many satisfied customers—usually will produce excellent supplements. If you are new to supplements, buy a brand name. Now this does not mean the new kid on the block is a bad guy, he just has to prove himself first. A good test is the tablet itself. A poorly manufactured tablet either will disintegrate in the bottle, or will not disintegrate in water, except those that are specially coated. These are called **enteric coated tablets**.[31] Large, well-established retailers also are a good source of reliable supplements.

Check claims

Claims on supplements are controlled by the Federal Trade Commission (FTC). A claim must be supported with quality research sufficient to establish the claim if reviewed by a scientific expert. Beware of products that knock other products, that claim superiority on some obscure finding, or state that "great research has been done" to support the claims. Often this research is public domain, was done years ago and is essential basic science research. What you want is sound clinical evidence that the product works.

All-natural. Nothing is more misleading, misrepresented and misinterpreted then the term **all-natural**. Somehow, the belief that anything that is all-natural is safe has seeped like a cancer into our culture. Cyanide is an all-natural chemical found in cherry pits. Spoiled clover contains coumadins that cause abortion in cattle, and rye bread that goes moldy can cause abortion or madness, a disease called ergotism. These are all natural phenomena, yet deadly. Snake venom is natural and so are poison ivy and the destroyer mushroom. All poisons used by the infamous murderers of old were obtained from natural sources, since no one could make synthetic drugs 300 years ago.

The major benefit of all-natural is that the chemical form is correct. This is discussed in the biochemical section of Chapter 6, "Basic Chemistry of Life" and in Chapter 7, "Biochemistry." Unfortunately the natural form of a product often is extremely expensive. I cannot go into great detail here, but when you hear that a product is "all-natural," ask about its origin. For instance, there is no all-natural glycolic acid; it is made by a major manufacturer as a petroleum derivative.

Combinations. Multiple vitamins combined with minerals serve as a good tablet; others are not so good. Ask yourself, why are these ingredients put into the same tablet? Are they synergistic, compatible, incompatible, additive, subtractive or what? Some combinations work well, such as arginine and lysine, but you really need to know what benefits accrue from the combination. First, search the Internet and then the scientific literature. Time is saved when searching the Internet because, often, many people with the same questions have searched and documented it there.

Beyond supplements

There are powerful natural and synthetic agents not found in food or food supplements. Chemicals such as growth hormone and nootropics and second-messenger stimulators are in a very gray area as far as the FDA is concerned. Frankly, some are drugs. This may be the future of age prevention or retardation. Certainly every esthetician should be knowledgeable on these topics. As time passes, the role of the esthetician will expand to include a holistic concept of health and attractiveness, far beyond what is being offered today. Only the swift, the intelligent and the energetic esthetician will survive in this new marketplace.

Some of the new agents related to health and longevity are being used by physicians to treat a number of medical conditions associated with aging. There are too many areas of research and too many compounds for comprehensive coverage; therefore, this section will narrow the topic to **nootropics**, **hormones** and **stem cell research**. Each of these areas is exciting and promising.

(*Author's note:* **This section is only an introduction to these compounds; it is not intended to be a guide. Do not use these compounds unless you have consulted with a physician or competent health practitioner knowledgeable in their use.**)

Nootropics, the smart drugs

Nootropics is word derived from two Greek words: *nous* for "mind," and *tropikos* for "turning." It means agents that work "toward the mind," or "turning the mind." If you don't like that word, call them cognitive enhancer substances or CES. While they are complex chemicals, a great deal of research explains how they work, how safe they are and how much to take, but still much remains to be done. The major nootropics are outlined below.

Piracetam. This was the first nootropic on the market. It works by increasing the nucleotide adenosine triphosphate (ATP) in the brain cells through more efficient use of glucose, increasing cerebral circulation, oxygen utilization and protein synthesis. An interesting function of this chemical is its ability to interconnect the right and left hemispheres of the brain, which increases the flow of information. The results suggest that brilliance, creativity and insight, along with peak performance, are the result of this integration and synergistic action. Piracetam is believed to enhance not only simple learning, but also creative and syntheses thinking. It is one of the safest of all nootropics, but it should not be taken with amphetamines and other psycho tropics. The dosage is 2,400–4,800 mg a day. It is available by prescription only in the United States, but it is likely that in time it will be an over-the-counter drug as it is in Mexico.[32]

Vasopressin. This is a natural peptide compound produced in the brain under stimulation by acetylcholine and released in the pituitary gland. Its action is to create, imprint and store memories, and it is essential to memory. In times of trauma it is excreted in large amounts, which probably is why there are such vivid imprints and recollection of these events. Anyone who takes cocaine, lysergic acid diethylamide (LSD), amphetamines or Ritalin* actually are causing vasopressin to be released, but frequent use of these agents depletes the natural source, producing more problems. Vasopressin really is a hormone, not a drug. There are side effects such as headaches, abdominal cramps and triggering of angina attacks when heart disease is present. The dosage is 12–16 USP, or United States Pharmacopoeia recommendation, per day, which is one spray in the both nostrils three to four times a day. It is available in a nasal spray by prescription only. This is a potent agent not to used without supervision.[33]

Acetyl-L-carnitine. L-Carnitine and acetyl-L-carnitine essentially have the same action, although acetyl-L-carnitine is used readily by the cells. The basic effect of this compound, which is an amino acid, is to enhance cellular energy metabolism and to promote nerve growth factor. Both aging and daily stress reduce nerve growth factor, which would prevent cellular repair in the brain. It appears that this compound will be used more widely in the near future as it is not a prescription item, can be obtained easily and is supported by a growing scientific literature base. There are no known side effects.

---

* Ritalin is manufactured by CIBA-Geigy Corp., Ardsley, NY

The dosage ranges from 100–2,000 mg a day. This is one of best anti-aging supplement compounds available.

Dimethylaminoethanol (DMAE). This drug has been around a long time and basically is an incomplete choline molecule. Choline is an amino acid that is converted to acetylcholine in the nervous system. Acetylcholine is essential for transmission of nerve impulses at the point where nerves join, called a **synapse**. DMAE gets into the brain easier than choline and once in the brain it is converted to choline by the addition of a methyl group. The use of DMAE is associated with increased memory, increased learning ability, an increase in intelligence and an increase in life span in laboratory animals. DMAE can be purchased over-the-counter. The dosage is between 150 mg up to 500 mg or more per day.

Xanthinol nicotinate. Xanthinol nicotinate is a niacin derivative. It increases the level of ATP in the brain as it crosses the cell membrane more easily than niacin. Once in the cell, xanthinol nicotinate increases glucose use and thus increases cell ATP. It also dilates blood vessels and lowers cholesterol. Like niacin, it causes flushing in some individuals along with abdominal cramps, headache and heartburn. Most of the symptoms are transient. The dosage is 900–1,800 mg a day. It is not available in the United States without a prescription.

There are many other nootropic drugs. I refer the interested reader to the book *Smart Drugs and Nutrients*.[34]

Hormone use in anti-aging therapy

In this section three hormones—human growth hormone (HGH), melatonin and dehydoxyepiandrosterone—will be discussed. While estrogen also is an extremely important anti-aging hormone I have not included here as it is discussed in Chapter 19 on "Estrogens and Phytoestrogens."

Human growth hormone. Human growth hormone (HGH) is secreted by the anterior pituitary gland under stimulation from the hypothalamus. The level of HGH peaks in adolescence even though it continues to be secreted by diminishing amounts throughout a lifetime. Many scientists believe HGH decline is a major source of aging since the levels of HGH decrease from 500 micrograms at 20, to 200 micrograms at 40, and to 25 micrograms at 80. HGH does many things for the body to keep it young in terms of both physiology and appearance. There are side effects from using HGH. For one, it cannot be given orally; it must be injected. It is expensive and must be continued for life. It also can produce bone growth in the hands and head. The alternative to HGH shots is the use of **secretagogues**, chemicals that increase the secretion of HGH.

Secretagogues will be the popular way to increase HGH in a short time. The agent most commonly used is the amino acid **arginine**. When combined with lysine or orthinine, two other amino acids, the effect in secreted HGH is increased. An effective combination uses lysine at 1,200 mg and arginine pyroglutamate at 1200 mg. The addition of the glutamate is important as glutamine is an essential amino acid for many body functions, particularly the immune system. Arginine, lysine and orthinine can be taken as a combination tablet and is available in health food stores. The Internet supplies a great deal of information on HGH, but a comprehensive source of information can be found in the book *Growth Hormone*.[35]

Melatonin. Melatonin is a neurotransmitter derived from serotonin and is produced in the pineal gland. **Serotonin** is made in the brain during the day and is converted to melatonin after sundown, peaking about 3 AM. Melatonin is a wonderful natural hormone that does many positive things for the body. I cannot even outline all the benefits in this section, so I refer the reader to the book *The Melatonin Miracle*.[36] While I do not believe melatonin is a miracle drug, it certainly is helpful, particularly if you travel over three time zones. The dosage is 0.3–3 mg, three times a week at bedtime. It is available at health food stores and pharmacies.

Dehydroxyepiandrosterone (DHEA). Estrogen and testosterone are derived from this basic hormone. The blood level drops with age, just as HGH. A great deal of information on DHEA has appeared recently, though there still is controversy on how it works, how much benefit there is to taking it and what are its side effects. For people over 50, there seems to be a lot of physiological and psychological benefits. Again, the use of this agent is extremely complex for it can produce both testosterone and estrogen in both men and women. Individuals under 40 need less than 15 mg; older individuals can tolerate and benefit from 25 mg or more a day. Consult with a physician before using this agent, though not all physicians are knowledgeable about these agents. A good text that covers this topic in detail along with many other aspects of anti-aging is *Age Right*.[37] This is one of the best practical use books among anti-aging literature.

The stem cell–promise of the future

Recently, stem cell research broke into the news with a fury. **Stem cells** are cells that are capable of producing many cells by almost endless divisions. Some of them also are capable of producing many different types of cells. For example, a bone marrow stem cell can produce both red and white blood cells, as well as other types of cells that are not blood cells. When an ovum and sperm combine for fertilization, a zygote is produced that divides, forming many cells. One week after fertilization until two months into the pregnancy the conceptus is called an embryo, and at the beginning of the third month it is called a fetus.

The earliest stages after fertilization produce the most diverse stem cells, those capable of producing every kind of cell in the body. What is not known at this time is whether the stem cells obtained from bone marrow or the brain are capable of producing the wide range of cells that embryonic stem cells can produce. Marrow stem cells produce liver cells, heart, bone and muscle cells, along with other types of cells. It is possible that a resting stem cell in the bone marrow can be an embryonic stem cell. We could therefore take these stem cells from a person's bone marrow, multiple them in tissue culture and inject them into damaged, or aged, tissue and have them repair or renew that tissue.[38]

Promise of youth

This research holds the promise of youth. Obviously we cannot live forever, but a longer life, such as 150–200 years or more, is possible with this technology. These truly are exciting times to be alive, but the future of biological research will be even more dazzling.

References

1. Saltman P, Gurin J and Mothner I, *The University of California San Diego Nutrition Book*. Boston: Little, Brown and Company (1993)

2. Wilson JW, Enns CW, Goldman JD, Tippett KS, Mickle SI, Cleveland LE and Chahil PS, Data tables: Combined results from USDA's 1994 and 1995 continuing survey of food intakes by individuals, and 1994 and 1995 diet and health knowledge survey. USDA/ARS Food Surveys Research Group. Beltsville Human Nutrition Research Center, Riverdale, MD. (1997)

3. Willett WC and Trichopoulos D, Nutrition and cancer: a summary of the evidence. *Cancer Causes Control* 7: 178–180 (1996)

4. Steinmetz KA and Potter JD, Vegetables, fruit, and cancer prevention: a review. *J Am Diet Assoc* 96:1027–1039 (1996)

5. Ames BN, Shigenaga MK and Hagen TM, Oxidants, antioxidants and the prevention of degenerative diseases of aging. *FASEB J* 11: 1041–1052 (1993)

6. Mills PK, Beeson WI, Phillips IL and Fraser GE, Cancer incidence among California Seventh-day Adventists. *Am J Clin Nutr* 59: 1136S–1142S (1994)

7. Blount BC, Mack MM and Wehr C, et al, Folate deficiency causes uracil misincorporation into human DNA and chromosome breakage: Implications for cancer and neuronal damage. *Proc Nail Mad Sd USA* 94: 3290–3295. (1997)

8. White E, Shannon, JS and Patterson, RE, Relationship between vitamin and calcium supplement use and colon cancer. *Cancer Epidemiol Biomarkers Prey* 6: 769–774 (1997)

9. Hartman TJ, Albanes D and Pietinen P, et al, The association between baseline vitamin E, selenium, and prostate cancer in the alpha-tocopherol beta-carotene cancer prevention study. *Cancer Epidemiol Biomarkers Prey* 7: 335–340 (1998)

10. Lethem I and Orrell M, Antioxidants and dementia. *Lancet* 349: 1189 (1997)

11. Brown KM, Morrlce PC and Duthie GG, Esythrocyte vitamin E and plasma ascorbate concentrations in relation to eiythrocyte peroxidation in smoker and nonsmokers: dose response to vitamin E supplementation. *Am J Clin Nutr* 65: 496–502 (1997)

12. Finch JM and Turner RJ, Effects of selenium and vitamin E on the immune responses of domestic animals. *Res Vet Sci* 60: 97–106 (1996)

13. Meydani SN, Meydani M and Blumberg JB, et al, Vitamin B supplementation and in vivo response in healthy elderly subjects: A randomized controlled trial. *J Am Med Assoc* 277: 1380–1386 (1997)

14. Fraga CG, Motchnik PA, Shigenaga MK, Helbock H, Jacob RA and Ames BN, Ascorbic acid protects against endogenous oxidative damage in human sperm. *Proc Natl Acad Sci USA* 88: 11003–11006 (1991).

15. Duthie SJ, Ma A, Roes MA and Coffin AR, Antioxidant supplementation decreases oxidative DNA damage in human lymphocytes. *Cancer Res* 56: 1291–1295 (1996)

16. Wolk A, Lindblad P and Adami HO, Nutrition and renal cell cancer. *Cancer Causes Control* 7: 5–18 (1996)

17. Fraga CG, Motchnik PA, Wyrobek AJ, Rempel DM and Ames,BN, Smoking and low antioxidant levels increase oxidative damage to sperm DNA. *Mutat Res* 351: 199–203 (1996)

18. Woodall AA and Ames BN, Nutritional prevention of DNA damage to sperm and

consequent risk reduction in birth defects and cancer in offspring. In: Bendich A, Deckelbaum R, eds, *Preventative Nutrition: The Comprehensive Guide for Health Professionals*, Totowa, NJ: Humana Press, 373–385 (1997)

19. Sorahan T, Lancashire RJ, Hulten MA, Peck L and Stewart AM, Childhood cancer and parental use of tobacco—deaths from 1953 to 1955. *Br J Cancer* 75: 134–138 (1991)

20. Sorahan T, Lancashire RJ, Prior P, Peck I and Stewart AM, Childhood cancer and parental use of alcohol and tobacco. *Ann Epidemiol* 5: 354–359 (1995)

21. Ji BT, Shu XO and Linet MS, et al,.Paternal cigarette smoking and the risk of childhood cancer among offspring of nonsmoking mothers. *J Natl Cancer* Inst 89: 238–244 (1997)

22. Ames BN, Motchnlk PA, Fraga CC, Shigenaga MK and Hagen TM, Antioxidant prevention of birth defects and cancer. In: Mattison, DR and Olshan A, eds, *Male-mediated Developmental Toxicity*, New York: Plenum Publishing Corporation 243–259 (1994)

23. Block GM, The data support a role for antioxidants in reducing cancer risk. *Nutr Rev* 50: 207–213 (1992)

24. Wilson JW, Enns CW, Goldman JD, Tippett KS, Mickle S, Cleveland LE and Chahil PS, Data tables: Combined results from USDA's 1994 and 1995 continuing survey of food intakes by individuals, and 1994 and 1995 diet and health knowledge survey. USDA/ARS Food Surveys Research Group. Beltsville Human Nutrition Research Center, Riverdale, MD (1997)

25. Yip R and Dallman PR, Iron. In: Ziegler EE, Filer, Jr LJ, eds, *Present Knowledge in Nutrition*, Washington, DC: ILSI Press, 277–292 (1996)

26. Sempos CT, Gillum RF, Looker AC, Iron and heart disease. In: Bendich, A and Deckelbaum RJ, eds, *Preventive Nutrition: The Comprehensive Guide for Health Professionals*, Totowa, NJ: Humana Press Inc. 181–192 (1997)

27. Olin KL, Shigenaga MK and Ames BN, et al, Maternal dietary zinc influences DNA strand break and 8-hydroxy-2-deoxyguanosine levels in infant rhesus monkey. *Proc Soc Exp Biol Med* 203: 461–466 (1993)

28. Fong LY, Li KM, Huebner K and Magee PN, Induction of esophageal tumors in zinc-deficient rats by single low doses of N-nitrosomethylbenzylamine (NMBA): Analysis of cell proliferation and mutation in p53 genes, *Carciogenesis* 18(8):1477–84(1997)

29. Oteiza PL, Olin KL, Fraga CE and Keen CL, Oxidative defense systems in testes from zinc-deficient rats (44040). *Proc Soc Exp Biol Med* 213: 85–91 (1996)

30. OTC means over-the-counter items. These are products that are regulated by the FDA such as sunscreens and arthritis products, but do not require a prescription.

31. Enteric coated tablets are designed to break up and be absorbed in the small bowel. These tablets usually have ingredients that are unstable in acid, so they are protected until they get to through the stomach.

32. Dimond SJ and Bowers EYM, Increase in the power of memory in normal man through the use of drugs. *Psychopharmacology* 5:307–309 (1976)

33. Legos JJ, et al, Influence of vassopressin on learning and memory. *Lancet* Jan 7: 41–42, (1978)

34. Dean W and Morgenthaler J, *Smart Drugs and Nutrients*, Smart Publications (1991)

35. Harvey S, Scanes CG and Daughaday WH, *Growth Hormone*, Boca Raton, FL: CRC Press, (1995)

36. Peirpaolo W, Regelson W and Coleman C, *The Melatonin Miracle*, New York: Simon and Schuster (1995)

37. Ullis K, *Age Right*, New York: Simon and Schuster (1999)

38. Quesenberry PJ, et al, *Stem Cell Biology and Gene Therapy*, New York: Wiley-Liss (1998). A very comprehensive and timely book but quite technical.

Chapter 23

The Power of Chemical Peels

Estheticians can develop a high level of expertise with superficial peels. Legally, estheticians cannot perform deep peels or laser peels. Estheticians know that reading a chapter on chemical peeling does not qualify them to do a peel. Adequate training in chemical peeling, which includes hands-on training, first must be obtained. Chemical peeling is one of the most exciting and financially rewarding areas of esthetics; learn it well.

History of chemical peeling

Chemical peeling, or skin resurfacing, is an ancient practice probably dating back to the early days of Egypt, more than 5,000 years ago. Only fruit acids and lactic acid from milk were available to Egyptians. Physicians began using salicylic acid, resorcinol, phenol and trichloroacetic acid in 1882. Around 1903, phenol first was used to remove acne scars.[1]

Antoinette la Gasse, who practiced peeling in Los Angeles from 1930 to the 1940s, was the first person to introduce chemical peeling to the United States. This was the first time chemical peeling was used to remove wrinkles, employing a phenol-type peel.[2] Her protégée Cora Galenti probably taught other lay people, because the practice of peeling soon turned up in Florida.

Throughout the years, chemical peeling became more popular with dermatologists and plastic surgeons. The advent of the alpha hydroxy and trichloracetic acids made the procedure safer in the hands of physicians. The light, or superficial, peel was developed in Europe during the 1930s and came to the United States by way of European-trained estheticians. The original resorcinol peel has changed little from the current Jessner's peel, named after Max Jessner, MD. It appears that as chemical peeling spread in the medical community, more clients sought the advice of estheticians on the efficacy of peeling.

Chemical peeling as a practice among estheticians seems to have started in earnest sometime in the 1980s.

The peeling process

Chemical peeling involves the use of destructive chemical agents that wound the skin. The key word here is **wound**. The healing of a wound is a complex process. New tissue is constructed in this process and damaged tissue is replaced. The skin looks better and actually feels better than before the wound. This is the basis for chemical peeling: *wound the skin and allow it to generate new skin in the healing process.*

This takes the magic and mystery out of chemical peeling, but it provides the scientific foundation for the use of peeling as a restructuring or rejuvenating technique. A clear knowledge of the process of wound healing goes a long way to help understand the benefits and limitations of chemical peeling. The principle of wound healing, the clinical indications for chemical peeling and the techniques used in superficial chemical peeling will be discussed.

Wound healing

Figure 23-1 is a drawing showing the four layers of the epidermis and the two layers of the dermis. Keeping these six layers in mind and knowing how far each penetrates into the skin—**skin depth**—is the primary anatomical fact needed to remember in the

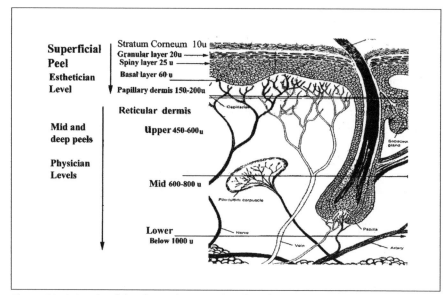

Figure 23-1. Levels of the skin to be considered in chemical peeling. The symbol μ stands for 1/1,000 of a millimeter.

peeling technique. The depth of skin peeling in superficial peels does not penetrate much below the stratum corneum. In this general discussion of wound healing, there is no dermal element in healing skin treated by superficial chemical peeling. The healing of deeper wounds will be left to the medical profession. It is the subject, as well, of pre- and post-operative care for laser surgery.

There are five stages of wound healing after all types of chemical peeling.

Stages of Wound Healing	Peeling Depth
Coagulation and inflammation	Superficial
Re-epithelialization	Superficial and mid
Granular tissue formation (dermal)	Mid and deep
Angiogenesis (dermal)	Mid and deep
Collagen remodeling (dermal)	Mainly deep

The first two stages are most relevant to estheticians.

Coagulation and inflammation

Any injury to the skin will elicit an inflammatory response. This is an extremely complex reaction that involves both cellular and biochemical reactions beginning the instant the injury occurs. The injured cell sends out the signals. The skin's defenses mobilize and the repair process begins. If the injury is deep enough to elicit bleeding, the coagulation process swings into action immediately. Superficial peeling should not be associated with bleeding.

Figure 23-2 shows the major biochemical routes of inflammation. Several types of white blood cells move into the wounded area, such as lymphocytes, granulocytes and

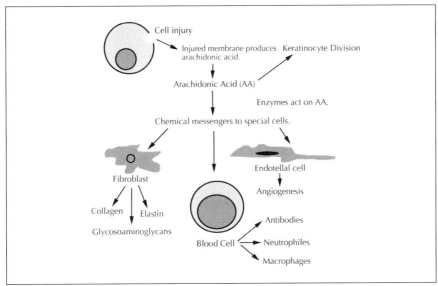

Figure 23-2. Inflammation routes.

macrophages. These cells combat infection and secrete chemicals that signal other cells to enter the area. They also send powerful messages to still other cells to start the healing process. It is important to know that an inflammatory reaction has started, because this is what promotes new skin cells and possibly new dermal elements.

Re-epithelialization

Undamaged keratinocytes start the process of resurfacing the wounded area by migrating in from the margins of the wound and from the lower surface of the wound. The process starts within 24 hours after wounding. Leaving the skin uncovered so that it actually dries helps promote separation of the epidermis. The different types of white blood cells moving into the wounded area begin to signal the dermal components, particularly the fibroblasts, to respond to the repair process. Since only minimal dermal elements are involved in superficial peeling, the response is not great. This process can differ depending on the chemical agent used. In the superficial peels done by estheticians, the major tissue lost is the stratum corneum.

Why peel?

There are at least four indications for superficial peels by the esthetician:

1. Sun-damaged skin (actinic keratosis)
2. Acne vulgaris types I and II
3. Pigmentation abnormalities
4. Aging skin, fine wrinkles

Sun-damaged skin. Sun damage can cover a wide spectrum of insults to the skin. Both UVA and UVB rays damage the skin. UVA has less energy but penetrates deeper into the dermis and is the cause of dermal damage. UVB has very high energy and operates mainly on the epidermis, producing skin cancers and ugly lesions. Discolorations and keratoses, along with deep wrinkles, are common findings among clients with sun-damaged skin. This syndrome often is called "South Florida skin."

Sun-damaged skin responds best to mid to deep peels, although superficial peels can be helpful if they go as deep as the lower layer of the epidermis. It is best to treat only mild cases. Anyone with deep wrinkles and leather-like skin should be referred to a physician. Unfortunately, repeated superficial peels are not effective in severely sun-damaged skin. Glogau types I and II respond well to superficial peeling. (See **Photoaging Groups—Glogau's Classification.**)

Acne vulgaris. Acne of the common Type I and Type II (pustules and comedones without deep cysts) will respond to superficial peels. Comedones will be lifted out and pustules will dry up quickly.

Pigmentation abnormalities. The most common types of pigmentation abnormalities seen are melasma and post-inflammation pigmentation. It is necessary to determine the level, or extent, of pigmentation before deciding to use a superficial peel. The pigmented granules, called melanosomes, will be found in either the epidermis or the dermis. In natural sunlight the epidermal pigmentation will appear light brown compared to dermal pigmentation which will appear dark brown, or gray. Use a Wood's lamp to further distinguish these two levels. The Wood's lamp emits ultraviolet between 320–400 in the UVA range.

With epidermal pigmentation the color will be enhanced, while in the dermal pigmentation there is no increase in color. In blacks and Asians, this technique can't be used because their skin pigments block fluorescent light.

Skin aging and resurfacing

A number of estheticians use the superficial peel on a regular basis to provide a smooth, blemish-free skin for their clients. This works very well and I encourage it as a sound practice as long as it is not overly used. Fine lines and small pigmented lesions will be removed, as well as topical debris, which no one recognizes as pathological but nevertheless produces an unattractive appearance. The skilled and experienced esthetician can tell best how often to repeat the peel. Every three months is not too frequent but a peel every month might be overdoing it. If it is done too often the skin will let you know!

Photoaging Groups — Glogau's Classification*

Group I—*Mild (usually 25–35)*
> No keratoses
> Little wrinkling
> No scarring
> Little or no makeup

Group II—*Moderate (usually 35–50)*
> Early actinic keratoses; slight yellow skin discoloration
> Early wrinkling; parallel smile lines
> Mild scarring
> Little makeup

Group III—*Advanced (usually 50–65)*
> Actinic keratoses; obvious yellow skin discoloration with telangiectasia
> Wrinkling; present at rest
> Moderate acne scarring
> Always wears makeup

Group IV—*Severe (usually 60–75)*
> Actinic keratoses and skin cancers have occurred
> Wrinkling; much cutis laxa of actinic, gravitational and dynamic origin
> Severe acne scarring
> Wears makeup that cakes on the skin

* Adapted from RG Glogau, Chemical Peel Symposium, American Academy of Dermatology, Atlanta, Dec 4, 1990.

Client selection

Whom do I peel? This is a critical question. Who is the best candidate? Who is the most risky candidate? How do I tell? Physicians and estheticians have a few standards to use in selecting suitable clients for peeling procedures. In his book *Chemical Peeling*, H. J. Brody, MD, outlines 13 factors to consider in the evaluation of clients for chemical peeling:

1. Fitzpatrick skin type
2. Degree of actinic damage
3. Philosophy of sun exposure
4. Philosophy of cosmetic use
5. Present and past sebaceous gland activity, and previous treatment (Accutane*, or radiation)
6. Previous cosmetic surgery
7. Philosophy of smoking
8. General state of physical and mental health
9. Medications
10. Pregnancy history
11. History of herpes simplex
12. History of hypertrophic scarring
13. Realistic expectations

For a superficial peel, all of these factors need not be considered, but the important ones are discussed in more detail.

The Fitzpatrick type. The Fitzpatrick types refer the reaction various people have to sun exposure depending on skin color. **Fitzpatrick's Classification of Sun-Reactive Skin Types**, shows the characteristics of skin types used in the chart. Check the hair and eye color also. A person with dark brown hair and blue or green eyes can react as Type I or II. Superficial peels can be used on Types I through VI, although the results are not always predictable on Types V and VI.

Degree of actinic damage and photoaging. For superficial peels, the Glogau Classification is a good assessment scale. This level of peeling can be used on Groups I–III, with less success, however, in Group III. See **Photoaging Groups — Glogau's Classification** for the complete classification characteristics.

Sebaceous gland activity. Chemical peeling will be less successful with clients who have high sebaceous gland activity; more success will be seen with those who have less oily skin. Peeling does not alter the activity of the sebaceous gland even though it is beneficial for acne.

Smoking. Generally, smokers do not do well with peeling. Smoking increases wrinkling and dilates blood vessels, so the effect of a peel on smokers is short-lived. Some smokers do have reasonably good results, but I strongly would urge you to discourage any client from smoking.

---

* Trademark of Hoffman LaRoche Pharmaceuticals, Nutley, NJ

Herpes simplex. A history of recurrent herpes simplex does not appear to be a problem with superficial peels. Deep and medium peels require treatment with anti-viral agents. Since these clients must be referred, physicians doing the peeling will provide the medication. I do not recommend that you use chemical peeling if there is an active herpetic infection present on the face.

Unrealistic expectations. This is a very important aspect of any beauty treatment. Spending time with clients to determine their expectations is time well spent. Clearly explain the benefits and limitations of the treatment, answer questions truthfully and do not oversell.

Preparation of the skin

Before the actual day a peeling is scheduled, a pre-operative skin care program should be followed to prepare the skin for optimal results. There are many variables, so there is no "standard" program. You really are the best judge of a pre-treatment program, and with some experience you will gain confidence as to what works best for you and your client. I recommend the following regimen as a starting point.

1. Ask about the client's regular diet and suggest ways to improve it if needed. Adequate protein and vitamins are needed to heal skin.

2. Use food supplements and vitamins such as vitamin E at 400 mg/day, and vitamin C at 500 mg to 1,000 mg/day.

3. A cream containing vitamin A and antioxidants is helpful. Use a preparatory program until you see an obvious improvement in the skin. This can take four to six weeks, or longer.

Fitzpatrick's Classification of Sun-Reactive Skin Types

Skin Type	Color	Reaction to First Summer Exposure
I	White	Always burn, never tan
II	White	Usually burn, tan with difficulty
III	White	Sometimes mild burn, tan average
IV	Moderate brown	Rarely burn, tan with ease
V	Dark Brown*	Very rarely burn, tan very easily
VI	Black	No burn, tan very easily

Asian Indian, Hispanic, or light African descent, for example.

Superficial peels

The Jessner's peel. The Jessner's peel also is known as the Coomb's peel, after F.C. Coombs, MD. The Jessner's peel originally was formulated by Jessner to help reduce the side effects of resorcinol. The use of resorcinol as a peeling agent, at 10–30% concentrations, dates back to the 1800s.

In France, S.M. Letessier modified the formula by increasing it to 50%.[3] The problems with high concentrations of resorcinol are its corrosive quality, its tendency for depigmentation and an occasional allergic reaction. While the product was used by estheticians for many years, I do not recommend its use unless adequate training has been received in all aspects of this product. Jessner developed his peel to circumvent some of these problems. This peel works well for the treatment of freckles, lentigenes (brown discoloration) and actinic damage.

Composition of the Jessner's Solution

Resorcinol	14 %
Salicylic acid	14 %
Lactic acid (85%)	14 %
Ethanol (95%)	58%

While this preparation can be made by estheticians, it is easier to buy the finished product. The solution is not stable and will turn pink if not kept in a sealed dark bottle. Wear gloves if you touch the solution; it will turn your fingernails a yellow-orange color.

Jessner's peeling is an art that must be learned—there are many variations in techniques. Above all, safety must be considered. Two of the ingredients are acids and resorcinol is similar to phenol; they will cause injury if they get into the eyes. Have some saline solution (0.9% salt in water) handy to wash out the eye if an accident occurs.

Alpha hydroxy acids (glycolic acid peel). Alpha hydroxy acids are naturally occurring acids found in foods. They include lactic acid from milk, glycolic acid from sugar, citric acid from fruits, tartaric acid from grapes and malic acid from apples. Most of these acids are made synthetically in whole or in part. Glycolic acid peels using 30% glycolic acid is a common strength. This is a safe procedure if used by a well-trained esthetician. Higher concentrations of these acids are corrosive and dangerous.

Alpha hydroxy acids are used to reduce wrinkling and to treat acne. The mechanism of action is unknown but appears to enhance synthesis of dermal components.[4] There are many techniques used in applying glycolic acid.

Salicylic acid peels. I believe the salicylic acid peel will become a major peeling method for estheticians. It is very safe when used properly and has many indications. Recent publications by Douglas Kligman, MD, and Albert Kligman, MD, describe in detail the use of the salicylic acid peel.[5, 6]

Post-peeling care

Once you have peeled away the old, unattractive skin with associated defects, estheticians have a new canvas on which to work their magic. Continue using retinol; antioxidants; bioflavanoids, which reduce enzymatic destruction of collagen and elastin; and vitamin C. Monitor the client's progress to determine when to do a second peel. I would caution not to use many products after a peel. The skin needs some time to adjust to the trauma, so it can't handle many additional chemical insults at the same time. Monthly visits for evaluation and possible additional peeling sessions should be part of your after-care program. This is also a good opportunity to discuss diet, exercise and lifestyle changes that will prevent additional, or future, skin damage. The client will have a lot of money invested in your services so follow through with a comprehensive program.

Training in chemical peels

Due to the purpose of chemical peels—to wound the skin and allow it to generate new skin in the healing process—and the potency of the acids used in chemical peels, it is necessary to receive proper training in the use of these treatments. Most suppliers of glycolic acid and Jessner's solution, as well as established esthetic schools, can provide training in chemical peel procedures. Trade associations and publications can provide you with information on training also. At least a two-day course at the minimum is recommended, and this should be followed up by working with an experienced skin care professional for hands-on experience.

Financial rewards

Generally I avoid discussions on the financial aspects of esthetics since this is not my area of expertise. I feel that chemical peeling is such an important part of esthetics, however, that every esthetician should take the time and invest in learning this skill. The financial rewards can be quite high. Your skill will be the determining factor of the price, because the satisfied client will be your best advertisement. Most physicians receive most of their referrals from other patients. Milton Hershey of the Hershey chocolate company believed that the product must be the best advertisement. So, send out beautiful clients and they will speak a thousand words without uttering a sound!

Author's note: I want to acknowledge and thank Christine Heathman of GlyMed Plus and Maria Forland of Esthetic Pathways for their expert help and knowledge in hands-on experience with chemical peels. Forland supplied me with several packages of product information from suppliers, shared her experiences with the technique, as well as formulated many of the questions presented here. I also wish to thank Brian Reedy, MD, a plastic and reconstructive surgeon in Reading, Pennsylvania, for the valuable information on chemical peels.

References

1. Brody HJ, *Chemical Peeling*, St. Louis, MO: Mosby Year Book (1992)

2. Gross BG and Maschek F, Phenol chemosurgery for the removal of deep facial wrinkles. *Int. J Dermatol* 19: 159–164 (1980)

3. Letessier SM, Chemical peeling with resorcinol. *In Roenigk, HH Dermatological Surgery: Principles and Practice*, New York: Marcel Dekker, Inc. 1017–1024 (1989)

4. Moy L, A Comparison of Chemical Peeling Agents. Presented at the American Society for Dermatological Surgery, Chemical Peeling Symposium, Orlando, FL. March 17, 1991

5. Kligman AM and Kligman D, Salicylic acid as a peeling agent for the treatment of acne. *Cosmetic Dermatology* 10: 44–47 (1997)

6. Kligman AM and Kligman D, Salicylic acid peels for the treatment of photo-aging, *Dermatological Surgery* 24: 325–328 (1998)

Chapter 24

Cellulite

Cellulite is a term used to express a visible physical change seen frequently in women, and only rarely in men. The characteristic appearance is one of an undulating skin surface associated with increased fatty deposits. About 80–90% of women either have or will have cellulite. Many attempts have been made to define cellulite, often incorrectly, with no adequate explanation.

For example, Scherwitz and Braun-Falco[1] offered a definition for cellulite in 1978. Nurnberger and Muller[2] are the most frequently quoted references in this article and in others. These investigators studied tissue from the thighs and buttocks of 150 cadavers and performed biopsies on tissue from 30 women with cellulite. They reported the following findings:

- Subcutaneous tissue of the thighs is composed of three layers of fat with two planes of connective tissue between them.

- The upper-most subcutaneous layer consists of large "standing fat-cell chambers" that average 0.0–1.5 cm and are separated by septa of connective tissue called retinacula cutis.

- The retinacula cutis runs a radial and arched pattern then anchors into the overlying corium.

- Papillae adiposae project from these chambers into the corium.

- The "mattress sign"—dimpling or orange-peel appearance—is characteristic of women, not of cellulite.

- In men, the upper part of the subcutaneous tissue is thinner and has a network of crisscrossing septa that divide the fat chamber into smaller polygonal units.

- The corium is thicker in the thighs of men than it is in women.

- The pinch test only is positive in androgen-deficient men.

- The sex differences in fetuses appear after the eighth month and present the above adult patterns.

These authors present very interesting photographs of four generations of women with cellulite, showing the presence of cellulite in an eight-year-old child progressing in severity to a 79-year-old great-grandmother.

In 1986, a paper by Markman and Barton[3] reported on the anatomy of the trunk of the body and lower extremities. These investigators corrected many of the errors and misconceptions stated by Nurnberger. Their findings included:

- The subcutaneous tissue in the trunk consists of two distinct layers: superficial layer and the deep layer. Each layer is separated and contained by a discreet continuous subcutaneous fascia that runs parallel to the skin. (See **Figure 24-1.**)

- The septal framework of the superficial adipose layers visibly is different from the deep layer.

- The fat lobules of the superficial layer are smaller than those in the deep layer and tightly packed within closely spaced septa.

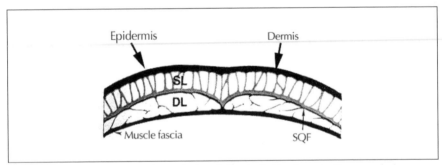

Figure 24-1. *A cross section through the abdominal skin down to the muscle layer. The superficial layer (SL) begins below the dermis. It is separated from the deep fatty layer (DL) by the superficial fascia, also called the subcutaneous fascia (SQF).*

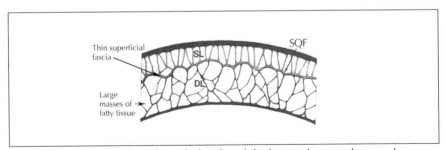

Figure 24-2. *A cross section through the gluteal-thigh area down to the muscle layer. There are two layers with the deeper layer (DL) being much thicker than the superficial layer (SL). It is the breakdown of this area that allows the fat to bulge into the dermis, causing the typical undulations of cellulite.*

- The deep layers are large, irregular and much less organized. This arrangement is more pronounced in the gluteal and trochanter-thigh region and is absent in the lower leg. The deep fascia is referred to as the fascia innominate, or Gallaudet's fascia. (See **Figure 24-2**.)

The diagrams of Markman and Barton are markedly different from those of Nurnberger's and more consistent with the human anatomy.

In 1991, Lockwood[4] reported on a new concept in superficial fascia based on the dissection of cadavers and observation of body-contour patients. He views the surface of the body as a function of the superficial fascia as it relates to the fascia of muscle and fat. The primary function of the superficial fascia system is to encase, support and shape fat of the trunk and extremities, and to fix the skin to the underlying tissues. The typical undulations of cellulite occur when this system fails.

Lockwood defines two types of cellulite as **primary cellulite**, characterized by hypertrophied superficial fat cells, and **secondary cellulite**, which results from laxity of the skin and soft tissues secondary to sun damage, aging or massive weight loss. The former type is not amenable to surgical correction while the latter is amenable to surgery.

Other published reports, to a large extent, only recant the data in these papers and add no significant information. Newer data presents a fresh look at cellulite.

Adipose and connective tissues

An understanding of cellulite requires an appreciation of the physiology of **adipose** and **connective** tissues. These two tissues are interwoven in a complex physiological system that primarily involves the sex hormones. While fat is the major source of energy reserve, it also plays a major roll in reproduction and postpartum nutrition. Fat deposits mainly in the hips, buttocks and breasts mold the female shape. Fat can be thought of as a sex organ, just as the skin is thought of as a sex organ. The hips and thighs are the most common target of cellulite, and how this fat is utilized depends on both metabolic and hormonal needs. (See **Figure 24-3**.)

Fat metabolism

The intake, utilization and storage of fat are under control of more than one system. Fat usually is ingested as a **triglyceride**, a compound containing three fatty acids attached to a glycerol molecule (see Figure **24-4**). A typical Western diet contains 30–45% fat. Eskimos, on the other hand, live on 80–90% of dietary fat. Yellow and white fat are common sights to everyone. Fat that comes from an edible animal is bound up with connective tissue, which is protein. Raw fat cannot be absorbed and must be broken down in a metabolic process called **lipolytic**. Fat is emulsified in the upper gastrointestinal tract by bile and partially digested by pancreatic lipase, a process called **hydrolysis**. Free fatty acids, monoglycerides and glycerol are produced. In the duodenum and upper jejunum the breakdown products are absorbed into the intestinal wall and through a complex process are resynthesized into triglycerides. In the cells of the intestinal wall the triglycerides are packed into **chylomicrons**, which are globules containing phospholipids, cholesterol and apoproteins. These chylomicrons must pass into the lymphatic system and then into the blood stream. Chylomicrons can remain in the blood stream for eight hours or longer. (See **Figure 24-5**.)

Using triglycerides

Chylomicrons are delivered to cells and used as fuel or for storage. **Lipoprotein lipase**, an important enzyme, is needed to breakdown the triglycerides into fatty acids so the cell can utilize them, and herein lies a problem. It is the existence or the absence of lipoprotein lipase associated with the blood vessels close to a cell that determines whether the lipid in the chylomicrons will be taken up by the cell. (See **Figure 24-6**.)

The fat cell, or adipocyte, will take up triglycerides from the chylomicrons only when the circulating chylomicrons are very high. It is the adipocyte that synthesizes and exports lipoprotein lipase under the stimulus of insulin and glucose. A key point to remember is the activity of lipoprotein lipase in other tissues is regulated by signals quite different from those that regulate the adipocyte enzyme. The breast, for example, increases the production of lipoprotein lipase at the time of birth since lipid is needed for milk formation.

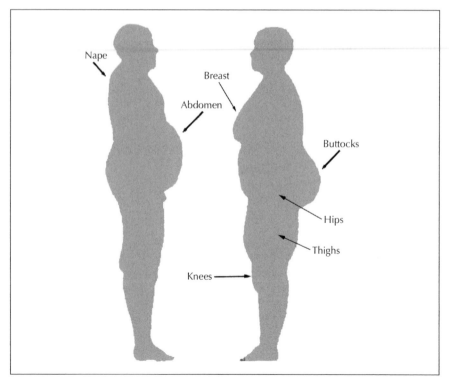

Figure 24-3. Male/female fat distribution. Note the thighs and buttocks on both sexes. Males have large abdominal fat masses, which predisposes them to heart disease. Women have large fat masses in the buttocks and thighs, which is reserved for pregnancy and lactation.

Carbohydrates

Carbohydrates and proteins are another indirect source of triglycerides. Carbohydrates, when in excess of the amount needed by the body for anabolic processes, are converted into lipid for storage. Conversion can occur either in adipocytes or in the liver. The liver synthesizes about 40–100 grams of fat every day, much of it coming from ingested glucose. Transport of triglycerides from the liver to the adipocytes occurs by means of very **low-density lipoproteins**, or VLDL. Like chylomicrons, VLDL require lipoprotein lipase for cellular uptake. Keep the storage concept in mind, for overweight simply is excess fat storage.

Stored lipids

Adipocytes serve as the major storage units for fat. Even though some cells contain droplets of lipid material, they are minor sources of stored energy. Where and why lipids are stored at certain sites remains a mystery, but much is known about some of the mechanisms that control the deposition of fat at certain sites, such as the hips and thighs. With a high-fat and high-carbohydrate diet, the lipid storage is initiated by insulin. *Insulin inhibits the utilization of fat whenever glucose is available.* When the body needs lipids, the triglycerides must be broken down again. This process is called **lipolytic**. The fat is stored in the adipocytes, sometimes called **lipocytes**, the size and number of which are highly regulated. The adipocytes originate from cells called **preadipocytes**, which are **fibroblasts**, cells that produce collagen in the connective tissue that surrounds the fatty tissue. (See **Figure 24-7**.) This connective tissue is called **stroma**. Cellulite formation is diagrammed in **Figures 24-8** and **24-9**.

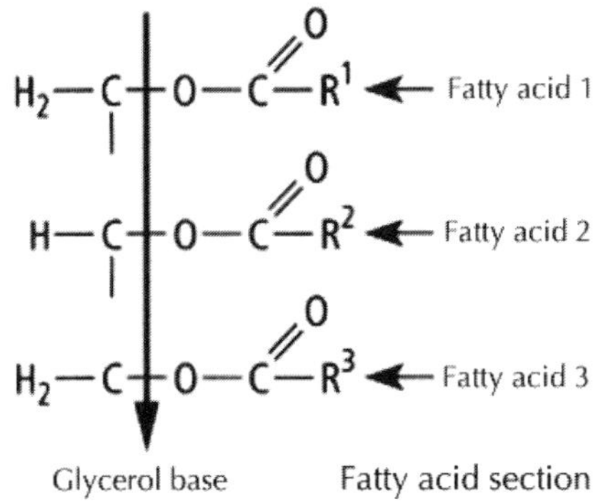

Figure 24-4. A typical triglyceride, or fat, molecule. The K's stand for long fatty acid chains such as palmitic, stearic or myristic acid. The lipolytic action breaks the triglyceride at the line, producing three fatty acid molecules and one glycerol molecule. The glycerol then is used again in another pathway.

Key summary points

1. Only the liver and the intestine make triglycerides that can enter the circulation.

2. Triglycerides that are circulating always are in the form of lipoproteins.

3. Uptake of lipid always requires hydrolysis, or lipolytic, to fatty acids.

4. Hydrolysis can occur at the surface of storage cells, such as adipocytes, or working cells such as in the heart muscle.

5. Lipid that is taken up as fatty acid either is re-stored as triglycerides or utilized for energy.

6. Stored lipid must be broken down into free fatty acids to be utilized as energy.

7. Adipocyte enlarge as more storage space is needed; new adipocytes are produced from preadipocytes.

This should be viewed as a process of fat—triglycerides—breaking down to free fatty acids, then stored as triglycerides and broken down again to free fatty acids to be used by the cell.

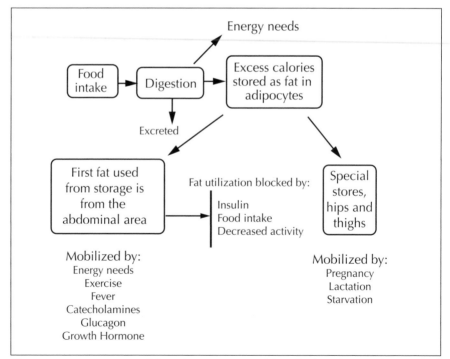

Figure 24-5. *An overview of fat utilization. Ingested fat is broken down to fatty acids. Some of the fatty acids are used for energy; the rest are stored as fat. Fat must be broken down again to fatty acids to be used for energy. Note the special storage areas. Fat cannot be used if the insulin level is high.*

Lipid release

Stored lipid is used as a source of energy under a variety of physiological conditions such as fasting, exercise or stress. These stored triglycerides are broken down again into fatty acids to then be used as an energy source by the cells. In the adipocyte, a special enzyme called **hormone sensitive lipase**, or HSL, catalyzes this reaction. What initiates this process is a fascinating story in itself for it involves many other substances. Epinephrine is one of the hormones that starts the process of lipolytic by acting on a cell receptor known as **cyclic adenosine monophosphate**, or cAMP. (See **Figure 24-10**.) For cellulite, this process is very important since stored fat must be mobilized at specific sites of cellulite in order to help the condition.

In **Figure 24-10**, epinephrine acts on the beta adrenergic receptor. This step activates a G protein, which activates adenylate cyclase to form cAMP. The cAMP activates protein kinase A, or PKA, which activates HSL by adding a phosphorus group to the enzyme. HSL then hydrolyzes triglycerides by removing two fatty acids. The final fatty acid is removed with a second enzyme known as **monoacylglycerol lipase**, or MAG. The activation of adenylate cyclase is inhibited by insulin, so this process occurs only at times when insulin levels are low. This is complex, but cellulite is a complex condition; treatments also are not simple.

These are the salient points in the mobilization of fat to form fatty acids. How the fatty acids are used is another story. Why does cellulite occur mainly in females? Can it be prevented? Is there a scientific basis for treatment?

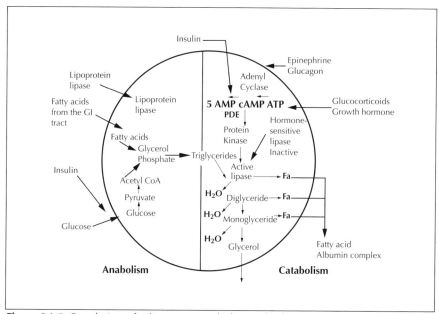

Figure 24-6. Regulation of adipocyte metabolism—the fat story at a glance. Looks complex, and it is, but in essence it is: free fatty acids in => stored as fat => free fatty acid out. The rest is the metabolic pathway.

Fat deposits

A good starting point in looking at cellulite is the regional distribution of fatty tissue. It is established that women have greater amounts of fat than men and that their fatty tissues are thicker than men.[5] (See **Figure 24-3**.) Is this a difference in fat cell number, fat cell size or a combination of both? Prins and O'Rahilly[6] reviewed the regulation of adipose cell numbers in humans and found that adipose mass is dependent of both size and number of adipocytes.

Differences in cell size vary with sites in subcutaneous tissue with a mean order that approximates gluteal> preperitoneal> abdominal> anterior thigh> mesentery> triceps> omentum.[7] These are not absolute relationships since other investigators have reported only small differences in cell size in the various regions.[8] While much data has been generated, there are no known mechanisms that define what areas of the body are to receive fat deposits. Hormones are the suspected agent which appears obvious, but how they accomplish this and why is yet to be discovered.

A new concept of cellulite

Cellulite is a natural process in females induced by the hormone **estrogen**. Since males have relatively little estrogen, they have very little cellulite. Estrogen's major function is to breakdown the collagen in the cervix at the time of delivery to allow the passage of the baby. This process starts at puberty and continues until well after menopause. The breakdown of collagen is a basic biological function of estrogen. In **Figure 24-8**, note the fatty tissue contained in collagen compartments in the skin—nice little boxes divided into two layers—superficial fat and deep fat.

Also notice that the fascial plane separates the deep layer from the superficial layer. This is the **superficial fascia**. Next, take a look at what happens when the collagen is relaxed or weakened—the square changes to a sphere. (See **Figure 24-9**.) The superficial

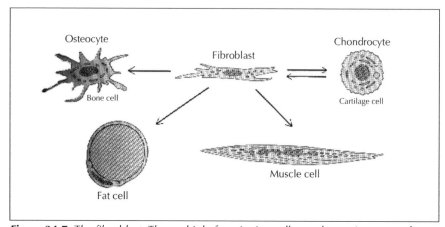

Figure 24-7. The fibroblast. The multiple-functioning cell can change into many forms. It may be possible to revert from one special type to a fibroblast again. The adipocyte starts as a presdipocyte, or fibroblast.

fascia weakens and gives way, and the fat bulges upward. There is more area for the fat to expand so adipocytes become bigger, and on reaching their maximum size they stimulate preadipocytes to form adipocytes. Estrogen stimulates the formation of new adipocytes from preadipocytes, and fat makes estrogen! Nice and neat, but a real vicious cycle is established.

This indicates that liposuction is at best temporary and that any mechanical means of fat removal will stimulate more fat to be produced. It is a physiological fact. Here are the steps in this cycle:

1. Fat cell mass equals body needs for organ protection and energy reserve.

2. Fat cell mass expands as caloric intake is greater than body needs.

3. Fat cell mass = adipocyte size + adipocyte number.

4. Increasing fatty intake increases fat cell mass; first adipocytes size enlarges, then number of adipocytes increases.

5. Preadipocytes must move out of the stroma—a framework of connective tissue—and become fully differentiated adipocytes.

All this physiology must be considered when planning a treatment for cellulite. What works and what doesn't work? We must pause and consider why 10–20% of women

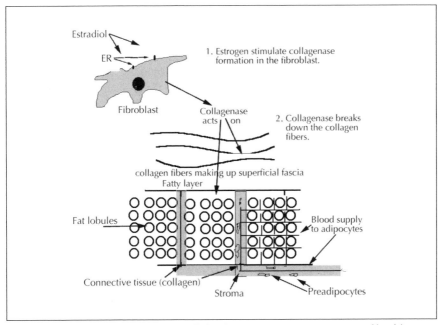

Figure 24-8. The general theory of cellulite formation. Estrogen activates fibroblasts to produce collagenase, which breaks down connective tissue around fat mass. These fibroblasts are in the stroma, or connective tissue that surrounds the fat mass. The retained fat now expands upward.

do not have cellulite. This fact provides hope, and perhaps will provide a clue to both the prevention and treatment of cellulite. Like baldness, the causes are known, but not the cure. There are some families in which all the females are free of cellulite, and other families in which the young females start to develop cellulite at 9. Since the origin of cellulite appears to be a physiological mechanism, a constellation of types can be expected, as well as degrees of severity. Either some genetic mechanism is missing to protect the connective tissue, or there is an excess of some enzyme or receptor that is overly active. In any event, I will take a guess and say the key to cellulite is in the fibroblast, and leave it at that.

Treatment methods

Cellulite treatments are about as confusing and nonsensical as the published causes for cellulite. Only a tiny glimmer of light has been shed on the topic during the last 20 years. I know of no present treatment for cellulite that totally eliminates the condition. There are some new, very promising treatments available, and some research is underway to provide more effective treatments based on new information as to the possible cause, or causes, of cellulite. Many different professional treatment methods billed as helping to reduce cellulite are available.

Packs and wraps. The basis of these methods is mechanical action used to "break up fat" or to "burn fat." They do neither. What these treatments actually do is move a

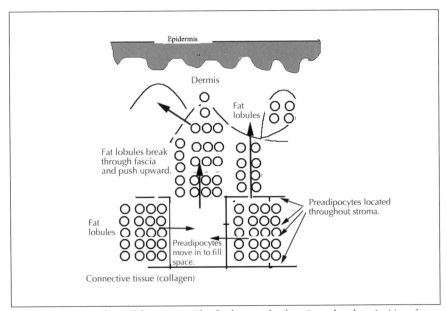

Figure 24-9. *New fat cell formation. The fat has pushed up into the dermis. New fat cells, or adipocytes, are created by the differentiation of preadipocytes to adipocytes. The adipocytes first increase in size, then increase their number. Now the fat mass is free to expand as the connective tissue gives way.*

small amount of interstitial water around, without changing cellulite. To claim that a pound of fat can be burned up with one of these treatments, or that an inch or two of thigh diameter can be lost is a misleading claim. Just think about the physiology involved; no basis exists to support this type of treatment. You are causing no harm in doing it and probably giving the client some psychological benefits, but you are not treating cellulite.

Wraps. Wraps combined with certain herbs have some positive effect. Herbs of choice include gotu kola, Paraquay tea, coleus forskolii and fennel.

Suction, rolling and pressure devices. None of the devices used have any positive effect on cellulite. In fact, I believe that the action of these mechanical devices actually can make the condition worse by inflicting further damage on an already weakened support structure.

Topical herbal treatments. To be effective, the active ingredients must reach the fatty layer, or at least the superficial layer. This means that water-soluble materials will not penetrate the skin easily unless they are formulated properly. Natural materials such as caffeine, theophylline and coleus forscholii have firm scientific basis for use in

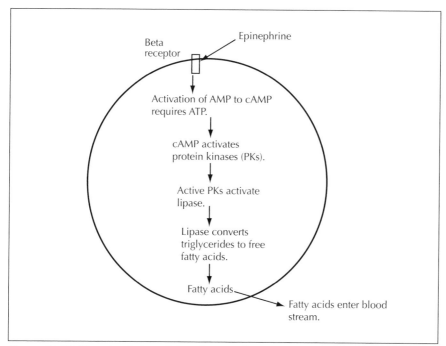

Figure 24-10. *The stimulation of the adipocyte by epinephrine. A process of activation is needed to utilize fat from the adipocyte. This process is tightly controlled and no steps can be omitted. Many body reactions require phosphorylation, or activation, of enzmes before they will work. The enzymes that activate other enzymes are called kinases.*

cellulite treatments as they actually can stimulate lipolytic. I have little experience with many of the other herbal ingredients used, but as a guide, any ingredient used must have an effect on increasing lipolytic to produce a reduction in thigh diameter.

Circulation enhancers and lymphatic drainage. One characteristic of cellulite is the reduced capillary blood flow. When the capillary flow is decreased, so is the flow of lymph fluid. The lymphatic vessels have no muscles to pump the fluid; they depend entirely on the tissue movement to work. Sluggish circulation slows down lipid metabolism and tends to increase interstitial fluid, and increases the appearance of the cellulite by aggravating the fatty mass.

Lymphatic drainage offers a positive treatment for the interstitial congestion associated with cellulite. It does not treat the cellulite, but treats associated conditions such as sluggish circulation and increased capillary pressure. Estheticians need to be skilled in this technique to make it work, for too much pressure will aggravate the cellulite. It also should be noted that lymphatic edema is not the same as cellulite.

Xanthines and xanthine derivative. Xanthines are a group of natural compounds that naturally occur as the body makes them every day. While they are by-products of tissue breakdown, they have many functions in the body.

Many natural products contain xanthines, such as coffee, tea and chocolate. One of the biological actions of the xanthines is to inhibit an enzyme called **phosphodiesterase**, or PDE. The enzyme PDE destroys the cAMP that stimulate lipolytic. By inhibiting PDE, the xanthine prolong the action of cAMP thereby increasing lipolytic. The key to using these products is to use them during the time when you are not eating, such as early morning and one hour before bedtime.

It is imperative for any lipolytic product to work that insulin not be active. Insulin production is stimulated when a person eats, shutting down fat utilization and lipolytic. One of the xanthine derivatives is known as aminophylline. This is a water-soluble form of theophylline and as such, it is a poor skin penetrator.

Collagenase-blocking agents. This is a promising area in cellulite treatment as it strikes at the underlying cause of cellulite—weakened connective tissue. The group of compounds known as bioflavanoids, some of which are known as proanthocyanidins, are quite effective blocking agents for enzyme action. Laboratory studies have shown that 1–1.5% of proanthocyanidins are quite effective as blockers of both collagenase and elastase. These agents are effective in that they prevent further breakdown of collagen. This is an expensive ingredient and very few products come close to the effective concentration. Having just a little amount of proanthocyanidins is not only worthless, but also misleading.

Other treatments. Liposuction is not recommended for cellulite; in fact it can make it worse. Keep in mind that there is no such thing as cellulite below the knees. If clients have fat legs below the knees, they do not have cellulite, they have fat legs. They need to lose weight—not have liposuction. These clients should wear a good pair of support hose, take walks, reduce caloric intake, put their feet up twice a day and do mild calisthenics. Liposuction will at times give a temporary relief and improve the appearance of the legs. In time, it will return, for nature will fill up the space with new fatty tissue, Remember this, the fat stored in the cellulite area is reserved for pregnancy when food intake is inadequate to nourish the fetus. Under rare circumstances will nature allow this reserve to be used, or to diminish.

Vitamin A and retinoic acid have some effect on cellulite, but they do not cure the condition.

Vitamin C is helpful, as is citric acid. They help to restore collagen but do not stop the destruction of it.

Oral products containing effective circulatory stimulants and collagenase-blocking agents as well as estrogen antagonists such as phytoestrogens from soy bean meal are well worth recommending as additional treatment.

The future

New treatments for cellulite will continue to be introduced. A revolutionary treatment currently is under development that involves pantyhose impregnated with anti-cellulite agents that are released slowly during the day. This action prevents the hills and valleys of dosage as seen with creams and lotions. An advantage of this method is the very low level of active ingredients needed to provide effective treatment.

A second treatment will be a multi-therapeutic approach involving natural ingredients that reduce the estrogen effect on collagen and simultaneously reduce the fat mass. These developments are in the research phase.

New oral approaches to the treatment of cellulite will be developed further with more sophisticated formulations. Some of these treatments will be combined with topical treatments for even more effective treatment. Keep a close eye on the ongoing research into the mechanisms of cellulite. At present there is not a great deal of published information on cellulite, but more will be coming forth.

Cellulite literature

The medical profession, unfortunately, is not well-versed on the topic of cellulite, and tends to make statements that are based solely on conjecture when asked about it. The press has a field day with cellulite, mocking any serious product or investigator. Some research workers in this area are making progress, but the problem covers many scientific disciplines; no one will ever master the whole subject. What is evident, however, is that from the study of this cosmetic condition will come some very significant biological findings that will improve the quality of life greatly.

Fat vs. cellulite

Many myths surround fat and cellulite. Fat is a fuel, a protective organ and a sex organ. The distribution of fat is controlled in part by hormones—mainly sex hormones, but other hormones such as growth hormones are involved. Cellulite is not a condition of fatty tissue primarily—it is a condition associated with estrogen activity. Estrogen is needed to effect pregnancy and birth, but it also has a relentless effect on collagen. The destruction of collagen associated with fatty tissue in the hips and thighs leads to the condition known as cellulite. Cellulite essentially is a herniation of superficial and deep fat into the dermis. The fascia, weakened by collagenase, no longer can contain the fat mass so it moves upward and produces a wavy surface.

As the space expands in the fatty layer due to movement of the fat mass, the remaining fat cells enlarge to maximum capacity. New fat cells are produced from preadipocytes in the connective tissue adding to the fat mass. Fat cells produce estrogen, which stimulates the fibroblast to produce collagenase, thus setting up a vicious cycle. Fatty tissue is removed only by a process called adipolysis. Adipolysis is a complex process involving many steps and hormones, as well as other controlling factors. Therapy that does not address this underlying etiology is useless. New research has lead to an understanding of cellulite and this new knowledge is producing new therapies. The small percentage of women who are cellulite-free can provide the answer to both the cause and the cure of cellulite.

References

1. Braun-Falco O and Scherwitz C, So-called cellulite. *J Dermatol Surg Oncolo* 4:230 (1978)

2. Muller G and Nurnberger F, So-called cellulite: an invested disease. *J Dermatol Surg Oncolo* 4:221-229 (1978)

3. Barton FE and Markman B, Anatomy of the subcutaneous tissues of the trunk and tower extremities. *Plastic and Reconstructive Surgery*, 248–254 (Aug 1987)

4. Lockwood TE, Superficial fascia system (SFS) of the trunk and extremities: a new concept. *Plastic and Reconstructive Surgery*, 1009–1018 (1991)

5. Lundgren H, Sex differences in body composition. Bosek J, (ed) *Human Body Composition*, Oxford Pergammon Press 129 (1965)

6. O'Rahilly S and Prins JB, The regulation of adipose cell number in man. *Clinical Science*, 92:3–11 (1997)

7. Roche AF, Research progress in the field of body composition. *Medicine and Science in Sports and Exercise*, 16:759–783 (1964)

8. Bjorntorp P, Effects of age, sex and clinical condition on adipose tissue cellularity in man. *Medicine*, 23:1091–1102 (1974)

General References

Author's note: I have included a list of more common references on cellulite. If you are computer literate, log on to the Web and search "cellulite." You will find at least a third of the most cited papers but keep in mind—caveat lector: let the reader beware.

Artz JS, Dinner MI. Treatment of cellulite deformities of the thighs with topical aminophylline gel. *The Canadian Journal of Plastic Surgery*, 3(4): 190–192 (1995)

Buscaglia DA, Conte ET, McCain W and Friedman S, The treatment of cellulite with methylxanthine and herbal extract- based cream: an ultrasonographic analysis. *Cosmetic Dermatology*, 9(11): 11 30–40 (Nov 1996)

Curri SB, Bombardelli E, Proposed etiology and therapeutic management of local lipodystrophy and distructual microcirculation. *Cosmetics & Toiletries*, 109: 51–65 (Sep 1994)

Dickinson BI, Gora-Harper M, Aminophylline for cellulite removal. *The Annals of Pharmaacotherapy*, 30: 292–293 (March 1996)

Di Salvo RM, Controlling the appearance of cellulite. *Cosmetics & Toiletries*, 110: 50–59 (July 1995)

Greenway FL, Bray GA, Herber D, Topical fat reduction. *Obesity Research*, 3(4): 561S–568S (Nov 1995)

Hermite R, Cellulite, *Cosmetics & Toiletries*, 102: 61–88 (Nov 1987)

Lotti T, Grappone C, Dini G, Proteoglycans in so-called cellulite, *International Journal of Dermatology*, 29: 272–274 (May 1990)

Mizutani T, Nishikawa Y, Adachi H, Enomoto T, Ikegami H, Kurachi H, Nomura T, Miyake A, Identification of Estrogen Receptor in Human Adipose Tissue and Adipocytes. *Journal of Clinical Endocrinology and Metabolism*, 78 (4) 950–954 (1994)

Nurnberger F, Muller G. So-called cellulite: an invented disease. *J Dermatol Surg Oncol*, 4: 3 221–229 (March 1978)

Rosenbaum M, Prieto V, Hellmer J, Boschmann M, Krueger J, Leibel RI, Ship AG, An exploratory investigation of the morphology and biochemistry of cellulite, presented at the annual meeting of the Am Soc Aesthetic Surgery, NY, May 1997. *Plastic & Reconstructive Surgery*, 101: 1934–1939 (1998)

Smith WP, Cellulite treatments: snake oils or skin science. *Cosmetics & Toiletries*, 110: 81–89 (July 1995)

Smyth MJ, Wharton W, Differentiation of A3116 proadipocytes to adipocytes: a flow cytometric analysis. *Experimental Cell Research*, 199: 29–38 (1992)

Van Robin LR, Bayliss CE, Roncari DAK, Cytological and enzymological characterization of adult human adipocyte precursors in culture. *Journal of Clinical Investigation*, 58: 699–704 (Sept 1976)

Chapter 25

Phytotherapy

Author's note: While writing this chapter, the goal was to be both practical and informative. I chose to supply a few uses for some of my favorite plants. The list is not all-encompassing, however, and you can have your own list. If I did not mention one of yours, it is not intentional. The chapter is limited to applications of plants to the skin. Refer to **Phytotherapy Defined** for a better understanding of the terminology used in the chapter.

There is a misconception in the skin care industry that **anything natural is safe. However, nothing is farther from the truth.** Every plant has some toxicity by its very nature; these toxins are the protective mechanisms of plants. It is very important that a healthy respect for plants be developed from the time you begin using them in your treatments. Remember this: **if a plant is active as a therapeutic material, it must have a physiological effect, which means it will alter the body biochemistry in some fashion, good or bad.**

Another belief is that plants can be used to treat every condition and are better than manufactured drugs. This isn't necessarily true. Between 50–70% of modern pharmacology uses plant materials or plant-derived materials, but some agents are synthesized from scratch. It doesn't matter if the agent is synthesized by a plant or by a human. What matters is the purity and strength of the agent.[1]

Others may feel that the cheapest is the best, and that it doesn't matter where you get the materials, they are all the same. Although this statement is not accurate, I hear it often. Many materials produced from plants contain insecticides, pesticides and herbicides. Often the material is adulterated with common weeds, or may not even contain the plant that is stated on the package. Organically grown plants are rare and quite expensive.

Skin care professionals should obtain specialized training before offering any new services.

Phytotherapy Defined

"Phyto" is from the Greek word meaning plant, and is used to form many words. The formal study of natural products used in medicine is called *pharmacognosy*. This study includes natural products from animals, minerals and plants. *Phytotherapy* is a branch of pharmacognosy that deals with the use of plant materials for therapy. *Phytochemistry* is the study of the composition of the plants and their active components. *Aromatherapy* is a division of phytochemistry. Following are terms used to describe the therapeutic action of plants:

Anodynes, also called analgesics, are substances that reduce pain.

Astringents cause tissue to contract; usually they react with proteins.

Antiseptics are externally applied agents that kill microbes.

Alteratives are strengtheners and detoxifiers which are used to help speed recovery from an illness.

Antibiotics are used internally and interfere with microbial action.

Cardiacs are substances that strengthen the heart muscle. Do not use them without medical supervision.

Carminatives are herbs that stimulate digestion and dispel gas.

Decoction is an essence or flavor extract produced by boiling.

Demulcents are soothing substances taken internally and contain mucilage, a type of fiber that absorbs water and acts to protect damaged or inflamed tissues.

Diaphoretics are herbs that cause perspiration, and often are used to "sweat out" a fever.

Diuretics stimulate the kidneys to increase the flow of urine.

Emollients are soothing substances used externally on the skin.

Emmenogogues promote menstruation, increase uterine contraction and reduce menstrual cramps. Overdoses to cause abortion can be very harmful; it is a dangerous practice.

Expectorants are agents that help to expel mucus from the lungs.

Immunostimulant is any substance that produces a significant change in the immune system and the body's defense system. The plants that stimulate it keep it in good shape.

Infusion is a liquid extract made by pouring or steeping a substance in hot water.

Macerate is to soften and break down plant material into parts by soaking in a cold liquid for a period of time.

Rubefacients increase blood flow near the skin's surface. They're often used for arthritis.

Stimulants increase metabolism and circulation. Excess stimulation may be detrimental.

Tincture is an alcoholic extract or solution of any plant or chemical material.

Tonics are herbs that strengthen the entire body. It's not really known what herbalists mean by the term "strengthen," but empirical use suggests that there is an increase in vigor or stamina experienced by the individual.

Vulneraries are healing agents for wounds or injuries.

In other cases, the preparation of the final product either can have destroyed or weakened the active ingredients. In addition, the product can be so diluted it is ineffective. To be safe, always buy from the best source, ask for analysis and how the product is prepared, and know its origin. Industry professionals who use plant extracts regularly can provide the names of good sources. This is the key to using plant material well. Keep in mind that if you do not have a reliable source, you can't obtain good results and even can do harm.

Ingredients

Please note that for the listed ingredients and each herb described in this chapter, I have listed the chemical names, but they are not explained in detail. Check these in any good herbal book; those that you cannot find will be found in textbooks on phytopharmacology or phytochemistry. The listed general references at the end of this chapter will give you a start.

Some teas, how they are prepared and the indications for their use will be discussed. Next, some popular plants and their uses will be covered, and a list of some poisonous plants you should be familiar with will be presented.

Working with plants, and using parts and extracts in any treatment, requires proper training. *Do not attempt to use plant parts or extracts in any segment of your treatments without this educational and practical background.*

A cup of tea

Teas are wonderful, both for enjoyment and therapy. Teas are made from leaves, stems, bark, flowers or a combination of all of these. Generally, teas are chopped rather than powdered. Coarsely chopped teas, above 6–8 mm sized particles, or finely chopped teas, around 4 mm, are the best to use because they provide a greater surface area than whole leaves or plant parts. Teas can be made in several ways, but there are some standards involved. A cup is equal to about 250 ml, eight ounces, or about $\frac{1}{2}$ of a pint. A pint is equal to 500 ml, 16 ounces, or two cups. A teaspoon is 5 ml and a tablespoon is 15 ml. In some cases, as in water, 5 ml equals 5 grams, but you can't make this assumption for powders or chopped material. Remember, *a milliliter is a volume measurement and gram is a weight measurement.*

To prepare an **infusion**, pour 250 ml of boiling water over 1–3 teaspoons of chopped tea, depending on the type of plant. Cover the container and let it stand for 5–10 minutes with occasional stirring. Strain. This method is good for leaves, flowers, soft roots and some types of bark.[2]

To prepare a **decoction**, begin with cold water. The amount of water and plant materials used will vary with the intent of use. For example, one cup of water usually is used as a general rule, so that would be about 8 ounces of water to 5 grams of tea. Place the prescribed amount of chopped plant substance in the water and heat to a boil. Boil for 5–10 minutes. Let stand for a few minutes to cool and strain. Wood barks and roots are made into teas this way.[2]

A **macerated** tea starts with cold water being poured over the prescribed amount of chopped plant material and allowed to stand for several hours. Some practitioners say overnight, but usually 3–5 hours is fine. Regarding the amount, use your judgment. It usually takes more water for harder materials, such as tough roots, to soften. A concentrated plant material also contains more concentrated natural toxins. A rule would be 1-1/2 teaspoons of chopped plant material to 8 ounces of water. You can drink the maceration cold or warm it slightly. This method is used to avoid certain constituents that are not desirable such as tannins, which are bitter.[2]

For example, a decoction of bearberry leaves yields 600 mg of tannin and 600 mg of arbutin, while a macerated tea contains 300 mg of tannin and 800 mg of arbutin. The macerated bearberry tea would be less bitter.

Another concern with macerated teas is the bacterial content. The bacteria problem increases the longer you keep the maceration going. If a plant is kept in water for a long time, it will decay and will decompose by bacteria. Bad bacteria types are found in fecal material from animals, birds or dogs. Soaking the plant material with this type of bacteria only a few hours will decrease the likelihood of further growth. For reasons such as this, it is best to subject all macerated teas to a brief boiling after extraction to kill any existing bacteria.

Commonly used plant material

Following is a list of my favorite commonly used plants that are safe for phytotherapy. In comparison, medical students are advised to learn to use a few drugs very well, rather than using many drugs less effectively. The skin care professional should do the same when using plants for phytotherapy.

It is crucial for the skin care professional to have a reliable material supplier, and not use home-grown plants to use for treatments. Knowing which plants are safe to use and which are toxic requires skill. Learning identification methods for plants grown in the wild is possible and many good books have been written on the subject. A good place to start is with *Identifying and Harvesting Edible Plants and Medicinal Plants*. (See **General References**.) Keep in mind, however, that if you plan to do this, special training is required.

Aloe. *(Aloe barbadensis, Aloe vera or Aloe vulgaris.)* The word aloe is derived from the Arabic word *alloeh* or the Hebrew word *halal*, meaning "a white, shining, bitter substance." The designation *barbadensis* is from the Barbados Island, where it was introduced from northern Africa.

Aloe is one of the most widely used herbal preparations in the treatment of skin disorders. It is obtained from the juice of the parenchyma, or inner portion, of the leaf. Do not confuse this aloe material with the bitter yellow juice obtained from the area under the rind of the leaf.

Many of the conflicting reports on the efficacy of aloe can be due to the wide variety of products sold, as well as the many different means of preparing and obtaining the juice. The juice is collected from the plant and allowed to harden into a brown mass. It is used as a powder or diluted with water at this stage, then sold. Commercial aloe gel usually is quite diluted and watery, but the freshly squeezed material has a gel-like consistency.

Uses: Most published studies have shown that aloe is effective in treating skin ulcerations, burns and frostbite injuries. It can be used for minor skin ailments such as cuts, bruises and abrasions, and can be applied fresh or in an ointment form with a water-soluble base. There are many products on the market claiming to contain aloe vera, but I have not seen one yet with a real aloe concentration listed. Generally, aloe should not be taken internally. If taken improperly it can produce drastic results.

Preparation: Aloe is supplied most often as an extract, either as a powder or a liquid. The aloe plant is tough to handle and extraction is not easy in quantity. To extract aloe, simply slice the leaf and gently press it to express the aloe juice.

Arnica. *(Arnica montana, or leopards bane, European arnica.)* Widely used in Europe and in the United States, this plant has many uses for injuries to the skin, including bruises, sores, lacerations and contused muscular structures. In addition, it can be used for muscular soreness, pain, breast soreness, severe injury, old sores and abscesses.

Uses: Arnica will help relieve rheumatic pain, and the inflammation of phlebitis and similar conditions when used externally. It can be used wherever there is pain or inflammation on the skin, as long as the skin is not broken. Arnica is believed to be an immuno-stimulant.

Preparation: Pour 1/2 liter, one pint, of 70% alcohol over 50 grams, 2 ounces, of freshly picked arnica flowers. Seal tightly in a clear glass container, and let stand for at least one week in the sun or a warm place. Filter, and the arnica is ready. It can be stored in a sealed container, but should be kept out of the direct sunlight to prevent the deterioration of constituents over prolonged periods of time. For a bad bruise, soak a 4 x 4-inch gauze sponge in the arnica solution and apply to the bruise.

Balm. *(Melissa officinalis, or lemon balm, sweet balm, melissa.)* Melissa, or balm, is taken from the Latin word *mela* meaning "honey." It is an excellent flavoring and can be used both internally and externally. This lotion-based extract can be used for skin lesions of Herpes simplex. The antiviral activity has been confirmed by both laboratory and clinical trials. Generally the balm leaves are used, but young shoots also can be cut and used fresh. Heat-drying appears to reduce the activity of balm.

Uses: Balm can be used topically as an anti-aging preparation since it contains high levels of antioxidants and immuno-stimulants. Taken internally, it is an antispasmodic and an antidepressant. It is a safe plant extract to use. Balm is an excellent carminative herb that relieves spasms in the digestive tract and helps flatulent dyspepsia. It also can be used for mild skin infections such as pustular acne in combination with other antiseptics. Individuals with hypothyroidism should not use balm because it inhibits the action of thyroid stimulating hormone (TSH). However, it can be effective for some forms of hyperthyroidism, such as Graves' disease. Of course, anyone with a thyroid disorder should see a physician before incorporating any balm preparations into a treatment.

Preparation: Pour one cup of boiling water onto 2–3 teaspoons of the dried herb, 4–6 fresh leaves, and soak for 10–15 minutes, keeping the container covered. Tinctures, creams and lotions prepared from balm can be used.

Calendula. *(Calendula officinalis, marigold, marybud, gold-bloom, Caltha officinalis.)* Calendula belongs to the *Compositiae* family of plant, as does the daisy. Either the entire flower head or the petals are used in phytotherapy. If you collect this common garden plant, be sure to dry with great care to ensure there is no discoloration.

Dry flowers by placing the petals, or whole flower if small, on gauze that is tightly stretched over a frame that will permit circulation of air around the flower. Do not overlap petals or flowers. Avoid placing in direct sunlight since ultraviolet light will fade the flower and denature the chemicals. The best temperature is around 90°F, or 32°C, for the first day, then between 75–80°F, or 24–28°C, for the next seven days for small flowers. Large flowers will take several weeks and should be turned once or twice.

Uses: Calendula is an anti-inflammatory, antispasmodic, astringent and anti-microbial. It is an excellent herb for treating skin problems, and can be used safely wherever there is an inflammation on the skin, whether due to infection or physical damage. It can be used for any external bleeding or wound, bruising or strains, and in slow-healing wounds and skin ulcers. Calendula makes a good first-aid treatment of minor burns and scalds. Its healing power can relate to the presence of terpenes, such as calendulozide B, which exerts a marked anti-ulcerous and sedative action. Calendula appears to be devoid of locally irritating properties and an insignificant toxicity. The extract has marked anti-fungal activity and can be used both internally and externally to combat infections such as monilia, or yeast. In addition, it can be used to help soothe severe burns, varicose veins, chronic ulcers, capillary engorgement, recent wounds and open sores.

Preparation: Pour one cup of boiling water onto 1–2 teaspoons of the calendula florets and soak for 10–15 minutes. Drink three times a day, or use externally as a lotion or ointment for cuts, bruises, diaper rash, sore nipples, burns and scalds.

Chamomile. Two herbs commonly are called chamomile. Roman chamomile, *Anthemus nobilis*, is a compact, low-growing perennial plant with tiny, daisy-like flowers. The German chamomile, *Matricaria recutita*, is taller and less compact in form. Both have a wonderful aroma, but many herbalists prefer German chamomile for medicinal purposes. Only the flowering tops of chamomile are used.

Uses: There are so many uses reported for chamomile that it is difficult to do justice to this herb. The anti-microbial action is effective against both staphylococcus and streptococci bacteria. It is safe in most types of stress- and anxiety-related problems, and can be taken at nighttime for a restful sleep. In essential oil form, it is safe to use added to the bath water of anxious children or teething infants. Putting the essential oil in a bath is beneficial both externally and internally, as it soothes skin and relaxes nerves. In addition, chamomile is a well-documented digestive aid and intestinal antispasmodic.

Chamomile can be used for any inflammatory condition of the skin to help reduce redness. It also is useful on areas where there is irritation or an abrasion. Often, it is combined with other plant materials to act as an anti-irritant. In general, chamomile is an effective agent that requires some experience to use, but the inexperienced person also will see results.

A recent study in Germany demonstrated the efficacy of chamomile on the healing of wounds caused by tattooing. With some tattoos, a "weeping" wound occurs where the skin has been abraded. The decrease of the weeping wound area, as well as the speed of drying, dramatically was improved when chamomile was applied to the wound.

Preparations: A tea is made in the usual way; 2–3 teaspoons soaked for 10 minutes, taken three to four times a day. A tincture of 1–4 ml can be ingested up to three times a day. With an alcohol tincture, all of the plant components are extracted and available for the body to readily use.

Echinacea. (*Echinacea spp., purple cornflower.*) Echinacea grows throughout North America as a wildflower. The best part is the root, although some use the entire plant.

A great deal of basic research is being conducted on the effects of echinacea. It seems to prevent infection and even repair tissue damaged by infection. This action is thought to be due to inhibition of the enzyme **hyaluronidase**. One of the primary defense mechanisms in the body is a connective tissue-ground substance called **hyaluronic acid**. It acts as a barrier against pathogenic organisms when they enter the body.

Some bacteria are able to activate the enzyme hyaluronidase, which destroys the ground substance by making it thin and allowing the bacteria to move about freely, reach cells, penetrate the cell membrane and kill the cell. This can result in an infection, but echinacea inhibits the action of hyaluronidase by bonding with the enzyme so that it can't act on the hyaluronic acid. The major component of echinacea that has this property is thought to be a complex polysaccharide called **echinacin B**.

Uses: Echinacea is effective against both bacterial and viral disorders. It works well with skin infections such as pustules and boils, and can be used alone or in conjunction with other herbs for any infection. Combined with yarrow or bearberry, echinacea is effective against cystitis, as well as respiratory infections. The tincture, or decoction, can be used as a mouthwash in the treatment of pyorrhea and gingivitis. It particularly is effective in treating vaginal infections such as *trichomonas vaginalis* and *candida albicans*, or yeast or monilia infections. Echinacea can be applied directly to the skin, or a preparation of lotions or creams can be used. Unfortunately, there are very few good commercial topical preparations available in the United States.

Preparation: To extract the flavor, put 1–2 teaspoons of the root in one cup of water and slowly bring to a boil. Simmer for 10–15 minutes. You can drink this tea up to three times a day. An echinacea tincture, 1–4 ml, can be taken internally up to three times a day. Do not ingest echinacea every day—a routine of three weeks on and two weeks off is recommended. If you are going to make your own lotion or cream, I suggest you use a reputable source for the ground root—one who has assayed the product for active ingredients.

Horse chestnut. (*Aesculus hippocastanum.*) This tree grows in northern Asia and England, and must not be confused with the American horse chestnut, *aesculus glabra*, also known as the buckeye. The actual fruit of the horse chestnut is used in phytotherapy, although some areas use both the bark and leaves.

Uses: Horse chestnut is a good remedy for many vascular problems. It is both astringent and anti-inflammatory, with a unique action on the vessels of the circulatory system that appears to be an increase in the strength and tone of the veins. It has been used to treat leg ulcers due to varicose vein breakdown, and is effective in spider vein treatment as well as in treating varicose veins.

Chronic venous insufficiency is associated with swelling and heaviness in the legs. I recommend trying the infusion along with application of topical horse chestnut cream or lotion. A 1–2% preparation is fine, and should be applied once or twice a day. The only side effects I know of are gastrointestinal irritation and the rare case of allergy to horse chestnut.

Preparations: Pour one cup of boiling water onto 1–2 teaspoons of the dried fruit and soak for 10–15 minutes. Drink this three times a day or use as a lotion. For tincture, take 1–4 ml three times a day.

Lavender. *(Avandula officinalis, garden lavender.)* Lavender is a very pleasant herb with many applications. Lavender essential oil is widely used in aromatherapy, and in my opinion, it is one of the safest phytochemicals. The flowers of the plant are used; they are gathered in June and September, and are dried below 35°C.

Uses: Lavender has many uses as a nerve tonic and calming agent, so it often is used in stress-related conditions, such as headaches. Externally, the oil acts as a stimulating liniment to help the aches and pains of rheumatism. The greatest use of lavender is in the perfume industry. Frequently, it is put on pillows as a sleep aid, and also acts as an antioxidant when used on the skin. Poured in bath water, it helps the skin heal minor injuries and wounds.

Meadowsweet. *(Filipendula ulmaria, queen of the meadow, bridewort.)* Meadowsweet is an unusual plant and is anything but sweet. Meadowsweet can be used for anti-inflammatory conditions and gastric distress. The aerial parts of the plant, better known as the flowers, leaves and stems, are used.

Uses: Meadowsweet is anti-rheumatic, anti-inflammatory, antacid, anti-emetic, analgesic and astringent. It is one of the best digestive remedies and is indicated in many conditions. Meadowsweet protects and soothes the gastrointestinal mucous membranes, reduces excess acidity and helps ease nausea. It is effective against heartburn, hyperacidity, gastritis and peptic ulceration, and can be used to treat diarrhea in children. The aspirin-like chemicals in meadowsweet reduce fever and relieve pain associated with connective tissue inflammation, rheumatism, in muscles and joints. Try meadowsweet on hyperkeratotic skin areas, such as elbows and knees, because it becomes keratolytic in higher concentrations. The pain relieving action can be increased if combined with willow bark or celery seed.

Preparation: An infusion is made by pouring one cup of boiling water onto 1–2 teaspoons of the dried herb. Soak for 10–15 minutes. Drink three times a day, or as needed. For tincture, take 1–4 ml three times a day.

Oats. *(Avena sativa.)* Oats have been known to be therapeutic for many centuries. The entire plant, excluding the roots, can be used—in fact, green oat shoots now are used as an aphrodisiac. In recent years, the oat grain has been refined into a powder that contains mainly proteins with some carbohydrates. Of special interest is the presence of 1,3 beta glucan in oats at a fairly high percentage. This glucan acts as an immuno-stimulant. Researchers also have found that eating oats is one means of preventing heart disease.

Uses: Oats have many uses. They are great for any type of skin inflammation associated with itching or burning, such as chickenpox. A bath with colloidal oatmeal was a standard, but now there is a much better form of highly refined oats containing almost pure protein. Oat protein can be taken internally and with milk as a nutritional supplement. The powder is excellent for sunburn and other environmental occurrences such as chigger bites. Oats can be used for eczema and any rash in either powder form or as a shake lotion-water and powder shaken together. It is one of the safest and most versatile herbs available.

Preparations: Use it as an oatmeal breakfast. I make mine by combining 1/2 cup of oatmeal, 1 cup of water, 1/8 teaspoon salt, plenty of cinnamon and some raisins. First, heat cold water to a gentle boil. For the skin, you can use a powder or a shake lotion, which can be made by putting one teaspoon of the powder in 1/2 pint of water and then shaking. It will keep in the refrigerator for a few days, but it is best fresh. The concoction is safe to use on any inflamed area, but not in the groin or intertrigonous areas where the skin is folded and wet-bacteria will grow and use the oat protein for food. When wet, without a preservative, most natural products will support microbial growth if they contain carbohydrate and/or protein.

Other effective plants

Here is a short list of additional plants that can be used in skin care. The items covered can be invaluable additions to your other treatment programs.

Jewelweed. *(Impatiens spp.)* This is a great plant for poison ivy treatment and prevention. Make an ointment by taking a handful of jewelweed stems and simmering in one quart of light vegetable oil for 10 minutes. Strain and add some beeswax to thicken, plus the contents of one capsule of vitamin E. Refrigerate, and it should last from 1–3 months or more.

Marshmallow. *(Althae officinalis, Malva species.)* This excellent common plant has many uses, particularly on the skin. Externally, the herb can be used in drawing ointments for abscesses and boils, or as an emollient for varicose veins and ulcers. It also softens the skin and acts as a moisturizer, antioxidant and keratolytic agent. An infusion can be prepared by soaking 2–4 grams of the root in one cup of cold water overnight. Tinctures, using alcohol, keep well and are quite effective.

Plantain. *(Plantago major.)* Plantain relieves inflammatory infection of the skin, especially if accompanied with burning pain or itching. Inflammation of the intestinal tract involving the mucous membranes and accompanied with colicky pains will be relieved by plantain. Apply plantain in the form of a saturated tincture as a dressing for fresh cuts and mild bleeding.

Goldenseal. *(Hydrastis canadensis.)* The roots of this plant contain many active ingredients including berberine, a versatile compound. It has antibiotic, immuno-stimulatory, antispasmodic, sedative, hypotensive, uterotonic, cholerectic and carminative activity. The anti-microbial properties appear due to berberine and other alkaloids present. It is highly effective against gram positive and gram-negative bacteria and fungi including yeast. Goldenseal can be used on eczema and other inflammatory conditions, and has a good history of use both internally and externally for acne treatment.

Toxic plants

There are plants to avoid that are toxic and poisonous. Most cases of plant poisoning occur in children under 3, and the majority of these cases occur with household plants. For this reason, I am listing the ten most common household plants that are poisonous. (See **Plants Most Frequently Reported to Poison Centers**.) The amount of plant ingested and the time the plant has remained in the stomach relate to the severity of the symptoms. Keeping toddlers away from plants is always a problem, but should be of paramount importance if you have children under 3.

Remember that plants mostly are cellulose and synthesize many chemicals for food and for protection. Some of the secondary metabolites of plants can be poisonous, such as **digitalis** in fox glove. Plants within a given family usually have similar chemicals. For example, the family *Solanaceae*, which is the nightshade family, all contain some alkaloids. The tomato and the potato are in this family. Never use a plant that is not identified, that you are not certain of, or with which you are not thoroughly familiar.

Phytotherapy fundamentals

Phytotherapy is a discipline that requires years of study and practice. While you can learn a great deal in a short time about the fundamentals, experience is needed to achieve skill, and this requires time. One way to learn phytotherapy is to work with an expert after you have obtained some basic training. Unfortunately, these experts do not abound. I have listed some general references for your use.

If you have access to a computer and can go on-line, there is a wealth of information waiting for you. For example, if you go to the World Wide Web via the Internet and type "Herb," you will retrieve a great deal of information.

Plants Most Frequently Reported to Poison Centers

Common Name	Plant	Annual number of exposures nationwide
Philodendron	*Philodendron spp*	5,657
Dumbcane	*Dieffenbachia spp*	2,776
Poinsettia	*Euphorbia pulcherrima*	2,048
Jade plant	*Crassula argentea*	2,015
Schefflera	*Brassaia actinophylla*	1,756
Holly	*Ilex spp*	1,657
Firethorn	*Pyracantha spp*	1,071
Pokeweed	*Phytolacca amencana* or *rigida*	949
Yew	*Taxus spp*	818
Rhododendron/Azalea	*Rhododendron spp*	803

The National Clearinghouse for Poison Control Centers in the U.S.

Phytotherapy is a rapidly growing field yet untapped by many, but waiting to be discovered. More and more natural materials are being used to process skin care products. There is a great deal of activity in the rain forest, where new applications for exotic plants are being explored. The skin care specialist will be faced with an array of new products in the coming years based on this technology.

Keeping abreast of phytotherapy will become necessary to understand and use the best materials available. Natural products provide many benefits, but since they also are potent chemical agents, they demand respect and a thorough knowledge of their properties. Phytotherapy can be very rewarding and definitely is worth the time to learn how to use effectively for skin care.

References

1. DerMarderosian A and Liberti L, *Natural Product Medicine*, Philadelphia: George F. Stickley Company (1988)

2. Wichtl M, edited by Bisset NG, *Herbal Drugs and Phytopharmaceuticals*, Boca Raton, FL: Medpharm, CRC Press (1994)

General References

Bremness L, *Herbs*, London-New York: Dorling Kindersley (1993). Helpful in identifying plants, easy-to-read and carry around.

Brill S "Wildman" and Dean E, *Identifying and Harvesting Edible Plants and Medicinal Plants*, New York: Hearst Books (1994). An informative and enjoyable book by an experienced herbalist who takes you afield. A must if you want to pick your own herbs.

Hoffman D, *The Information Source Book of Herbal Medicine*, Freeman, CA: The Crossing Press (1994). If you seriously are searching for information on herbal medicine, this book is an answer to a prayer. It covers just about everything there is on the subject.

Mowery DB, *The Scientific Validation of Herbal Medicine*, New Canaan, CA: Keats Publishing (1986). An excellent reference book.

Murray M and Pizzaorno J, *Encyclopedia of Natural Medicine*, Rocklin, CA: Prima Publications (1991). Good reference, comprehensive clinical data.

Tisserant R and Balacs T, *Essential Oil Safety*, New York: Churchill Livingston (1995). A new book that tells it as it is, and covers the dangers of essential oils as well as the use of them. Well-written.

Tyler VE, *Herbs of Choice*, New York: Pharmaceutical Products Press (1994). Complex, but an excellent reference standard and my favorite herbal reference.

Tyler VE, *The Honest Herbal*, Philadelphia: George F. Stickley Company, (1981). A great first book on herbs.

Tyler VE, Brady LR and Robbers JE, *Pharmacognosy*, Philadelphia: Lea and Febiger (1988). The standard text in the field. This is the ninth edition.

Werbach MR and Murray MT, *Botanical Influences on Illness*, Tarzana, CA: Third Line Press (1994). A well-written clinical book. Not a first book for the neophyte.

Computer sources are highly recommended. There are many new Web sites to choose from. All of the following sites I have investigated and are worth visiting. The list is not exhaustive:

www.ars-grin.gov/duke
The best, most comprehensive source of information on medicinal plants.

www.herbs.org
The Herb Research Foundation site. Really great with many links and current information in all areas.

www.herb.com
Much herbal information including schools, herbalists and an herbal medical dictionary.

www.rt66.com/hrbmoore/homepage/homepage.html
An excellent site managed by Michael Moor, director of the Southwest School of Botanical Medicine.

www.algy.com/herb
One of the best sites on the Web; very comprehensive information on herbs.

Chapter 26

Sterilization

The Acquired Immune Deficiency Syndrome (AIDS) epidemic has heightened the awareness of communicable diseases and the risk of infection that all providers of health and personal care services now face. In the past, tuberculosis was one of the most communicable of all bacterial diseases. Understanding how tuberculosis was spread and how to control the infection by isolation and treatment of the carriers went a long way to reduce the spread of this deadly disease.

Today, there are three communicable diseases that put the skin care specialist at risk. They are: AIDS, tuberculosis and hepatitis. All three are spread primarily from person to person, but can be spread by contamination with blood or body fluids. Knowledge of how these diseases are spread and what precautions are needed for protection from contracting the disease is essential. Keep in mind that infectious diseases can be spread in two directions, from the esthetician to the client and from the client to the esthetician. Within the office, salon, spa or skin care clinic, general hygiene, sanitation and sterilization measures used together will help reduce or even prevent this cross infection. Before you can sterilize, you first must have a clean working environment. This chapter mainly will deal with sterilization techniques.

What is sterilization?

Sterilization is defined as the killing of all microbes that can cause infection. For the purposes of this chapter, discussion will be limited to the control of infection in the skin care clinic. A basic knowledge of microbiology, the infectious agents involved and the specific microorganisms found on the skin is essential to understand the principles of sterilization. The sterilization techniques that are available to the esthetician will be covered in detail.

In preparing to write this chapter, I was guided by the need for the skin care specialist to have available a ready reference that covered all possible needs and situations that can arise requiring a knowledge of sterilization. I have included many "how-to-do's," as well as the "why-we-must-do's." The result is a practical reference manual for sterilization for the skin care specialist. **Microbes** are the source of all infection; this is our starting point.

The term microbe is a general, comprehensive term used for all infectious agents. The unbroken skin is a very effective protection against bacterial infection because most microorganisms cannot penetrate the skin barrier. Microbes enter the skin through breaks, such as cuts, punctures, scratches, abrasions and insect bites. Each body surface has a unique colonization of normal flora—bacteria—ranging from 10,000–100,000 bacteria per square centimeter. That would be more than 60,000–600,000 in square inches. This can seem like a lot, but considering several million bacteria fit on a pinhead, it is not a great number. The hair and skin both contain bacteria such as staphylococcus and diptheroids, and yeasts.

Essential microbiology

At one time microbiology was just bacteriology, or the study of bacteria. Today it covers all bacteria, fungi and viruses, as well as some organisms in between these groups. Bacteria, fungi and viruses will be discussed since these are the major contaminants of human skin. A brief description of each of these microbial groups follows.

Bacteria. Derived from the Latin *bacterium,* meaning "a rod" or "staff," bacteria are free-living, one-cell organisms without a visible nucleus. They are classified in many ways, but their shape provides an easy method to categorize the major groups. They can be spherical, the cocci group; rodlike, the bacillus group; or spiral, the spirillum group. Bacteria multiply by dividing, some dividing at a rate of one division every 15 minutes, resulting in billions of bacteria forming from a single bacterium in 24 hours.

It is not important to memorize the names of the bacteria, only to know that they are present in various forms. (See **Major Bacteria on Skin.**) Many bacteria will go into a resting state under adverse conditions such as too hot, cold or dry, or lack of an

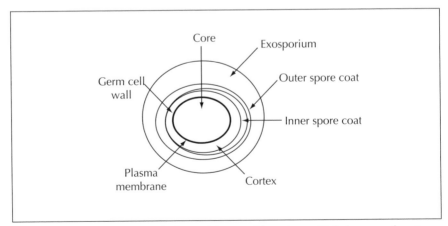

Figure 26-1. *Basic structure of a bacterial spore. Note the multiple layers and coats. These structures provide barriers and resistance to many chemical germicides.*

available food source, forming a ball-like mass called a spore. Spores are hard to kill. They can withstand boiling water, chemical treatment for hours, and extreme cold. (See **Figure 26-1**.)

Fungi. Derived from the Latin word *fungus*, meaning "a mushroom," fungi actually are plants that contain no chlorophyll. They include a large group of organisms such as yeast, molds, mushrooms, mildew and plant rust. While a few are pathological to humans, many are beneficial. A world without fungi would be a world without bread, beer, mushrooms and penicillin, to name a few.

Fungi live on both dead and living matter. They obtain food by secreting enzymes that digest the plant or animal material so it can pass through the walls of the fungi. Fungi that feed on dead material are called saprophytes, from the Greek words *sapros*, meaning "decay," and *phyte*, meaning "plant." Those fungi that feed on living tissues, either plant or animal, are parasites, from the Greek words *parasitos,* meaning "a guest," which in turn comes from *para*, meaning "beside" and *sitos*, meaning "food."

Major Bacteria on Skin

Staphylococcus epidermidis accounts for 90% of bacteria on the scalp.

Staphylococcus aureus is found on the perineum and in the nose. Carriers range from 0–40% of the population. (This is a very nasty bacterium.)

Micrococcus look and act like staphylococcus but metabolize sugar differently.

Streptococcus are spherical bacteria that grow in chains. They are rarely seen on the skin, though they may occur on infants and on older individuals.

Diphtheroids cover a wide range of rod-shaped bacteria belonging to the genus *Corynebacterium*. They are found in the axillae as lipophyllic (fat-loving) and non-lipophyllic types, and in the sebaceous glands as a special group called propionibacteria, associated with acne.

Gram-negative bacilli are also known as coliforms since they are a normal inhabitant of the colon. They occur frequently in the groin, the webs of the toes and in the axilla. They are called gram-negative because they stain red with a specific staining process known as Gram's stain (after the Danish scientist Hans Christian Gram, 1853-1935).

Spirochetes are Gram-negative, slender, helically coiled organisms.

Syphilis is a sexually transmitted disease caused by a spirochete called *Treponema pallidum*.

Yeast are the most common fungi on the skin. There are 160 different types, but the one most often seen is *Candida albicans*, though *Candida tropicalis* also occurs. Yeast can't penetrate intact dry skin, so they prefer moist surfaces, such as cracks and folds. Common sites are the mouth, vagina and rectum, and skin folds.

Ringworm is caused by a group of fungi called dermatophytes, which includes the epidermophyton, microsporum and tricophyton groups. Infection is spread through the keratin by digestion of both protein and lipids. Rarely do these organisms invade the dermis except in immune-compromised individuals, such as in AIDS patients. The infection is spread to other individuals by direct contact with a carrier of the disease, either human or animal. The most common fungal infections seen in the skin and hair are caused by yeast and ringworm.

Viruses. Derived from the Latin word *virus*, meaning "poison," viruses are mankind's deadliest enemy, besides ourselves. The virus is not living material and cannot carry on a life process outside a living cell. However, while very small—only 0.02–0.25 microns—the virus is ingenious in attacking living tissue and propagating itself. It is beyond the scope of this chapter to discuss the cycle of infection with viruses, even though it's a fascinating topic. Here the common viral diseases of the skin will be outlined, and then the AIDS virus and its relation to skin care will be discussed.

Viral diseases of the skin

The common viral skin diseases are called dermatropic viruses and include: chickenpox; smallpox; herpes simplex, which causes common fever blisters; herpes zoster; rubella, the German measles; rubeoloa, regular measles; and human warts. Warts are caused by a human papillomavirus. Only humans are infected with this virus, which causes an excessive proliferation of keratin as it grows. Most warts go away with time and require no treatment, unless painful or secondarily infected with bacteria.

There are several other viral infections that need to be discussed, even though they are not seen primarily on the skin. These are the viruses that cause hepatitis and AIDS.

Viral hepatitis. Hepatitis is an acute infection of the liver. The most common cause, and the infectious agent that concerns us, is a virus. When you provide a service to humans which requires close contact, you risk being infected with hepatitis. The major types include:

Hepatitis A. Formerly called infectious hepatitis, this form of hepatitis is spread orally by contaminated water and food such as shellfish in particular, and by fecal contamination. It is not communicable after the first week of jaundice. Once contracted, the disease can persist for several months.

Hepatitis B. Formerly called serum hepatitis, hepatitis B is the most common hepatitis infection spread in hospitals, since carriers are the main source of infection. The hepatitis B virus can be harbored for up to 15 years, and is found in practically all body fluids of an infected person. It is transmitted percutaneously, via skin puncture or wound; or permucosally, through kissing or sexual contact, but actual infection requires the presence of serum, blood or other body fluids of the infected person.

If you are a carrier of hepatitis B, you need to be especially careful with your clients.

It makes good sense when you take a medical history of a client to inquire if the client ever had hepatitis, or tested positive for hepatitis B. If there are any open lesions on the skin, such as pimples or cuts, extra precautions, such as wearing rubber gloves and thoroughly washing your hands after contact, must be taken when working with these individuals.

Non-A and non-B hepatitis. Also known as post transfusion hepatitis, it is responsible for 90% of transfusion hepatitis. It is a worldwide infection that is carried in the blood, and transmitted by blood transfusion and the use of blood and serum products.

Hepatitis C. The hepatitis C virus (HCV) is a form of hepatitis caused by a ribonucleic acid (RNA) virus. HCV accounts for the majority of the hepatitis cases previously referred to as non-A and non-B hepatitis. The hepatitis C virus was first identified and described in 1987, and in 1990 a hepatitis C antibody test, anti-HCV, became available commercially to help identify individuals exposed to HCV. In mid-1995, the hepatitis C virus was seen for the first time ever by scientists with the aid of an electron microscope. It is a linear single-strand RNA virus 40-50 nanometers in size. It is covered with a lipid envelope and is encased with glycoprotein peplomers or "spikes."

Hepatitis C is believed to cause between 150,000–250,000 new cases in the United States each year. Hemophiliacs and drug abusers are at the greatest risk, but anyone, of any status or age, and in any walk of life, is at risk for acquiring the hepatitis C virus. Researchers have found that many people infected with hepatitis C don't even know it. From 20–40% of patients in inner-city hospitals are infected, as are 80% of drug users.

Most people with hepatitis C contracted it either through a blood transfusion or receiving blood products such as plasma, which was contaminated with hepatitis C, or by sharing needles with intravenous drug users that were infected with hepatitis C. Before 1990, blood could not be screened for HCV. Thanks to HCV testing with modern sensitive methods, the risk of acquiring hepatitis C from blood transfusion is now less than 1%.

The other means of acquiring hepatitis C include health care and laboratory workers that can get stuck with an infected needle or instrument, people receiving medical/dental procedures or people with tattoos that were performed with poorly sterilized equipment. Infected mothers can pass the virus to the fetus in utero, but this occurs less than 1% of the time. It can occur more readily if the mother also is infected with the human immunodeficiency virus (HIV) that causes AIDS.

Cases of hepatitis C with no evidence of exposure through blood transfusions, needle sticks or needle sharing are called "sporadic." How these individuals became infected is unknown.

What you should know about HCV. The hepatitis C virus cannot be transmitted through the air—it is not airborne, and it is not spread by sneezing and coughing, holding hands, kissing, using the same bathroom, eating food prepared by someone with HCV, holding a child in your arms, or swimming in the same pool.

The virus is in the blood of an infected person and can be spread by using something with infected blood on it, such as razors, nail clippers or scissors, toothbrushes and water pics, tattoo or body-piercing needles, illicit intravenous drug needles, tampons and sanitary napkins.

The virus must enter the body through the skin or mucous membrane.

To help prevent HCV, avoid risk behaviors. Shots of gamma globulin after a person has been stuck with a needle do not seem to work.

Some people carry the virus in their bloodstream and can remain contagious for years. The disease can occur in the acute form and be followed by recovery, but the majority of the cases become chronic and cause symptoms for years.

AIDS and HIV. Probably not since the Black Plague of the Middle Ages has an infection struck more terror into the hearts of people than has AIDS. The initial lack of knowledge about this condition produced most of the fear, just as ignorance did about the plague in the Middle Ages. Since it's now known how AIDS is spread, precautions can be taken to prevent and contain it.

The primary sources of infection are by sexual intercourse or by direct contact with blood and blood products that contain the virus. The virus is known to survive in blood, semen, vaginal secretions, saliva, tears and breast milk. Any body fluid that contains white blood cells will support the reproduction of human immunodeficiency virus (HIV). The virus is not transmitted by casual contact with an infected person. It is relatively fragile and easily destroyed outside the body.

After contact or exposure, the antibodies to HIV, which are needed to give a positive test, may not appear for 6–12 weeks. The incubation period, before symptoms develop, can last from six months to five years or longer. People who have the antibodies of HIV are considered infected and infectious. Carefully handling all needles and sharp instruments that come into contact with an HIV positive person and using barriers, such as gloves, to avoid direct contact with blood and body fluids, is the best way to prevent transmission from the client.

The transmission of infection

How are infectious agents spread? Hands probably are the main source of transmitted infection in the practice of skin care, though I know of no study carried out with estheticians showing the number of infections transmitted in a typical salon or clinic. At one time barbers were responsible for transmitting *Tinea capitis*, or ringworm of the scalp, with contaminated scissors and combs. This situation was corrected a long time ago. The best database on transmission of infections comes from studying the infection rate in hospitals. It was found in a recent study that the following means attributed to the spread of infection to patients within a hospital. These findings are:

1. Hospital personnel–physicians, nurses, orderlies and nurses' aids
2. Medications or treatments–catheters, injections and inhalation devices
3. Patients' own flora, that is, their own body microbes
4. Surgery
5. Inanimate articles—fomites—beds, sheets, glasses and instruments
6. Visitors
7. Water and food

Control measures. To prevent the spread of infection in the skin care salon, the following are possible sources of infection:

1. The esthetician
2. The client
3. Instruments and other equipment
4. The air

The skin itself. The skin of both the client and the skin care specialist contain countless bacteria, particularly in the hair follicles and the sebaceous glands. About 4,000–10,000 viable particles are shed per minute by an average individual, while some people shed up to 30,000 particles per minute. Shedders are individuals with densely populated skin containing many organisms, particularly *Staphylococcus aureus*. These people, numbering about 1 out of every 50 individuals, have frequent wound infections. The hair is grossly contaminated with microbes, and a major source of staphylococci. The more abundant and longer the hair, the more microbes since the number of microbes directly relates to the length and the cleanliness of the hair.

To prevent these infectious agents from spreading, keep the skin and hair well-covered. Clean, tightly pulled-back hair or clean, short hair plus gloves for the hands, offer the best assurance for control of these organisms.

The nasopharynx. When a person coughs, sneezes or talks, bacteria are forced into the air, mix with the dust and land on the skin. A certain group of people are carriers for streptococcus Group A and staphylococcus, and when they have an open sore or infection they become hazardous to other people. Covering the nose with a mask when you have a cold helps somewhat, but doesn't offer complete protection to the other person. When you work on the facial area and are in close contact with the client, do not talk.

Fomites. Derived from the Latin word *fomes*, meaning "tinder," fomites are inanimate articles. This is a very large group. It includes all furniture, rugs, curtains, linen, equipment, instruments, cosmetic products and water. Clean rooms, well-vacuumed rugs, and clean curtains or blinds are general housekeeping measures. Equipment and instrument sterilization will be covered separately, but a source of clean, sterile water is important in infection control, particularly if you use basins and dip your hands and cloth into the basin frequently. Never use water, cloth or linen on a client that has been used on another client. Consider every object that has been used once as unclean or contaminated.

Make sure your products are not contaminated. Sometimes, despite all the precautions taken by manufacturers, products become contaminated with bacteria and fungi. The product will be cloudy, show microbial growth or have an unpleasant odor if it is contaminated with microbes. Contact your regional Occupational Safety & Health Administration (OSHA) office for guidelines to follow. Your regional OSHA office will be listed in the *White Pages* of your telephone directory under United States: Labor Department.

Air. One of the most serious sources of infection is the air. About 80–90% of contamination in an operating room comes from the air in the room. Consider the fact that microbes settle on the floor, equipment, lights and linen. When there's movement or when settled microbes are stirred up, they become airborne and settle again on large flat surfaces, such as the clients' skin. One effective method of keeping the air contamination down is to have a good ventilation system that filters the air in your treatment rooms to extract these microbes.

These are the four methods by which infection spreads. Add to this human error, the times you forget to wash your hands, cough or sneeze on someone, or break a routine in sterilization of equipment—all these things increase the possibility of infection being transmitted.

Major methods of sterilization

The major methods of sterilization include: heat, or thermal methods, and chemical methods. These methods will be discussed in detail, with an explanation of how they are used, and for what purpose they are used. Please note the terms in **Definitions of Sterilization and Disinfection**.

Thermal, or heat, sterilization. While the science behind heat sterilization is very complex, this information is not needed to use thermal sterilization methods. What is important is that the heat reaches the microbes in order to kill them. While this sounds extremely simple, it is one of the major reasons for failure of sterilization techniques. Remember that heat must travel over distance and that takes time. Also, the heat must be at an effective temperature and held there long enough to kill the microbes. A good analogy is that if you touch a red-hot stove for a very brief instant you may or may not get burned, but if you leave your hand on the stove for even a second you will suffer a burn. Let's look first at steam under pressure as a method of sterilization in detail.

Steam under pressure sterilization. Steam by itself is not an effective means of sterilization because it requires pressure to develop sufficient heat to kill microbes. Both

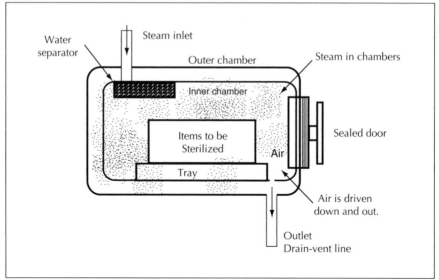

Figure 26-2. *Cross section of an autoclave.*

liquids and solids can be sterilized by steam under pressure. For our purpose, this will be called the autoclaving technique, because the autoclave is widely used to sterilize many types of material.

The autoclave, designed to provide pressure, steam and timing for safe and effective sterilization, is the best means to sterilize both equipment and solutions. Essentially, it is a two-chambered stainless steel shell that is closed at one end and opened at the other by a sealable door. Both chambers receive steam and are equipped with safety valves and relief valves. There is a chamber temperature indicator and control switch to set the temperature, as well as a pressure indicator and pressure regulator.

The key factor in autoclaving is removing the inner chamber air. Trapped air results in both cold and hot spots in the autoclave, which removes these areas from effective sterilization. There are many methods to remove the air, but the gravity displacement method is most widely used. Steam is lighter than air and rises to the top of the autoclave and displaces the air down and out of the bottom of the chamber much like a piston. A water separator keeps water trapped in the steam from wetting the materials to be sterilized. (See **Figure 26-2**.)

Preparation of material to be sterilized in the autoclave requires that it first be cleaned by washing, so that no particulate matter remains. This step is vital, and includes soaking and brushing of instruments, thorough washing of glassware and basins, and washing and rinsing of rubber tubing and other long hollow items. Always allow a little clean rinse water to remain in long tubing. It helps to displace the air when the steam heats it.

Packaging the material to be sterilized is important for two reasons. First, the material must be exposed on all surfaces to the steam, and second, the sterilized material must be removed and stored in a sterile condition. Muslin wrapping or woven cotton of 140–180 thread commonly is used. Paper is used, also, particularly water-repellent paper, but glassine paper and parchment also are effective. These supplies can be purchased from a laboratory or medical supply store. The technique of wrapping is not complex. Make sure the material is completely covered with two layers of paper or cloth so that the object can be removed easily from the wrapper after being sterilized without contamination. Seal the package with autoclave tape which has a visible indicator showing the package has been autoclaved after being processed. Do not use rubber bands or staples to close a package. Rubber bands don't allow steam to penetrate and staples make holes in the package.

Envelopes of various sizes can be purchased for one or more articles. They are very convenient, easy to use and inexpensive. Metal containers also can be used to contain several instruments or large objects. They often have a wire mesh inner container with a handle that can be removed to retrieve the instruments. Care must be exercised when removing an instrument so that other instruments in the container are not contaminated. This is usually done with sterile forceps, stored in a germicidal solution.

Loading the autoclave requires care. Items must be placed carefully in the autoclave so that they don't touch each other. This allows the steam to penetrate all surfaces of the package. Overloading an autoclave can result in incomplete sterilization of the material. Objects are placed on a removable tray in the autoclave. Make sure that everything is contained on the tray and that nothing touches the interior autoclave walls.

Definitions of Sterilization and Disinfection

Antiseptic—an organic or inorganic compound that inhibits bacterial growth, but may not necessarily kill bacteria. It is used on the skin to stop the growth of endogenous microbes, and also is used on surfaces.

Asepsis—the absence of microbes that cause disease; exclusion of microbes; free of infection.

Bactericide—agents that kill bacteria.

Bacteriostasis—the inhibition of bacterial growth, but note that bacteria are not killed!

Bioburden—the degree of microbial contamination on an object before sterilization.

Disinfectants—agents that kill all growing or vegetative forms of microorganisms. There are four types:

Bactericide—kills bacteria
Fungicide—kills fungi
Sporocides—kills spores
Viricide—kills viruses

Endogenous—source of infection within or on the body.

Exogenous—source of infection from outside the body.

Flora—bacteria and fungi found inhabiting the body, also called resident, or transient microbes.

Fomite—any inanimate object that can be contaminated with microbes and transmit infection.

Gram's Stain—a chemical stain used to identify bacteria. Gram-positive bacteria stain blue and Gram-negative bacteria stain red or pink.

Microbe—a general, comprehensive term used for all infectious agents.

Microorganisms—living organisms invisible to the naked eye. This includes all microbes.

Opportunists—organisms that normally do not invade the body, but are capable of causing infection if introduced by wounds, or when resistance of the host is low.

Sanitation—the practice of maintaining a clean, hygienic environment.

Sepsis—severe toxic state caused by infection with pyrogenic organisms. Pyrogenic organisms are the type that produce a fever or elevation of body temperature (from the Greek "pyr" meaning fire).

Septicemia—a spread of infection into the blood stream.

Spores—inactive, but living organisms. They are highly resistant to heat, chemicals and other methods of destruction.

Sterile—free of all organisms, including spores.

Sterilization—a process by which all microbes are killed, including spores.

Sterilizer—a chamber, or equipment used to obtain either physical or chemical sterilization.

Unsterile—all objects that have not been subjected to a sterilization procedure.

Some indicator of the correct temperature and time also should be added to each load; these are commercially available pieces of tape or colored tablets. The best assurance is to incorporate a vial of bacterial spores in one package. The standard is a vial of *bacillus stearothermophilis*, which can be purchased from a medical supply store. After the material is autoclaved, remove the package, and culture the vial of bacteria in a broth. If there is no growth, you effectively have killed all bacteria, even the spores. If you do not have basic bacteriological media available, send the vial of bacteria to a hospital or medical laboratory for culture.

To operate the autoclave after loading, follow the directions on the instrument. Some autoclaves require adding the water first, then loading the items for sterilization, closing the door and sealing it, adjusting the heat and pressure with the controls, and finally setting the timer for the length of autoclaving. When the timer goes off, if the unit is not fully automatic, vent the system by releasing the steam pressure through a special vent, or valve, and wait until the pressure is reduced to zero. Next, open the sealed door a crack; steam will continue to escape and the outer jacket will remain hot in order to dry the material inside. After the material is dry, turn off the autoclave, let it cool, and then remove the sterilized material. Remember, an autoclave is very hot and contains steam under high pressure, so follow the directions carefully.

This is not as complicated as it can sound. When you purchase an autoclave, instructions for its use will come with it. The cost of an autoclave appropriate for a small clinic or an office, ranges from $1,000–6,000, depending upon the size of the unit. Try to purchase a used instrument if possible; many supply houses take used autoclaves as trade-ins and recondition them. An autoclave will last 10–20 years if properly maintained. It will give you the best assurance of sterile instruments and equipment. To determine the temperature and time needed to autoclave a specific item, consult the autoclave instruction manual or call the item's manufacturer.

Dry heat sterilization. Dry heat in an oven-like sterilizer is used to kill microbes where steam heat or ethylene oxide gas can't be used. The mechanism of dry heat, essentially hot air, is the production of a physical oxidation or burning of protein molecules in the microbes, which eventually results in coagulation of the protein. The primary use for dry heat sterilization is oil-based materials, such as petroleum jelly or other lipid based materials, as well as dry powders.

Materials that often are sterilized by this method include gauze impregnated with petroleum jelly, mineral oil and instruments that can't be exposed to water because of possible corrosion. The time required for sterilization relates to the load, but high temperatures are needed. Typically, manufacturer's directions should be followed, but as a rule, one hour is required for small loads at a temperature of 340° F or 141° C. The lower the temperature, the longer the time. Only small quantities of lipids can be sterilized by dry heat. Large quantities require very long exposure periods.

Chemical methods of sterilization and disinfection. There are many chemicals available for sterilization and disinfection, however there is no perfect one that is effective against all bacteria. Keep this in mind as you read this section. The basic groups of chemical agents used to kill microbes will be covered, and then the ones that can best serve the skin care specialist will be discussed. Broad chemical grouping forms the basis of this classification.

There is one other classification, and associated definitions, that needs to be covered before the actual chemicals can be discussed. This classification is the strength, or efficiency of kill, of the chemical agent. High-level germicides kill all forms of life including endospores, or bacterial spores; intermediate-level germicides kill tuberculosis bacteria, *M. tuberculosis*. They also kill hepatitis virus, but not endospores. Low-level germicides are not effective against tuberculosis bacteria, viruses, certain kinds of fungi or endospores. These germicides can be bought in the supermarket.

Phenolic compounds. Plain phenol is the benchmark activity level. It is less than half as strong as cresol (Lysol[a]). Hexylresorcinol is more than 300 times as strong as phenol. You often will see the term phenol coefficient on a germicide bottle; this is a number that relates to the relative strength of the solution compared to a standard solution of phenol, usually 5%; the higher the number the stronger the product. Hexachlorophene is used in soaps to kill bacteria, and is very effective against staphylococci. Phenolic compounds kill microbes by disrupting the plasma membrane and inactivating proteins and nucleic acids

The parabens, which are widely used as preservatives in cosmetics, are phenolic compounds. Chemically they are hydroxyben-zoic acid derivatives of phenol.

Alcohols. Ethanol and isopropanol are effective at 70–80% concentration. They kill most fungi, some viruses and vegetative, or actively growing, bacteria, but they do not kill bacterial spores. Since 100% alcohol extracts water from microbial cells, it helps the bacteria to survive as spores. Do not use 100% alcohol as a germicide. Alcohol can be used to cleanse wounds and disinfect skin before injections. It is sometimes used as a hand rinse before surgery.

The time required to kill microbes after exposure to alcohol relates to the concentration of the alcohol. Using 70% ethyl alcohol, most common bacteria will be killed in less than 60 seconds. As the concentration of alcohol decreases, the time to kill increases. Concentrations of alcohol under 30% requires kill times that are too long to be practical.

Detergents. There are three types: anionic detergents, cationic detergents and nonionic detergents, which are not germicidal. Sodium lauryl sulfate is an anionic detergent, while benzalkonium chloride is a powerful cationic detergent. Quaternary ammonium compounds are cationic detergents with high germicidal activity. They kill bacteria, viruses and fungi, but not spores. They also are not effective against a bacterium known as *pseudomonas aeruginosa*.

Detergents are used to clean surfaces, including the skin, since they are quite mild. They function by emulsifying and disrupting the plasma membrane of the microbes. Zephiran[b] is the common trade name for a frequently used quaternary ammonium product.

Halogens. This family of compounds includes chlorine, bromine, iodine and fluorine. These elements are toxic to most forms of life. They react with cellular components to reproduce powerful oxidizing agents, which in turn react with other

---

[a] Trade name of L&F Consumer Products, Montvale, NJ
[b] Trade name of Sanofi Winthrop, Ltd., Surrey, UK

cellular compounds to inactivate or destroy them. Chlorine is used as a disinfectant, not as an antiseptic.

Household bleach contains 5% sodium hypochlorite which is a very effective germicide, even in dilute forms. Clorox[c], a common commercial form, contains 5.25% active chlorine, Cl_2. The kill time for chlorine is a matter of seconds for bacteria, but it relates to the concentration of active chlorine. Spore-forming bacteria are more resistant to chlorine than vegetative bacteria.

Iodine has a long history of use in medicine as both an antiseptic and a disinfectant. Iodine is highly effective in killing microbes. Compounds such as polyvinyl pyrrolidone (PVP) plus iodine, known as povidone-iodine, contain at least 9% available iodine. These agents are used widely in hospitals and in the sanitation industry.

Aqueous solutions of iodine are not as effective as tinctures of iodine, which are alcohol solutions of iodine. A 1% tincture of iodine will kill bacteria on the skin in 90 seconds, while a 2% aqueous solution requires three minutes.

Alkylating agents. Common types include formaldehyde and glutaraldehyde, which also are two powerful germicides. A 2% solution of glutaraldehyde is virucidal, bactericidal, tuberculocidal, fungicidal and sporicidal. This agent can be used to sterilize items that can't stand heat, such as tubing and complex surgical optical instruments. The solution is water-soluble so it can be rinsed off the item with sterile water before storage or use. It must be buffered before use to a pH of 7.5–8.5, and is not stable at this pH for more than two weeks. Care also must be used to avoid hand contact for any prolonged period; in fact, it is possible to become sensitized to glutaraldehyde. I believe this is one of the best chemical sterilizing agents available.

Ultraviolet light sterilization. I have included the use of ultraviolet light (UVL) as a sterilizing agent under chemical sterilizers because it kills microbes by a photochemical action. Ultraviolet radiation is electromagnetic radiation, not to be confused with ionizing radiation such as X-rays or gamma rays. The electromagnetic spectrum for UVL is 100–400 nanometers (nm), but the most important range for biological material is around 260 nm. To be effective, the UVL must reach the microbe for a sufficient period of time, depending on the energy of the UVL.

UVL does not penetrate glass, opaque solids, liquids or thick cloth. It is best used as a surface sterilizer, such as countertops, sterile laboratory benches and other clean germ-free work areas. Many skin care specialists rely on UVL for sterilization of instruments and fabrics. This is a very poor choice.

Gases used for sterilization. Three gases are used for sterilization: ozone, hydrogen peroxide gas and ethylene oxide. These are used primarily in industrial applications and therefore are not practical for the skin care specialist.

Sterilization routine

Now, what can be done with this information about microbes and sterilization procedures? First, the hazard of working in close contact with people must be recognized.

---

[c] Trade name of Clorox Company, Oakland, CA

Second, understand how your client can infect you or how you can infect your client. Third, recognize that there are means to protect both your client and yourself from spreading infection. I have prepared a detailed outline of sanitization and sterilization procedures that I recommend for use by skin care specialists.

Supplies. Use disposable, sterilized lancets and individually wrapped surgical gauze (2x2 and 4x4). If you use large volumes, buy sterile packs. Buy sterile cotton. Anything that can be thrown away or disposed of after contact with a client makes the job easier and safer. Paper towels, paper drapes, and paper covers for head rests, tops of examining tables and chairs all are convenient and safe. Review your spa supplies to see what items could be replaced with disposable items. Cost-effectiveness should be carefully estimated using time spent cleaning and sterilizing the item as well as convenience of use.

Specific sterilization techniques. If you can afford an autoclave, buy one. It will be one of your best investments. You can sterilize gauze, linen and instruments such as extractors and tweezers, needles for electrolysis, brushes, basins and other stainless steel items. An autoclave is not for plastic items, unless they are thermostable.

Glutaraldehyde. If you can't afford an autoclave, I recommend using either a 2% solution of glutaraldehyde or a 0.5% solution of sodium hypochlorite. Of the two, glutaraldehyde is better. The trade name for glutaraldehyde is Cidex[d], and Clorox for sodium hypochlorite. Sterilize glassware, instruments, plastics, rubber items and hoses with glutaraldehyde, but make sure each item is rinsed with sterile water and then stored in a sterile area such as a closed container or cabinet that has been sterilized. The acid-stable form of glutaraldehyde will kill spores in 20 minutes. The ultraviolet sterilizing cabinet used by estheticians is ineffective, unless used to store pre-sterilized items. Following is the recommended time and concentrations for the above items.

Make up fresh glutaraldehyde at 2% concentration that is not older than two weeks, and soak items for 12 hours to kill all bacteria and spores. Rinse all items in sterile water and store in a sterile area.

Sodium hypochlorite, commercial type bleach, 5.25% available chlorine. Dilute 1 part bleach to 10 parts water, 1:10. It is not necessary to use sterile water; the bleach will sterilize the water. This solution can be used to kill bacteria on surfaces of tables, floors, examining tables, lamp housings, sinks, toilets, walls and tile surfaces. It also can be used to sterilize esthetic sponges, or cleansing clothes. Dilute 1:10 and soak the sponge or cloth for five minutes. Remove sponge or cloth and dilute bleach 1:100, and soak for an additional five minutes. Rinse in sterile clean water, dry and store in a sterile area.

Bleach can be added to spa hot tubs at a concentration of 1–2.5 ppm to keep bacteria down. This concentration can be achieved by using one teaspoon, five mls, of 5% bleach per liter of water, or four teaspoons for every gallon of water in the tub.

Alcohol. For skin asepsis on small areas such as pimples and comedones, use 70% alcohol. It doesn't matter if you use 70% ethanol or 70% isopropanol, they are equally

---

[d] Trade name of Johnson & Johnson, New Brunswick, NJ

effective. For larger areas use Zephiran, which is quaternary ammonium chloride, as a 1:1,000 concentration of 0.1%. The tincture of Zephiran is more effective as an antiseptic, but it stings on open skin.

Iodine. For infected wounds, I prefer tincture of iodine, a very old product, but still one of the best around. For larger areas there is Betadine[e], or tamed iodine, which is not as effective as the iodine tincture, but is more gentle.

Chlorhexadine. A 4% solution of chlorhexadine is effective as a hand cleanser in a soap base, but it is not as effective against gram-negative bacteria as iodine is. It, along with the quaternary ammonium compounds, is not effective against pseudomonas.

Your salon or spa should have at least three of the above items for both sterilization and sanitation. If you have any questions about the use of these items, contact the manufacturer. You must be familiar with the correct use and limitations of all germicides and sanitation products you employ. There are many resources available for help in sterilization and sanitation procedures and regulations. Contact your State Health Department, your regional OSHA office or the Communicable Disease Center (CDC) in Atlanta, Georgia, for specific information about a particular problem or regulation.

Using gloves and face masks. Keep a supply of disposable latex gloves on hand. Use them whenever you open a pimple, express a comedo, or anytime you perform a facial on a client with an open face lesion. Gloves absolutely should be worn if you have any break in the skin on your hands, or even chapped hands. Dry, inflamed skin has tiny invisible cracks that could be portals of entry.

Wear a face mask if you have a cold or cough, a sore throat, or a macule or pimple on your face. If the client has a cold or a chronic cough, protect yourself with a face mask, even though the protection is not complete.

Remember the value of frequent hand washing, and always keep your fingers away from your face. Safety measures are sometimes burdensome, but illness is far worse.

General References

I haven't listed single specific references in this chapter because the list would have been too long. Instead, I have listed general references from which I have gathered most of this information. You can find ample specific references in these texts for any particular interest you can wish to pursue.

Atkinson LJ, *Operating Room Technique*, 7th Edition, Philadelphia: Mosby (1992). An excellent reference written by a nurse for nurses. It contains many practical techniques, and is a very valuable text for estheticians working in a physician's office. Easy-to-read with many definitions and helpful explanations.

Block SS, Disinfection, *Sterilization and Preservation*, 4th Edition, Philadelphia: Lea and Febiger (1991). This is the standard text in the field. While it does provide many answers to tough questions, it is complex and intended mainly as an advanced reference book for scientists.

Cano RJ and Colome JS, *Microbiology*, New York: West Publishing Company (1986). This is a comprehensive text on all phases of microbiology, and is easy to read and understand.

---

[e] Trade name of Purdue Frederick Company, Stamford, CT

Osol A, ed, *Remington's Pharmaceutical Sciences,* 16th Edition, Easton, PA: Mack Publishing Company (1980). A good reference for specific action of chemical agents, dosage form and use. Available in most hospital libraries. Some pharmacists may have it.

Pugliese PT, *Advanced Professional Skin Care,* Bernville, PA: APSC Publishing (1991). Includes topics on microbiology, skin disorders and infections as well as sterilization techniques.

Glossary

A

Acid H⁺(proton) donor A substance that associates to release H⁺ and thus cause the pH of the solution to be less than 7.0.

Acquired Immune Deficiency (AIDS) A viral disease that destroys the body's ability to fight infections, leaving it susceptible to many other diseases.

Addison's disease A disorder of the adrenal glands in which insufficient adrenal hormones are made.

Adenine A nitrogenous base, one member of the base pair A-T, adenine-thymine.

Adenoma A benign tumor made up of glandular tissue. For example, an adenoma of the pituitary gland can cause it to produce abnormal amounts of hormones.

Adenosine diphosphate (ADP) A nucleotide diphosphate that often is phosphorylated to form ATP.

Adenosine triphosphate (ATP) A complex organic compound composed of the molecule adenosine and three phosphates that serves in short-term energy storage and conversion in all organisms.

Adipose (L *adeps*, fat) Fatty tissue.

Adrenocorticotrophic (L *adreno*, near the kidneys; *cortico*, bark; G *trophikos*, nourishing) A hormone secreted by the pituitary that stimulates cortisone production.

Alkaline Denoting substances that release hydroxyl (OH⁻) ions into a solution.

Alleles Alternative forms of a genetic locus; a single allele for each locus is inherited separately from each parent (e.g., at a locus for eye color, the allele can result in blue or brown eyes).

Alopecia (al-oh-PEE-she-ah) Loss of hair.

Amino acid Any of a class of 20 molecules that are combined to form proteins in living things. The sequence of amino acids in a protein and hence protein function are determined by the genetic code.

Amplification An increase in the number of copies of a specific DNA fragment; can be in vivo or in vitro.

Anabolism The building up in the body of complex chemical compounds from smaller simpler compounds (e.g., proteins from amino acids); it is the opposite of catabolism.

Anagen The growing phase of hair.

Analgesic Any drug that relieves pain. Aspirin and acetaminophen are mild analgesics.

Androgen Any substance that produces masculinization, such as testosterone.

Aneuploidy (G *an*, without, not; *eu*, good, well; *ploid*, multiple of). Loss or gain of a chromosome. Cells of the organism have one fewer than normal chromosome number, or one extra chromosome; for example, trisomy 21 (Down's syndrome).

Anhydrous (G *anydros*, without; *hydor* water). Deprived of water.

Anorexia The loss of appetite.

Anthocyanins A group of water-soluble red to blue flavonoid pigments found in certain plants; especially important pigmentation in flower petals.

Antibody A substance formed by the body to help defend it against infection.

Antigen Any substance that causes the body to produce natural antibodies A foreign (nonself) substance such as a protein, nucleoprotein, polysaccharide, and some glycolipids, to which lymphocytes respond; also known as an immunogen because it induces the immune response.

Apocrine (G *apo*, away; *krinein*, to separate). Applies to a type of mammalian sweat gland that produces a viscous secretion by breaking off a part of the cytoplasm of secreting cells.

Apoptosis (ap-oh-TOE-sis) (G *apo*, away; *ptosis*, a falling). Genetically determined cell death, or "programmed" cell death in which the cell membrane and genetic material disintegrate; death.

Appendages The hair, glands and nails of the skin.

Arbutin A natural skin lightening agent composed of glucose and hydroquinone.

Atherogenic Having the capacity to start or accelerate the process of atherogenesis or the formation of lipid deposits in the arteries.

Autoimmunity A condition in which the body's immune system mistakenly fights and rejects the body's own tissues.

Autosome A chromosome not involved in sex determination. The diploid human genome consists of 46 chromosomes, 22 pairs of autosomes and a pair of sex chromosomes—the X and Y chromosomes.

Auxins A group of natural and synthetic compounds that aid plant growth. Some are finding their way into cosmetic products.

Azelaic acid An acid derived from mushrooms used in skin lightening.

B

B cell A type of lymphocyte derived from bone marrow stem cells that matures into an immunologically competent cell under the influence of the bursa of Fabricius in the chicken, and the bone marrow in nonavian species; following interaction with antigen, it becomes a plasma cell, that synthesizes and secretes antibody molecules involved in humoral immunity; B lymphocyte.

Base pair (bp) Two nitrogenous bases—adenine and thymine *or* guanine and cytosine— held together by weak bonds. Two strands of DNA are held together in the shape of a double helix by the bonds between base pairs.

Base sequence The order of nucleotide bases in a DNA molecule.

Basic Possessing a large number of hydroxyl (OH⁻) ions; a pH of more than 7.0.

Benign growth A swelling or growth that is not cancerous and does not spread from one part of the body to another.

Bicarbonate ion Carbonic acid ionizes to produce a bicarbonate ion, HCO_3 and a proton, H^+ in rainfall.

Biochemistry The study of those molecules used and manufactured by living things.

Biocide A broad-spectrum poison that kills a wide range of organisms.

Biological clock An internal timing mechanism that involves both an internal self-sustaining pacemaker and cyclic environmental synchronizers.

Biopsy The surgical removal of tissue for microscopic examination to aid in diagnosis.

C

Calorie (L *calere*, to be warm). Unit of heat defined as the amount of heat required to heat 1 g of water from 14.5 to 15.5C; 1 cal = 4.184 joules in the International System of Units.

Cancer A group of diseases in which malignant cells grow out of control and spread to other parts of the body.

Cancer in situ The stage where the cancer is still confined to the tissue in which it started.

Candidiasis A common fungal infection, known as a yeast infection, found in the mouth, vagina and nails.

Carbohydrates (L *carbo*, charcoal; G *hydor*, water). Compounds of carbon, hydrogen and oxygen having the generalized formula (CH_2O); aldehyde or ketone derivatives of polyhydric alcohols, with hydrogen and oxygen atoms attached.

Carboxyl group An acid group attached to a molecule; ⁻COOH.

Carcinogen A substance that causes cancer. For example, nicotine in cigarettes is a carcinogen that causes lung cancer.

Carcinoma A type of cancer that starts in the skin or the lining of organs.

Carotenoids Class of plant pigments that includes carotenes and xanthophylls; most are yellow, orange or red.

Catagen The transitional phase of hair growth, between anagen and telogen.

Catalyze (KAT-ah-lies) To greatly accelerate a chemical reaction; enzymes, for example, are protein catalysts that speed up biochemical reactions in the body; the enzyme is not consumed in the process.

Cell Fundamental structural unit of all life. The cell consists primarily of an outer plasma membrane, which separates it from the environment; the genetic material deoxyribonucleic acid (DNA), which encodes heritable information for the maintenance of life; and the cytoplasm, a heterogeneous assemblage of ions, molecules, and fluid.

Cell cycle Complete sequence of steps that must be performed by a cell in order to replicate itself, as seen from mitotic event to mitotic event. Most of the cycle consists of a growth period in which the cell takes on mass and replicates its DNA. Arrest of the cell cycle is an important feature in the reproduction of many organisms, including humans.

Cell Mediated Immunity (CMI) Immunity in which antigen is bound to receptor sites on the surface of sensitized T lymphocytes that have been produced in response to prior immunizing experience with that antigen and in which manifestation is through macrophage response with no intervention of antibody.

Cell membrane The outer membrane of a cell that separates it from the environment. Also called a plasma membrane, or plasmalemma.

Cellular immune response Binding of antigen with receptor sites on sensitized T lymphocytes to cause release of lymphokines that affect macrophages, a direct response with no intervention of antibody. Also, the entire process by which the body responds to an antigen, resulting in a condition of cell-mediated immunity.

Cellular respiration The process in which a cell breaks down sugar or other organic compounds to release energy used for cellular work; can be anaerobic or aerobic, depending on the availability of oxygen.

Centromere A specialized chromosome region to which spindle fibers attach during cell division.

Chemical bond The force that holds molecules together.

Chemical element A substance that cannot be separated into different substances by ordinary chemical methods; see element.

Chemistry The science dealing with the elements and atomic relations of matter, and various elemental compounds. The study of the properties of substances and how substances react with one another.

Chiral (G *chier*, hand). A term used to describe an asymmetrical molecule that cannot be superimposed on its mirror image.

Chromosomes The self-replicating genetic structures of cells containing the cellular DNA that bears in its nucleotide sequence the linear array of genes. In prokaryotes, chromosomal DNA is circular, and the entire genome is carried on one chromosome. Eukaryotic genomes consist of a number of chromosomes whose DNA is associated with different kinds of proteins.

Chylomicron A particle of the class of lipoproteins responsible for the transport of cholesterol and triglycerides from the small intestine to tissues after meals.

Circadian (L *circa*, around; *dies*, day). Occurring in a period of approximately 24 hours.

Circadian rhythms Daily cycles of activity. Circadian rhythms usually are based upon photoperiods.

Clones A group of cells derived from a single ancestor.

Cloning The process of asexually producing a group of cells (clones), all genetically identical, from a single ancestor.

Coliform bacteria Bacteria that live in the intestines, including the colon, of humans and other animals; used as a measure of the presence of feces in water or soil. E.coli is an example.

Collagen (G *kolla*, glue; *genos*, descent). A tough, fibrous protein occurring in vertebrates as the chief constituent of collagenous connective tissue; also occurs in invertebrates, for example, the cuticle of worms. They are long proteins whose structure is wound into a triple helix. The resulting fibers have a high tensile strength. The major protein of the skin.

Complementary DNA (cDNA) DNA that is synthesized from a messenger RNA template; the single-stranded form often is used as a probe in physical mapping.

Constitutive skin color The natural color of skin.

Cornification The biochemical process of converting a keratinocyte to a hard squamous cell.

Crossing over The breaking, during meiosis, of one maternal and one paternal chromosome, the exchange of corresponding sections of DNA, and the rejoining of the chromosomes. This process can result in an exchange of alleles between chromosomes.

Cyst An accumulation of fluid or semisolid material within a sac.

Cytoplasm The contents of a cell, including the plasma membrane, but not including the nucleus.

Cytosine A nitrogenous base; one member of the base pair G-C, guanine and cytosine.

Cytoskeleton In the cytoplasm of eukaryotic cells, an internal framework of microtubules, microfilaments and intermediate filaments by which organelles and other structures are anchored, organized and moved about in the cell.

D

Dehydroxyepiandrosterone (DHEA) A steroid compound that is converted to testosterone and estrogen.

Dendrite Long thread-like projection from cells. The Langerhans cell is a dendritic cell.

Deoxyribonucleotide (See **DNA**).

Dermatome Anatomical surface locations of the peripheral sensory nerves.

Dermis The layer of skin that separated the epidermis from the fatty layer. Contains blood vessels, nerves, and connective tissue.

Differentiate The cellular process of acquiring a specific identity and function. Usually an irreversible pathway. A corneocyte is the end stage of differentiation of a keratinocyte.

Diploid A full set of genetic material, consisting of paired chromosomes—one chromosome from each parental set. Most animal cells, except the gametes, have a diploid set of chromosomes. The diploid human genome has 46 chromosomes.

DNA (deoxyribonucleic acid) The molecule that encodes genetic information. DNA is a double-stranded molecule held together by weak bonds between base pairs of nucleotides. The four nucleotides in DNA contain the bases: adenine (A), guanine (G), cytosine (C), and thymine (T). In nature, base pairs form only between A and T and between G and C; thus the base sequence of each single strand can be deduced from that of its partner.

DNA replication The use of existing DNA as a template for the synthesis of new DNA strands.

Dorsal Pertaining to the back, such as the back of the hands.

Double helix The shape that two linear strands of DNA assume when bonded together.

E

E. coli Common bacterium that has been studied intensively by geneticists because of its small genome size, normal lack of pathogenicity and ease of growth in the laboratory.

Eccrine sweat Thermoregulatory sweat from the eccrine sweat gland. It is mainly water.

Edema (eh-DEE-mah) Excess fluid buid up in cells or tissues.

Electrophoresis A method of separating large molecules, such as DNA fragments or proteins, from a mixture of similar molecules. An electric current is passed through a medium containing the mixture and each kind of molecule travels through the medium at a different rate, depending on its electrical charge and size. Separation is based on these differences. Agarose andacrylamide gels are the media commonly used for electrophoresis of proteins and nucleic acids.

Endocrine A system of ductless glands secreting hormones into the bloodstream and targeting another organ to produce a response.

Endocrinology The study of the endocrine system and its role in the physiology of an animal.

Endoplasmic reticulum (ER) Network of membranes in eukaryotic cells that helps in control of protein synthesis and cellular organization.

Entropy A measure of the degree of disorganization of a system; how much energy in a system has become so dispersed, usually as heat, so that it is no longer available to do work. The higher the entropy, the greater the disorder.

Environmental insults Any factor in the physical environment that inhibits the growth or development of an organism.

Enzyme A protein that acts as a catalyst, speeding the rate at which a biochemical reaction proceeds but not altering the direction, or nature of the reaction. Enzymes are important in the construction and degradation of other molecules.

Enzyme-substrate complex The binding of a substrate molecule to the active site of an enzyme.

Ephilides (G *ephelis*, a freckle). Freckles.

Epidermis (G *epi*, on, upon; *derma*, skin). The outer, nonvascular layer of skin of ecto-dermal origin; in invertebrates, animals without backbones, it is a single layer of ectodermal epithelium.

Epithelium (ep-i-THEE-lee-um) The cellular layer without blood vessels that covers free surfaces of the body such as the skin.

Epitope Antigenic determinant; the portion of the antigen molecule displayed on the surface of an antigen-presenting cell (APC).

Estrogen A female hormone produced primarily by the ovaries.

Etiology (ee-tee-OL-oh-gee) The science of the causes and modes of operation of diseases.

Eukaryote Cell or organism with a membrane-bound, structurally discrete nucleus and other well-developed sub-cellular compartments. Eukaryotes include all organisms except viruses, bacteria and blue-green algae.

Exfoliate (eks-FO-lee-ate) To shed cells from the epithelium layer of the skin.

Exons The protein-coding DNA sequences of a gene. (See **introns**.)

Exponential growth Growth at a constant rate of increase per unit of time; can be expressed as a constant fraction or exponent.

Extracellular matrix (ECM) Region outside of metazoan cells which includes compounds attached to the plasma membrane, as well as dissolved substances attracted to the surface charge of the cells. The ECM functions both to keep animal cells adhered together, as well as buffering them from their environment.

F

Faculative pigmentation Reversible pigmentation—tanning—due to external sources.

Fat Triglyceride that is solid at room temperature; usually of animal origin. Organic molecules containing high levels of carbon and hydrogen, but little oxygen. Oils are merely fats in liquid state.

Fatty acid Any of a series of saturated organic acids that occur in natural fats of animals and plants.

Fibroblast A cell that makes connective tissue components, such as collagen and elastin.

Fibroblastic (fi-bro-BLAS-tik) Pertaining to fibroblasts, or connective tissue cells.

Flavanoids A group of secondary compounds produced by plants and important in chemical identification of those plants; believed to be contained in petals that reflect ultraviolet patterns and thus an element in pollinator attraction.

Folic acid A member of the viatmin B complex involved in the formation of red blood cells.

Follicular (L *follies*, a leather bag). Pertaining to a follicle with reference to a secretory gland.

G

Genetics The study of the patterns of inheritance of specific traits.

Genome All the genetic material in the chromosomes of a particular organism; its size is generally given as its total number of base pairs.

Genomic library A collection of clones made from a set of randomly generated overlapping DNA fragments representing the entire genome of an organism.

Glucose Simple sugar, and the primary product of photosynthesis. It is polymerized to make starch and other complex sugars such as glycogen.

Glycerol An organic molecule to which fatty acids are attached to form a fat.

Glycogen (G *glykys*, sweet; *genes*, produced). A polysaccharide constituting the principal form in which carbohydrate is stored in animals; animal starch.

Glycolysis The conversion of glucose to pyruvic acid (pyruvate) with the release of some energy in the form of ATP. Occurs in the cytosol; literally "sugar splitting."

Glycoprotein A membrane-bound protein which has attached branching carbohydrates. These can function in cell recognition, such as in human blood groups and immune system response, as well as in resisting compression of cells.

Glycosoaminoglycans Large and complex molecules mainly in the dermis and joints that contain sugars and proteins.

Golgi apparatus Eukaryotic organelle which package cell products, such as enzymes and hormones, and coordinate their transport to the outside of the cell.

Gonads   Glands responsible for the production of gametes and where certain gonadal hormones are produced. These consist of the ovaries in females and the testes in males.

Gotu kola   (*Centella asiatica*) An herb that has the property to stimulate collagen formation.

Gram-negative   Denoting bacterial cells that do not stain with crystal violet and iodine.

Gram-positive   Denoting bacterial cells that are readily stained with crystal violet and iodine.

Granular layer   The third layer of cells in the epidermis.

Guanine   A nitrogenous base, one member of the base pair G-C, guanine and cytosine.

H

Haploid: (G *haploos*, single). The reduced, or N, number of chromosomes, typical of gametes, as opposed to the diploid, or 2N, number found in somatic cells. In certain groups, mature organisms can have a haploid number of chromosomes.

Haptens   Molecules, usually of small molecular weight, that are immunogenic only when attached to carrier molecules, usually proteins.

Hemoglobin   A protein complex found in the blood of most chordates and the roots of certain legumes. It binds oxygen molecules, and in chordates serves as the means by which the oxygen is supplied to the cells of the body.

Herpes simplex   The most common virus that causes sores often seen around the mouth, commonly called cold sores.

Heterozygosity   The presence of different alleles at one or more loci on homologous chromosomes.

Histology   (G *histos*, web or tissue). The microscopic study of tissues, also called microanatomy. Histology uses many beautiful dyes to stain specific biochemical in the tissues.

Histopathology   The histology of diseased tissues.

Hormones   Substances secreted by various organs of the body that regulate growth, metabolism and reproduction.

Hydrocarbon   An organic molecule that contains only carbon and hydrogen and has its carbons bonded in a linear fashion.

Hydrogen   An element that is one of the constituents of water, organic matter and many other chemicals. Hydrogen gas (H_2) is composed of two hydrogen atoms.

Hydrogenation   Addition of one or more hydrogens to monunsaturated and polyunsaturated fatty acid chains.

Hydrolysis   (G *hydor*, water; *lysis*, a loosening). The decomposition of a chemical compound by the addition of water; the splitting of a molecule into its groupings so that the split products acquire hydrogen and hydroxyl groups.

Hydrophilic—"water loving" Hydrophilic compounds dissolve easily in water, and are usually polar, that is, they have a positive, or negative charge.

Hydrophobic—"water fearing" Hydrophobic compounds do not dissolve easily in water, and are usually non-polar. Oils and other long hydrocarbons are hydrophobic.

Hydroxyl Containing an OH⁻ group, a negatively charged ion formed by alkalies in water.

Hydroxyproline An amino acid involved in the cross-linking of collagen.

Hypodermic Under the dermis, usually in the fat layer; refers mostly to injections.

I

Icthyosis (G *icthyos*, fish). A constellation of genetic diseases marked by scaly thick skin.

Immunity State in which a host is more or less resistant to an infective agent; preferably used in reference to resistance arising from tissues that are capable of recognizing and protecting the animal against "nonself."

Immunization The process of making one immune. The induction of protective immunity by administration of either (1) a vaccine or toxoid, active immunization; or (2) preformed antibodies, passive immunization.

Immunogenic Refers to any substance that is antigenic; that is, stimulates production of antibody or cell-mediated immunity.

Immunoglobulin (L *immunis*, free; *globus*, globe). Any one of five classes of proteins in blood serum that function as antibodies; abbreviated IgM, IgG, IgA, IgD, and IgE, and participates in the immune response by combining with the antigen that stimulated its production.

Immunological Pertaining to the immune response, in which a protein antibody is synthesized by an organism to counteract some pathogenic factor.

Immunology The study of the immune system. This study reveals the many phenomena that are responsible for both acquired and innate immunity. It also includes the use of antibody-antigen reactions in other laboratory work such as serology and immunochemistry.

In vitro (in VEE-troh) From the Latin meaning in glass; in an artificial environment such as a test tube, or the equivalent laboratory apparatus.

Inflammatory response A complex series of interactions between fragments of damaged cells, surrounding tissues, circulating blood cells and specific antibodies; typical of infections.

Integrin Adhesive protein of the extracellular matrix in animals.

Intermediate filament The chemically heterogeneous group of protein fibers; the specific proteins of which can vary with cell type. One of the three most prominent types of cytoskeletal filaments.

Interphase The period in the cell cycle when DNA is replicated in the nucleus; followed by mitosis.

Introns The DNA base sequences interrupting the protein-coding sequences of a gene. These sequences are transcribed into RNA, but are cut out of the message before it is translated into protein. Compare exons.

Isoprene A chemical from petroleum also known as 2-methylbutadiene. It is a major building block of synthetic rubber, but it also forms the basic structure of many of the essential oils.

K

Karyotype A photomicrograph of an individuals chromosomes arranged in a standard format showing the number, size, and shape of each chromosome type; used in low-resolution physical mapping to correlate gross chromosomal abnormalities with the characteristics of specific diseases.

Keratin The major protein in the epidermis of the skin.

Keratinocyte A cell that makes keratin; all the cells of the epidermis can be called keratinocytes.

L

Lanugo hair (L *lana*, wool). The fine hair that covers the fetus.

Lipase (G *lipos*, fat; *ase*, enzyme suffix). An enzyme that accelerates the hydrolysis or synthesis of fats.

Lipid A fat, oil, or fat-like compound that usually has fatty acids in its molecular structure. An organic compound consisting mainly of carbon and hydrogen atoms linked by nonpolar covalent bonds. Examples include fats, waxes, phospholipids and steroids that are insoluble in water.

Liposome Artificial lipoid particles.

Lymphatic system A network that includes lymph nodes, lymph and lymph vessels which serves as a filtering system for the blood.

M

Macromolecule (G *makros*, large; L *moliculus*, a little mass). A very large molecule, generally used in reference to carbohydrates, lipids, proteins and nucleic acids.

Macrophage (G *makros*, long, large; *phago*, to eat). A phagocytic cell type in vertebrates that performs crucial functions in the immune response and inflammation, such as presenting antigenic epitopes to T cells and producing several cytokines.

Major histocompatibility complex (MHC) Complex of genes coding for proteins inserted in the cell membrane; the proteins are the basis of self-nonself recognition by the immune system.

Mastectomy The surgical removal of the breast.

Meiosis Process of cell division by which egg and sperm cells are formed, involving a diminution in the amount of genetic material. Comprises two successive nuclear divisions with only one round of DNA replication, which produces four haploid daughter cells from an initial diploid cell.

Meissner's corpuscles (Georg Meissner, German physiologist, 1829-1901) (L *corpusc*, a small body) Tactile sensory receptors in the superficial dermis.

Melanin (G *melas*, black) Black or dark brown pigment found in plant, or animal structures.

Melanosome A pigmented particle found in melanocyte that imparts color to skin.

Melatonin A hormone secreted by the pineal gland. Functions in regulating photoperiodicity.

Menopause (G *men*, month; *pauein*, to cease). In the human female, that time of life when ovulation ceases; cessation of the menstrual cycle.

Menses The period of shedding of the lining, endometrium, of the uterus and associated fluids if an ovum is not fertilized, most notably in primates.

Menstrual cycle The period of the regularly recurring physiologic changes in the endometrium that culminates in its shedding—menstruation.

Menstruation (L *menstrua*, the menses; *mensis*, month). Loss of blood and tissue from the uterus at the end of a female primate's reproductive cycle.

Merkel cell (Friedrich Merkel a German anatomist 1845–1919) Touch corpuscles in the epidermis.

Mesenchyme Undifferentiated mesoderm. It eventually will develop into muscle, blood vessels, skeletal elements and other connective tissues.

Mesoderm (G *mesos*, middle; *derma*, skin). The third germ layer, formed in the gastrula between the ectoderm and endoderm; gives rise to connective tissues, muscle, urogenital and vascular systems, and the peritoneum.

Messenger RNA (mRNA) RNA that serves as a template for protein synthesis. (See **genetic code**.)

Metabolism (G *metabole*, change). A group of processes that includes digestion, production of energy (respiration), and synthesis of molecules and structures by organisms; the sum of the constructive (anabolic) and destructive (catabolic) processes.

Metaphase A stage in mitosis or meiosis during which the chromosomes are aligned along the equatorial plane of the cell.

Metastasis To spread from the first cancer site to other sites in the body in vitro.

Microfilament Component of the cytoskeleton; involved in cell shape, motion, and growth. Helical protein filament formed by the polymerization of globular action molecules.

Microtubules Type of filament in eukaryotic cells composed of units of the protein tubulin. Among other functions, it is the primary structural component of the eukaryotic flagellum.

Mitochondrion Complex organelle found in most eukaryotes; believed to be descended from free-living bacteria that established a symbiotic relationship with a primitive eukaryote. Mitochondria are the site of energy production in most eukaryotes; they require oxygen to function.

Mitosis The process of nuclear division in cells that produces daughter cells which are genetically identical to each other and to the parent cell.

N

Neoplasm A new growth of tissue or cells; a tumor that generally is malignant.

Nucleic acid A class of biochemical compounds that includes DNA and RNA. They are among the largest known molecules.

Nucleotide Unit from which nucleic acids are constructed by polymerization. It contains a sugar, a phosphate group and an organic base. ATP is a nucleotide.

Nucleus Membrane-bound organelle that contains the DNA in the form of chromosomes. It is the site of DNA replication and the site of RNA synthesis.

O

Ochronosis (G *ochros*, yellow). A metabolic disorder characterized by yellow deposits in the tissues.

Osmosis The passage of solvent from a lesser concentration to a greater concentration when two solutions are separated by a membrane that will allow passage of the solvent but not the solute.

Oxidation (F *oxider*, to oxidize; G *oxys*, sharp). The loss of an electron by an atom or molecule; sometimes addition of oxygen chemically to a substance. Opposite of reduction, in which an electron is accepted by an atom or molecule.

Oxidative phosphorylation The electron transport system associated with aerobic respiration and mitochondria. In the release of energy through a series of cytochromes, three molecules of ATP are made.

Oxygen An element that is one of the constituents of water, organic matter and many other chemicals.

Oxygen gas (O_2) Composed of two oxygen atoms, it is needed for respiration and is produced by photosynthesis.

P

p53 protein A tumor suppressor protein with critical functions in normal cells.

A mutation in the gene that encodes p53, can result in loss of control over cell division and thus cancer.

Pacinian corpuscle (Filippo Pacini, Italian anatomist, 1812–1883). A sensory receptor in skin, muscles, body joints, body organs and tendons that is involved with the vibratory sense and firm pressure on the skin; also called a lamellated corpuscle.

Papilla (L *nipple*). A small nipple-like projection. A vascular process that nourishes the root of a hair, feather or developing tooth. The papillary dermis is so called because of the nipple-like projection from the epidermis in the dermis and the upward projection of the papillary dermis into the epidermis.

Papillary dermis The papillary dermis is so called because of the nipple-like projection from the epidermis in the dermis and the upward projection of the papillary dermis into the epidermis.

Parenchyma A spongy mass of mesenchyme cells filling spaces around viscera, muscles or epithelia in invertebrates. Depending on the species, parenchyma can provide skeletal support, nutrient storage, motility, reserves of regenerative cells, transport of materials, structural interactions with other tissues, modifiable tissue for morphogenesis, oxygen storage and perhaps other functions that have yet to be determined.

Pathogen An organism that produces disease in a host organism, disease being an alteration of one or more metabolic functions in response to the presence of the organism.

Pathogenesis Production and development of disease.

Pathogenic (G *pathos*, disease; NL *genic*, giving rise to). Producing or capable of producing disease.

Pathogenicity Capability of an agent to produce disease.

Pentose A 5-carbon sugar that is critical in cell division. Ribose in DNA is a pentose sugar.

Peptidase (G *peptein*, to digest; *ase*, enzyme suffix). An enzyme that breaks down simple peptides, releasing amino acids.

Peptide bond A chemical bond formed between the amino group of one amino acid and the carboxyl (acidic) group of an adjacent amino acid. It also binds amino acids together into a polypeptide chain, formed by removing an OH from the carboxyl group of one amino acid and an H from the amino group of another to form an amide group.

Peptides Two or more amino acids linked by a peptide bond.

Peroxidase An enzyme that converts peroxides into water and oxygen.

Peroxisome A cellular microbody containing enzymes involved with photorespiration and photosynthesis in plants, but is intimately associated with energy metabolism and lipid metabolism in humans.

Petechiae Tiny areas of bleeding under the skin, usually caused by a low platelet count.

pH scale The numerical scale that measures acidity and alkalinity, ranging from 0 (most acidic) to 14 (most basic); pH stands for potential hydrogen and refers to the concentration of hydrogen ions (H^+).

pH (potential of hydrogen) A symbol referring to the relative concentration of hydrogen ions in a solution; pH values are from 0 to 14, and the lower the value, the more acid or hydrogen ions in the solution. Equal to the negative logarithm of the hydrogen ion concentration.

Phacomelanin (or pheomelanin) (G *phaios*, dusky). A chemically different melanin from black or eumelanin. It is reponsible for red and yellow colors in skin and hair.

Phagocyte (G *phagein*, to eat; kytos, *hollow vessel*). Any cell that engulfs and devours microorganisms or other particles.

Phagocytosis (G *phagein*, to eat; *kytos*, hollow vessel). The engulfment of a particle by a phagocyte or a protozoan.

Phenotype The expression that results from an interaction of one or more gene pairs and the environment. Blond hair and blue eyes are phenotypes of the genes that cause them.

Pheromone (G *pherein*, to carry; *hormon*, exciting, stirring up). Chemical substance released by one organism that influences the behavior, or physiological processes of another organism.

Phlebitis A painful inflammation of the veins.

Phosphatide A lipid with phosphorus, such as lecithin. A complex phosphoric ester lipid, such as lecithin, found in all cells.

Phospholipid A type of lipid molecule occurring in a bilayer in biological membranes; a lipid with two fatty acids and a phosphate group attached to glycerol.

Phosphorylation The addition of a phosphate group to a molecule.

Photon A unit of light energy.

Photooxidation The change in the structure of a molecule due to exposure to light; an example is bleaching.

Photosynthesis The biochemical process by which green plants and some bacteria capture light energy and use it to produce chemical bonds. Carbon dioxide and water are consumed while oxygen and simple sugars are produced.

Physiology (L *physiologia*, natural science). A branch of biology dealing with the organic processes and phenomena of anvorganism, or any of its parts, or of a particular bodily process.

Pigments Molecules that reflect and absorb light at particular wavelengths, such as melanin.

Placebo An inert substance often used in clinical trials as control substance when determining the effectiveness of a new product.

Plasmid (G *plasma*, a form, mold). A small circle of DNA that can be carried by a bacterium in addition to its genomic DNA. Widely used in genetic engineering.

Polarization (L *polaris*, polar; G *iz*, make). The arrangement of positive electrical charges on one side of a surface membrane and negative electrical charges on the other side, as in nerves and muscles.

Polarized A description for a membrane that has a potential difference due to an unequal distribution of ions across the membrane.

Polymer (G *polys*, many; *meros*, part). A chemical compound composed of repeated structural units called monomers.

Polynucleotide chains Attachment of one nucleotide to another in a linear fashion.

Polypeptide (G *polys*, many; *peptein*, to digest). A molecule consisting of many joined amino acids; not as complex as a protein.

Polyploidy Having more than two sets of chromosomes.

Polysaccharide (G *polys*, many; *sakcharon*, sugar; Sanskrit *sarkara*, gravel, sugar). A carbohydrate composed of many monosaccharide units, for example, glycogen, starch and cellulose.

Primary immune response The initial immune response following antigen exposure.

Primer Short, pre-existing polynucleotide chain to which new deoxyribonucleotides can be added by DNA polymerase.

Progesterone One of the female hormones produced by the ovaries after ovulation.

Prokarocyte Cell or organism lacking a membrane-bound, structurally discrete nucleus and other sub-cellular compartments. Bacteria are prokaryotes.

Promoter A site on DNA to which RNA polymerase will bind and initiate transcription.

Prostaglandins A family of fatty acid hormones, originally discovered in semen, known to have powerful effects on smooth muscle, nerves, circulation and reproductive organs.

Prostate gland Gland located around the male urethra below the urinary bladder that adds its secretions to seminal fluid during ejaculation.

Prosthetic group Non-protein groups that are attached to an enzyme or other protein and necessary for its function.

Protease An enzyme that digests proteins; includes proteinases and peptidases.

Protein A large molecule composed of one or more chains of amino acids in a specific order; the order is determined by the base sequence of nucleotides in the gene coding for the protein. Proteins are required for the structure, function and regulation of the body's cells, tissues and organs, and each protein has unique functions. Examples are hormones, enzymes and antibodies.

Psoriasis A proliferative, red, scaly disease of the epidermis that seems to have its origin in the dermis.

Puberty The age at which an organism can first reproduce.

Pubescence Having hairs or trichomes on the surface.

Pubis The hair that appears at puberty.

Pudendo (L *pudenda*, to be ashamed). External female genitalia.

Purine A nitrogen-containing, single-ring, basic compound that occurs in nucleic acids. The purines in DNA and RNA are adenine and guanine.

Pyrimidine A nitrogen-containing, double-ring, basic compound that occurs in nucleic acids. The pyrimidines in DNA are cytosine and thymine; in RNA, cytosine and uracil.

Pyruvic acid The end product 3-carbon compound resulting from glycolysis of glucose that enters the Krebs cycle in aerobic respiration.

R

Radiation A form of energy that includes visible light, ultraviolet light and X-rays; also a means by which body heat is lost in the form of infrared rays.

Radioactive An unstable isotope that decays spontaneously and releases subatomic particles or units of energy.

Recombinant DNA technologies Procedures used to join DNA segments in a cell-free system, an environment outside a cell or organism. Under appropriate conditions, a recombinant DNA molecule can enter a cell and replicate there, either autonomously or after it has become integrated into a cellular chromosome.

Recombination The process by which progeny derive a combination of genes different from that of either parent. In higher organisms, this can occur by crossing over.

Redox reactions Oxidation-reduction reaction; a chemical reaction involving the transfer of electrons from one molecule to another.

Reduction In chemistry, the gain of an electron by an atom or molecule of a substance; also the addition of hydrogen to, or the removal of oxygen from, a substance.

Refraction The change in the direction of a light wave as it moves, for example, into shallow water. Actually light will change properties whenever it encounters a medium that is more dense, or more rare then the one through which it is currently is traveling.

Repressor A compound that binds to and controls the regulator in gene regulation.

Reticular (L *reticulum*, small net). Resembling a net in appearance or structure.

Reticular dermis The part of the dermis that contains most of the connective tissue. It is immediately above the fat layer.

Reticuloendothelial (RE) system Total complement of fixed macrophages in the body, especially reticular connective tissue and the lining epithelium of the blood vascular system. Some authorities also include the phagocytic white blood cells.

Ribonucleic acid (RNA) A chemical found in the nucleus and cytoplasm of cells; it plays an important role in protein synthesis and other chemical activities of the cell. The structure of RNA is similar to that of DNA. There are several classes of RNA molecules, including messenger RNA, transfer RNA, ribosomal RNA and other small RNAs, each serving a different purpose.

Ribose A 5-carbon sugar important in RNA and many other compounds.

Ribosomal RNA (rRNA) A class of RNA found in the ribosomes of cells.

Ribosome Subcellular structure composed of protein and ribonucleic acid. Can be free in the cytoplasm or attached to the membranes of the endoplasmic reticulum; functions in protein synthesis.

S

Salicylic acid A compound with pain-relieving characteristics, found in willow bark and other plants; the basic ingredient of aspirin.

Salt (L *sal*, salt). The reaction product of an acid and a base; dissociates in water solution to negative and positive ions, but not H^+ or OH^-.

Saponin A glycoside with a steroid molecule as the active component, such as diosgenin from yams.

Saturated fat A fat in which all the carbons in the fatty acids are connected by single bonds, thereby having the maximum number of hygrogen atoms.

Scabies Disease caused by mites of the genus Sarcoptes. Also called sarcoptic mange.

Sclerotic (G *skleros*; hard). Pertaining to the tough outer coat of the eyeball.

Sebaceous (L *sebaceus*, made of tallow). A type of mammalian epidermal gland that produces a fatty substance.

Sebum Oily secretion from the sebaceous gland, mainly containing triglycerides.

Second law of thermodynamics States that, with each successive energy transfer or transformation in a system, less energy is available to do work. Basic law of the universe and of aging.

Sensitization An immune reaction from enhanced responsiveness to a repeated stimulus.

Serotonin (L *whey*, serum). A phenolic amine, found in the serum of clotted blood and in many other tissues, that possesses several poorly understood metabolic, vascular, and neural functions; chemicaly it is 5-hydroxytryptamine.

Serous (L *whey*, serum). Watery, resembling serum; applied to glands, tissue, cells, fluid.

Serum (L *whey*, serum). The liquid that separates from the blood after coagulation; blood plasma from which fibrinogen has been removed. Also, the clear portion of a biological fluid separated from its particulate elements.

Sex chromosome The X and Y chromosomes in human beings that determine the sex of an individual. Females have two X chromosomes in diploid cells; males have an X and a Y chromosome. The sex chromosomes comprise the 23rd chromosome pair in a karyotype.

Sex hormone A hormone that controls the timing of reproduction and sexual characteristics in vertebrates.

Shingles (Herpes zoster) A painful viral infection of peripheral nerves.

Solute Any material dissolved in a solution.

Solvent The liquid matrix in which a solute is dissolved.

Soma The whole of an organism except the germ cells.

Somatic cell Ordinary body cell; pertaining to or characteristic of a body cell. Any cell other than a germ cell or germ-cell precursor.

Spiny layer The layer above the basal layer that contains desmosomes that have fibrils which have the appearance of spines. Together with the basal layer the two are called the malpighian layer.

Spore A reproductive, often unicellular, unit that is capable of developing into a new organism without fusion with another cell. Spores are very resistant to killing.

Sprain As a term in physics it is a deformation of a structure, or a stretching; in medicine it is a slight tear in a ligament or muscle without breaking the continuity of the structure.

Squamous Flat, or scale-like.

Squamous epithelium (L *squama*, scale; *osus*, full of). Simple epithelium of flat, nucleated cells.

Starch A polysaccharide composed of a thousand or more glucose molecules; the chief food storage material of most plants.

Stem cells Undifferentiated, or partially differentiated cells capable of continuous division.

Sterol (G *stereos*, solid; L *ol*, from *oleum*, oil). One of a class of organic compounds containing a molecular skeleton of four fused carbon rings; it includes cholesterol, sex hormones, adrenocortical hormones and vitamin D.

Stimulant A psychoactive compound that excites and enhances mental alertness and physical activity; often reduces fatigue and suppresses hunger.

Strain In medicine it applies to a condition of a muscle or ligament that has been exerted beyond its normal capacity for stress.

Stress Physical, chemical or emotional factors that place a strain on an animal. Plants also experience physiological stress under adverse environmental conditions.

Stretch receptor Sensory receptor that responds to stretch; found in muscle tissue, lungs and other organs that undergo changes in position or size.

Stroma (G *stromata*, anything to sit or lie upon). In anatomy it refers to the structural components of a tissue or organ. The trabeculae make up the stroma of the fatty tissue.

Subcutaneous injection An injection into the fatty tissue under the skin.

Sucrose A disaccharide (glucose + fructose) found in many plants; the primary form in which sugar produced by photosynthesis is translocated, and most of the sugar we eat.

Sudoriferous gland A sweat gland.

Sympathetic nervous system Portion of the autonomic nervous system that arises from the thoracic and lumbar regions of the spinal cord; also called thoracolumbar division.

Synapsis The pairing of homologous chromosomes that occurs in Prophase I of meiosis.

Syndrome (G *syn*, with; *dramein*, to run). A group of symptoms characteristic of a particular disease or abnormality.

Synergism The interaction of two or more agents or forces so that their combined effect is greater than the sum of their individual effects, as when two hormones combine to affect target tissues.

T

T cell Type of lymphocyte with a vital regulatory role in immune response; so called because they are processed through the thymus. Subsets of T cells can be stimulatory or inhibitory. They communicate with other cells by protein hormones called cytokines. T cells are involved in a variety of cell-mediated immune reactions; also known as a T lymphocyte.

Tactile receptor (L *tactilis*, able to be touched). A sensory receptor in the skin that detects light pressure; formerly called Meissner's corpuscle; pertaining to touch.

Tannin A secondary product found in many plants that has been widely utilized as stains, dyes, inks or tanning agents for leather; believed to function in plants by discouraging herbivores. A potent astringent.

Teleology (G *telos*, end; L *logia*, study of; G *logos*, word). The philosophical view that natural events are goal-directed and are preordained, as opposed to the scientific view of mechanical determinism.

Telogen The resting stage of the hair follicle.

Telomeres The ends of chromosomes. These specialized structures are involved in the replication and stability of linear DNA molecules.

Telophase Stage in mitosis during which daughter cells become separate structures; the two sets of separated chromosomes decondense and become enclosed by nuclear envelopes.

Teratogens Chemicals or other factors that specifically cause abnormalities during embryonic growth and development.

Terminal hair A thick, pigmented hair that eventually will die and be lost.

Terpene An unsaturated hydrocarbon formed from an isoprene building block; found in many plants in the form of essential oils. There can be two or more isoprene units in a chain or ring; sometimes categorized as hydrocarbons only, sometimes to include terpenoids, a term referring to all compounds composed of isoprene units. (See **isoprene**.)

Testosterone Male sex hormone secreted by the interstitial cells of the testes.

TEWL Transepidermal water loss; the insensible loss of water from the skin.

Thalamus An oval mass of gray matter within the brain that serves as a sensory relay area.

Thermogenesis The generation of heat by muscle contraction.

Thermoregulation Heat regulation.

Threshold The minimum stimulus necessary to initiate an all-or-none response.

Thymine A pyrimidine base occurring in DNA, but not in RNA. A nitrogenous base, one member of the base pair A-T, adenine-thymine.

Thymus gland A ductless mass of flattened lymphoid tissue situated behind the top of the sternum; it forms antibodies in the newborn and is involved in the development of the immune system.

Thyroid gland (G *thyreos*, a shield). An endocrine gland located in the neck and involved with the metabolic functions of the body. An endocrine gland near the shield-shaped cartilage of the larynx.

Tight junction Region of actual fusion of cell membranes between two adjacent cells.

Tissue A group of similar cells that performs a specialized function.

Toxins Poisonous chemicals that react with specific cellular components to kill cells or to alter growth or development in undesirable ways; often harmful, even in dilute concentrations.

Trabecula (L *trabecula*, a small beam). In general anatomical usage, a septum extending from an envelope through an enclosed substance, which, together with other trabeculae, forms part of the framework of various organs; here referring specifically to the cell processes connecting group of cells, such as the trabeculae that hold fats together.

Transcription The formation of a messenger RNA molecule that carries the genetic code from the nucleus to the cytoplasm of a cell. The synthesis of an RNA copy from a sequence of DNA, a gene; the first step in gene expression

Transducer A receptor that converts one form of energy into another.

Transduction. Condition in which bacterial DNA, and the genetic characteristics it bears, is transferred from one bacterium to another by the agent of viral infection.

Transfer RNA (tRNA) A class of RNA having structures with triplet nucleotide sequences that are complementary to the triplet nucleotide coding sequences of mRNA. The role of tRNAs in protein synthesis is to bond with amino acids and transfer them to the ribosomes, where proteins are assembled according to the genetic code carried by mRNA.

Transgenic Cells or organisms that contain genes that were inserted into them from other organisms using the techniques of genetic engineering.

Translation The process in which the genetic code carried by mRNA directs the synthesis of proteins from amino acids. The second stage of protein synthesis in which the codon of mRNA pairs with the anticodon of tRNA at the surface of the ribosome.

Trauma Injury caused by accident or violence.

Triglyceride A type of lipid formed from three fatty acids bonded to a molecule of glycerol; a fat or oil.

Trophic (G *trophe*, food). Pertaining to feeding and nutrition.

Trophic hormones (trophic neurosecretions) Hormonal or neurosecretory products from endocrine glands or neurosecretory cells that influence the production and release of other hormone products from endocrine glands.

Tropic (G *trope*, to turn toward). Related to the tropics (tropical); in endocrinology, a hormone that influences the action of another hormone or endocrine gland.

Tubercle (L *tuberculum*, small hump). Small protuberance, knob or swelling.

Tumor A spherical mass of cells in which cell divisions occur at random and often in an uncontrolled fashion.

Tyrosinase An enzyme that converts tyrosine to melanin in the first stages.

Tyrosine An essential amino acid with multifunctions.

U

Ulcer Area of inflammation that opens out to the skin or a mucous surface.

Ultraviolet That portion of the sun's total range of radiation having wavelengths immediately shorter than the shortest of the visible spectrum (purple); between approximately 5–400 nanometers.

Unsaturated fat A fat containing one or more double bonds between carbon atoms.

Uracil A nitrogenous base normally found in RNA but not DNA; uracil is capable of forming a base pair with adenine.

Urea A nitrogen-containing waste product excreted in the urine of many vertebrates.

Uric acid The main nitrogenous excretory product in birds, reptiles, some invertebrates and insects.

Uterus (womb) The portion of female mammals' reproductive tract in which the embryo develops.

UVA Long wavelength ultraviolet light 320–400 nanometers. Penetrates to the dermis.

UVB Short wavelength ultraviolet light 290–320 nanometers. Pentrates the epidermis only.

V

Vaccine A preparation of either killed microorganisms; living, weakened (attenuated) microorganisms; or inactivated bacterial toxins (toxoids); administered to induce development of the immune response and protect the individual against a pathogen or toxin.

Vacuole (L *vacuus*, empty; F *ole*, dim). A membrane-bounded, fluid-filled space in a cell.

Varicose veins Dilated weak veins often with tortuous appearance.

Veins Blood vessels conducting blood toward the heart in any animal.

Vellus hair (L *vellis*, covering). Hair that is light and soft.

Viroid An infectious agent consisting of a single-stranded RNA molecule with no protein coat; produces diseases in plants.

Virulence Degree of pathogenicity of an agent; how much damage the agent can cause.

Virus A submicroscopic noncellular particle composed of a nucleoprotein core and a protein shell; parasitic; will grow and reproduce in a host cell. Viruses consist of nucleic acid covered by protein; some animal viruses also are surrounded by membrane. Inside the infected cell, the virus uses the synthetic capability of the host to produce progeny virus.

Viscosity The resistance of water molecules to external forces that would separate them.

Vitamin An organic substance other than a carbohydrate, lipid or protein that is needed for normal metabolism but cannot be synthesized in adequate amounts by the body.

Volatile oils Terpenes composed of two to four isoprene units; also known as essential oils, such as lemon and peppermint.

W

Wax A lipid material with considerable oxygen inserted in the molecule; high melting point and relatively impermeable to water.

X

Xerosis Dryness of the skin.

Z

Zygote Diploid cell produced by the fusion of an egg and sperm; fertilized egg cell.

Zygotic meiosis Meiosis that takes place within the first few divisions after zygote formation; thus all stages in the life cycle other than the zygote are haploid.

Index